SOLUTIONS TO RED EXERCISES

Roxy Wilson
University of Illinois

CHEMISTRY
THE CENTRAL SCIENCE

Brown ▲ LeMay ▲ Bursten
EIGHTH EDITION

PRENTICE HALL, Upper Saddle River, NJ 07458

Senior Editor: *John Challice*
Associate Editor: *Mary Hornby*
Editorial Assistants: *Amanda Griffith, Gillian Buonano*
Manufacturing Manager: *Trudy Pisciotti*
Special Projects Manager: *Barbara A. Murray*
Production Editor: *Ann Marie Kalajian*
Supplement Cover Manager: *Paul Gourhan*
Supplement Cover Design: *PM Workshop Inc.*
Cover Art: © *Kenneth Eward/BioGrafx, 1999*

Printed in the United States of America

10 9 8 7 6 5 4

ISBN 0-13-084099-8

Prentice-Hall International (UK) Limited, *London*
Prentice-Hall of Australia Pty. Limited, *Sydney*
Prentice-Hall Canada, Inc., *Toronto*
Prentice-Hall Hispanoamericana, S.A., *Mexico*
Prentice-Hall of India Private Limited, *New Delhi*
Prentice-Hall of (Singapore) Pte. Ltd.
Prentice-Hall of Japan, Inc., *Tokyo*
Editora Prentice-Hall do Brasil, Ltda., *Rio de Janeiro*

Contents

Introduction v

Chapter 1   Introduction: Matter and Measurement 1

Chapter 2   Atoms, Molecules, and Ions 7

Chapter 3   Stoichiometry: Calculations with
                  Chemical Formulas and Equations 11

Chapter 4   Aqueous Reactions and Solution Stoichiometry 26

Chapter 5   Thermochemistry 36

Chapter 6   Electronic Structure of Atoms 46

Chapter 7   Periodic Properties of the Elements 54

Chapter 8   Basic Concepts of Chemical Bonding 61

Chapter 9   Molecular Geometry and Bonding Theories 74

Chapter 10 Gases 87

Chapter 11 Intermolecular Forces, Liquids and Solids 98

Chapter 12 Modern Materials 109

Chapter 13   Properties of Solutions   115

Chapter 14   Chemical Kinetics   126

Chapter 15   Chemical Equilibrium   136

Chapter 16   Acid-Base Equilibria   145

Chapter 17   Additional Aspects of Aqueous Equilibria   160

Chapter 18   Chemistry of the Environment   176

Chapter 19   Chemical Thermodynamics   183

Chapter 20   Electrochemistry   193

Chapter 21   Nuclear Chemistry   206

Chapter 22   Chemistry of the Nonmetals   215

Chapter 23   Metals and Metallurgy   223

Chapter 24   Chemistry of Coordination Compounds   229

Chapter 25   The Chemistry of Life:
Organic and Biological Chemistry   235

Introduction

Chemistry: The Central Science, 8th edition, contains nearly 2300 end-of-chapter exercises. Considerable attention has been given to these exercises because one of the best ways for students to master chemistry is by solving problems. Grouping the exercises according to subject matter is intended to aid the student in selecting and recognizing particular types of problems. Within each subject matter group, similar problems are arranged in pairs. This provides the student with an opportunity to reinforce a particular kind of problem. There are also a substantial number of general exercises in each chapter to supplement those grouped by topic. Integrative exercises, which require students to integrate concepts from several chapters, are a continuing feature of the 8th edition. Answers to the odd numbered topical exercises plus selected general and integrative exercises, about 900 in all, are provided in the text. These appendix answers help to make the text a useful self-contained vehicle for learning.

This manual, **Solutions to Red Exercises in Chemistry: The Central Science, 8th edition**, was written to enhance the end-of-chapter exercises by providing documented solutions for those problems answered in the appendix of the text. The manual assists the instructor by saving time spent generating solutions for assigned problem sets and aids the student by offering a convenient independent source to check their understanding of the material. Most solutions have been worked in the same detail as the in-chapter sample exercises to help guide students in their studies.

When using this manual, keep in mind that the numerical result of any calculation is influenced by the precision of the numbers used in the calculation. In this manual, for example, atomic masses and physical constants are typically expressed to four significant figures, or at least as precisely as the data given in the problem. If students use slightly different values to solve problems, their answers will differ slightly from those listed in the appendix of the text or this manual. This is a normal and a common occurrence when comparing results from different calculations or experiments.

Rounding methods are another source of differences between calculated values. In this manual, when a solution is given in steps, intermediate results will be rounded to the correct number of significant figures; however, unrounded numbers will be used in subsequent calculations. By following this scheme, calculators need not be cleared to re-enter rounded intermediate results in the middle of a calculation sequence. The final answer will appear with the correct number of significant figures. This may result in a small discrepancy in the last significant digit between student-calculated answers and those given in this manual. Variations due to rounding can occur in any analysis of numerical data.

The first step in checking your solution and resolving differences between your answer and the listed value is to look for similarities and differences in problem-solving methods. Ultimately, resolving the small numerical differences described above is less important than understanding the general method for solving a problem. The goal of this manual is to provide a reference for sound and consistent problem-solving methods in addition to accurate answers to text exercises.

Extraordinary efforts have been made to keep this manual as error-free as possible. All exercises were worked and proof-read by at least three chemists to ensure clarity in methods and accuracy in mathematics. The work of Patricia Amateis, Nolan Flynn and Scott Wilson has been invaluable to this project. However, in a written work as technically challenging as this manual, typos and errors inevitably creep in. Please help us find and eliminate them. We hope that both instructors and students will find this manual accurate, helpful and instructive.

Roxy B. Wilson
University of Illinois
School of Chemical Sciences
601 S. Mathews Ave.
Urbana, IL 61801

1 Introduction: Matter and Measurement

Classification and Properties of Matter

1.1   (a) gas   (b) solid   (c) liquid   (d) gas

1.3   (a) heterogeneous mixture (b) homogeneous mixture   (If there are undissolved particles, such as sand or decaying plants, the mixture is heterogeneous.)   (c) pure substance (d) homogeneous mixture

1.5   Pure water is a pure substance, while a solution of salt in water is a mixture. We should be able to separate the components of the mixture by a physical process such as evaporation. Take a small quantity of the liquid and allow it to evaporate. If the liquid is salt water, there will be a solid white residue (salt). If the liquid is water, there will be no residue.

1.7   (a) C   (b) Cd   (c) Cr   (d) Zn   (e) I   (f) S   (g) O   (h) Ne

1.9   (a) hydrogen   (b) magnesium   (c) lead   (d) silicon   (e) fluorine   (f) tin (g) copper   (h) calcium

1.11 $A(s) \xrightarrow{heat} B(s) + C(g)$

When carbon(s) is burned in excess oxygen the two elements combine to form a gaseous compound, carbon dioxide. Clearly substance C is this compound.
Since C is produced when A is heated in the absence of oxygen (from air), both the carbon and oxygen in C must have been present in A originally. A is, therefore, a compound composed of two or more elements chemically combined. Without more information on the chemical or physical properties of B, we cannot determine absolutely whether it is an element or a compound. However, few if any elements exist as white solids, so B is probably also a compound.

1.13   Physical properties: silvery white (color); lustrous; melting point = 649°C; boiling point = 1105°C; density at 20°C = 1.738 g/cm^3; pounded into sheets (malleable); drawn into wires (ductile); good conductor. Chemical properties: burns in air to give intense white light; reacts with Cl$_2$ to produce brittle white solid.

1.15   (a) chemical   (b) physical   (c) physical   (d) chemical   (e) chemical

Units and Measurement

1.17 (a) 1×10^{-1} (b) 1×10^{-2} (c) 1×10^{-15} (d) 1×10^{-6} (e) 1×10^{6} (f) 1×10^{3}
      (g) 1×10^{-9} (h) 1×10^{-3} (i) 1×10^{-12}

1.19 (a) $454 \text{ mg} \times \dfrac{1 \times 10^{-3} \text{ g}}{1 \text{ mg}} = 0.454 \text{ g}$

      (b) $5.0 \times 10^{-9} \text{ m} \times \dfrac{1 \text{ pm}}{1 \times 10^{-12} \text{ m}} = 5.0 \times 10^{3} \text{ pm}$

      (c) $3.5 \times 10^{-2} \text{ mm} \times \dfrac{1 \times 10^{-3} \text{ m}}{1 \text{ mm}} \times \dfrac{1 \text{ μm}}{1 \times 10^{-6} \text{ m}} = 35 \text{ μm}$

1.21 (a) time   (b) density   (c) length   (d) area   (e) temperature
      (f) volume   (g) temperature

1.23 (a) $\text{density} = \dfrac{\text{mass}}{\text{volume}} = \dfrac{39.75 \text{ g}}{25.0 \text{ mL}} \times \dfrac{1 \text{ mL}}{1 \text{ cm}^3} = 1.59 \text{ g/cm}^3$

      The units cm^3 and mL will be used interchangeably in this manual.

      (b) $75.0 \text{ cm}^3 \times 23.4 \dfrac{\text{g}}{\text{cm}^3} = 1.76 \times 10^{3} \text{ g}$ (1.76 kg)

      (c) $275 \text{ g} \times \dfrac{1 \text{ cm}^3}{1.74 \text{ g}} = 158 \text{ cm}^3$ (158 mL)

1.25 (a) $\text{density} = \dfrac{38.5 \text{ g}}{45 \text{ mL}} = 0.86 \text{ g/mL}$

      The substance is probably toluene, density = 0.866 g/mL.

      (b) $45.0 \text{ g} \times \dfrac{1 \text{ mL}}{1.114 \text{ g}} = 40.4 \text{ mL}$ ethylene glycol

      (c) $(5.00)^3 \text{ cm}^3 \times \dfrac{8.90 \text{ g}}{1 \text{ cm}^3} = 1.11 \times 10^{3} \text{ g}$ (1.11 kg) nickel

1.27 thickness = volume/area

      $\text{volume} = 200 \text{ mg} \times \dfrac{1 \times 10^{-3} \text{ g}}{1 \text{ mg}} \times \dfrac{1 \text{ cm}^3}{19.32} = 0.01035 = 0.0104 \text{ cm}^3$

      $\text{area} = 2.4 \text{ ft} \times 1.0 \text{ ft} \times \dfrac{12^2 \text{ in}^2}{1 \text{ ft}^2} \times \dfrac{2.54^2 \text{ cm}^2}{\text{in}^2} = 2.23 \times 10^{3} = 2.2 \times 10^{3} \text{ cm}^2$

      $\text{thickness} = \dfrac{0.01035 \text{ cm}^3}{2,230 \text{ cm}^2} \times \dfrac{1 \times 10^{-2} \text{ m}}{1 \text{ cm}} = 4.6 \times 10^{-8} \text{ m}$

      $4.6 \times 10^{-8} \text{ m} \times \dfrac{1 \text{ nm}}{1 \times 10^{-9} \text{ m}} = 46 \text{ nm thick}$

1.29   (a) $°C = 5/9 (°F - 32°)$; $5/9 (62 - 32) = 17°C$

      (b) $°F = 9/5 (°C) + 32°$; $9/5 (216.7) + 32 = 422.1°F$

      (c) $K = °C + 273.15$; $233°C + 273.15 = 506 K$

      (d) $315 K - 273 = 42°C$; $9/5 (42°C) + 32 = 108°F$

      (e) $°C = 5/9 (°F - 32°)$; $5/9 (2500 - 32) = 1371°C$; $1371°C + 273 = 1644 K$

      (assuming 2500 °C has 4 sig figs)

Uncertainty In Measurement

1.31   Exact: (c), (d), and (f)   (All others depend on measurements and standards that have margins of error, e.g., the length of a week as defined by the earth's rotation.)

1.33   (a) 4   (b) 3   (c) 4   (d) 3   (e) 5

1.35   (a) 3.002×10^2 (b) 4.565×10^5 (c) 6.543×10^{-3}
      (d) 9.578×10^{-4} (e) 5.078×10^4 (f) -3.500×10^{-2}

1.37   (a) 77.04   (b) -51   (c) 9.995×10^4 (d) 3.13×10^4

Dimensional Analysis

1.39   Arrange conversion factors so that the starting units cancel and the new units remain in the appropriate place, either numerator or denominator.

1.41   (a) $0.076 \text{ L} \times \dfrac{1000 \text{ mL}}{1 \text{ L}} = 76 \text{ mL}$

      (b) $5.0 \times 10^{-8} \text{ m} \times \dfrac{1 \text{ nm}}{1 \times 10^{-9} \text{ m}} = 50. \text{ nm}$

      (c) $6.88 \times 10^5 \text{ ns} \times \dfrac{1 \times 10^{-9} \text{ s}}{1 \text{ ns}} = 6.88 \times 10^{-4} \text{ s}$

      (d) $1.55 \dfrac{\text{kg}}{\text{m}^3} \times \dfrac{1000 \text{ g}}{1 \text{ kg}} \times \dfrac{1 \text{ m}^3}{(10)^3 \text{ dm}^3} \times \dfrac{1 \text{ dm}^3}{1 \text{ L}} = 1.55 \text{ g/L}$

1.43   (a) $8.60 \text{ mi} \times \dfrac{1.609 \text{ km}}{1 \text{ mi}} \times \dfrac{1000 \text{ m}}{1 \text{ km}} = 1.38 \times 10^4 \text{ m}$

      (b) $3.00 \text{ days} \times \dfrac{24 \text{ hr}}{1 \text{ day}} \times \dfrac{60 \text{ min}}{1 \text{ hr}} \times \dfrac{60 \text{ s}}{1 \text{ min}} = 2.59 \times 10^5 \text{ s}$

      (c) $\dfrac{\$1.55}{\text{gal}} \times \dfrac{1 \text{ gal}}{4 \text{ qt}} \times \dfrac{1.057 \text{ qt}}{1 \text{ L}} = \dfrac{\$0.410}{\text{L}}$

(d) $\dfrac{5.0 \text{ pm}}{\text{ms}} \times \dfrac{1 \times 10^{-12} \text{ m}}{1 \text{ pm}} \times \dfrac{1 \text{ ms}}{1 \times 10^{-3} \text{ s}} = 5.0 \times 10^{-9} \text{ m/s}$

(e) $\dfrac{75.00 \text{ mi}}{\text{hr}} \times \dfrac{1.609 \text{ km}}{1 \text{ mi}} \times \dfrac{1000 \text{ m}}{1 \text{ km}} \times \dfrac{1 \text{ hr}}{60 \text{ min}} \times \dfrac{1 \text{ min}}{60 \text{ s}} = 33.52 \text{ m/s}$

(f) $55.35 \text{ ft}^3 \times \dfrac{(12)^3 \text{ in}^3}{1 \text{ ft}^3} \times \dfrac{(2.54)^3 \text{ cm}^3}{1 \text{ in}^3} = 1.567 \times 10^6 \text{ cm}^3$

1.45   (a) $31 \text{ gal} \times \dfrac{4 \text{ qt}}{1 \text{ gal}} \times \dfrac{1 \text{ L}}{1.057 \text{ qt}} = 1.2 \times 10^2 \text{ L}$

      (b) $\dfrac{6 \text{ mg}}{\text{kg (body)}} \times \dfrac{1 \text{ kg}}{2.205 \text{ lb}} \times 150 \text{ lb} = 4 \times 10^2 \text{ mg}$

      (c) $\dfrac{254 \text{ mi}}{11.2 \text{ gal}} \times \dfrac{1.609 \text{ km}}{1 \text{ mi}} \times \dfrac{1 \text{ gal}}{4 \text{ qt}} \times \dfrac{1.057 \text{ qt}}{1 \text{ L}} = \dfrac{9.64 \text{ km}}{\text{L}}$

      (d) $\dfrac{50 \text{ cups}}{1 \text{ lb}} \times \dfrac{1 \text{ qt}}{4 \text{ cups}} \times \dfrac{1 \text{ L}}{1.057 \text{ qt}} \times \dfrac{1000 \text{ mL}}{1 \text{ L}} \times \dfrac{1 \text{ lb}}{453.6 \text{ g}} = \dfrac{26 \text{ mL}}{\text{g}}$

1.47 $12.5 \text{ ft} \times 15.5 \text{ ft} \times 8.0 \text{ ft} = 1.6 \times 10^3 \text{ ft}^3$ (2 sig figs)

$1550 \text{ ft}^3 \times \dfrac{(1 \text{ yd})^3}{(3 \text{ ft})^3} \times \dfrac{(1 \text{ m})^3}{(1.0936)^3 \text{ yd}^3} \times \dfrac{10^3 \text{ dm}^3}{1 \text{ m}^3} \times \dfrac{1 \text{ L}}{1 \text{ dm}^3} \times \dfrac{1.19 \text{ g}}{\text{L}} \times \dfrac{1 \text{ kg}}{1000 \text{ g}} = 52 \text{ kg air}$

1.49   A wire is a very long, thin cylinder of volume, $V = \pi r^2 h$, where h is the length of the wire and πr^2 is the cross-sectional area of the wire.

      Strategy: 1)   Calculate total volume of copper in cm^3 from mass and density

              2)   h (length in cm) $= \dfrac{V}{\pi r^2}$

              3)   Change cm $\rightarrow$ ft

$150 \text{ lb Cu} \times \dfrac{453.6 \text{ g}}{1 \text{ lb Cu}} \times \dfrac{1 \text{ cm}^3}{8.94 \text{ g}} = 7.61 \times 10^3 \text{ cm}^3$

$r = d/2 = 8.25 \text{ mm} \times \dfrac{1 \text{ cm}}{10 \text{ mm}} \times \dfrac{1}{2} = 0.4125 = 0.413 \text{ cm}$

$h = \dfrac{V}{\pi r^2} = \dfrac{7610.7 \text{ cm}^3}{\pi (0.4125)^2 \text{ cm}^2} = 1.4237 \times 10^4 = 1.42 \times 10^4 \text{ cm}$

$1.4237 \times 10^4 \text{ cm} \times \dfrac{1 \text{ in}}{2.54 \text{ cm}} \times \dfrac{1 \text{ ft}}{12 \text{ in}} = 467 \text{ ft}$

Additional Exercises

1.51   Composition is the contents of a substance, the kinds of elements that are present and their relative amounts. Structure is the arrangement of these contents.

1.54   Any sample of vitamin C has the same relative amount of carbon and oxygen; the ratio of oxygen to carbon in the isolated sample is the same as the ratio in synthesized vitamin C.

$$\frac{2.00\,g\,O}{1.50\,g\,C} = \frac{x\,g\,O}{6.35\,g\,C}; \quad x = \frac{(2.00\,g\,O)(6.35\,g\,C)}{1.50\,g\,C} = 8.47\,g\,O$$

This calculation assumes the *law of constant composition*.

1.56   (a) $\dfrac{m}{s^2}$ (b) $\dfrac{kg \cdot m}{s^2}$ (c) $\dfrac{kg \cdot m}{s^2} \times m = \dfrac{kg \cdot m^2}{s^2}$

        (d) $\dfrac{kg \cdot m}{s^2} \times \dfrac{1}{m^2} = \dfrac{kg}{m \cdot s^2}$ (e) $\dfrac{kg \cdot m^2}{s^2} \times \dfrac{1}{s} = \dfrac{kg \cdot m^2}{s^3}$

1.60   (a)   I.   (22.52 + 22.48 + 22.54)/3 = 22.51
               II.   (22.64 + 22.58 + 22.62)/3 = 22.61

            Based on the average, set I is more accurate. That is, it is closer to the true value of 22.52%.

       (b)   Average deviation = $\sum$ | value – average |/3

            I. | 22.52 – 22.51 | + |22.48 – 22.51 | + |22.54 – 22.51 |/3 = 0.02
            II. | 22.64 – 22.61 | + |22.58 – 22.61 | + |22.62 – 22.61 |/3 = 0.02

            The two sets display the same precision, even though set I is more accurate.

1.62   (a) $25.83 \times 10^9\,lb \times \dfrac{453.6\,g}{1\,lb} = 1.17165 \times 10^{13} = 1.172 \times 10^{13}\,g\,NaOH$

       (b) $1.17165 \times 10^{13}\,g \times \dfrac{1\,cm^3}{2.130\,g} \times \dfrac{1\,m^3}{(100)^3\,cm^3} \times \dfrac{1\,km^3}{(1000)^3\,m^3} = 5.501 \times 10^{-3}\,km^3$

1.65   There are 209.1 degrees between the freezing and boiling points on the Celsius (C) scale and 100 degrees on the glycol (G) scale. Also, -11.5°C = 0°G. By analogy with °F and °C,

       $°G = \dfrac{100}{209.1}\,(°C + 11.5)$ or $°C = \dfrac{209.1}{100}(°G) - 11.5$

These equations correctly relate the freezing point and boiling point of ethylene glycol on the two scales.

f.p. of H_2O: $°G = \dfrac{100}{209.1}\,(0°C + 11.5) = 5.50°G$

b.p. of H_2O: $°G = \dfrac{100}{209.1}\,(100°C + 11.5) = 53.3°G$

1.68   (a) 2.4×10^5 mi $\times \dfrac{1.609 \text{ km}}{1 \text{ mi}} \times \dfrac{1000 \text{ m}}{1 \text{ km}} = 3.9 \times 10^8$ m

       (b) 2.4×10^5 mi $\times \dfrac{1.609 \text{ km}}{1 \text{ mi}} \times \dfrac{1 \text{ hr}}{2.4 \times 10^3 \text{ km}} \times \dfrac{60 \text{ min}}{1 \text{ hr}} \times \dfrac{60 \text{ s}}{1 \text{ min}} = 5.8 \times 10^5$ s

1.72   9.64 g ethanol $\times \dfrac{1 \text{ cm}^3}{0.789 \text{ g ethanol}} = 12.2 \text{ cm}^3$, volume of cylinder

$V = \pi r^2 h$; $r = (V/\pi h)^{1/2} = \left[\dfrac{12.218 \text{ cm}^3}{\pi \times 15.0 \text{ cm}}\right]^{1/2} = 0.509$ cm

$d = 2r = 1.02$ cm

1.76   The densities are:

carbon tetrachloride (methane, tetrachloro) - 1.5940 g/cm^3

hexane - 0.6603 g/cm^3

benzene - 0.87654 g/cm^3

methylene iodide (methane, diiodo) - 3.3254 g/cm^3

Only methylene iodide will separate the two granular solids.   The undesirable solid (2.04 g/cm^3) is less dense than methylene iodide and will float; the desired material is more dense than methylene iodide and will sink. The other three liquids are less dense than both solids and will not produce separation.

2 Atoms, Molecules, and Ions

Atomic Theory and Atomic Structure

2.1   Postulate 4 of the atomic theory is the *law of constant composition*. It states that the relative number and kinds of atoms in a compound are constant, regardless of the source. Therefore, 1.0 g of pure water should always contain the same relative amounts of hydrogen and oxygen, no matter where or how the sample is obtained.

2.3   (a) $\dfrac{17.37 \text{ g oxygen}}{15.20 \text{ g nitrogen}} = \dfrac{1.143 \text{ g O}}{1 \text{ g N}}$; 1.143/1.143 = 1.0; 1.0 × 2 = 2

$\dfrac{34.74 \text{ g oxygen}}{15.20 \text{ g nitrogen}} = \dfrac{2.286 \text{ g O}}{1 \text{ g N}}$; 2.286/1.143 = 2.0; 2.0 × 2 = 4

$\dfrac{43.43 \text{ g oxygen}}{15.20 \text{ g nitrogen}} = \dfrac{2.857 \text{ g O}}{1 \text{ g N}}$; 2.857/1.143 = 2.5; 2.5 × 2 = 5

(b)   These masses of oxygen per one gram nitrogen are in the ratio of 2:4:5 and thus obey the *law of multiple proportions*. Multiple proportions arise because atoms are the indivisible entities combining, so they must combine in ratios of small whole numbers.

2.5   Evidence that cathode rays were negatively charged particles was (1) that electric and magnetic fields deflected the rays in the same way they would deflect negatively charged particles and (2) that a metal plate exposed to cathode rays acquired a negative charge.

2.7   The droplets contain different charges because there may be 1, 2, 3 or more excess electrons on the droplet. The electronic charge is likely to be the lowest common factor in all the observed charges. Assuming this is so, we calculate the apparent electronic charge from each drop as follows:

A: $1.60 \times 10^{-19} / 1 = 1.60 \times 10^{-19}$ C

B: $3.15 \times 10^{-19} / 2 = 1.58 \times 10^{-19}$ C

C: $4.81 \times 10^{-19} / 3 = 1.60 \times 10^{-19}$ C

D: $6.31 \times 10^{-19} / 4 = 1.58 \times 10^{-19}$ C

The reported value is the average of these four values. Since each calculated charge has three significant figures, the average will also have three significant figures.

$(1.60 \times 10^{-19} \text{ C} + 1.58 \times 10^{-19} \text{ C} + 1.60 \times 10^{-19} \text{ C} + 1.58 \times 10^{-19} \text{ C}) / 4 = 1.59 \times 10^{-19}$ C

2.9   The Be nuclei have a much smaller volume and positive charge than the Au nuclei; the charge repulsion between the alpha particles and the Be nuclei will be less, and there will be fewer direct hits because the Be nuclei have an even smaller volume than the Au nuclei. Fewer alpha particles will be scattered in general and fewer will be strongly back scattered.

2.11   (a) $2.4 \text{ Å} \times \dfrac{1 \times 10^{-10} \text{ m}}{1 \text{ Å}} \times \dfrac{1 \text{ nm}}{1 \times 10^{-9} \text{ m}} = 0.24 \text{ nm}$

$2.4 \text{ Å} \times \dfrac{1 \times 10^{-10} \text{ m}}{1 \text{ Å}} \times \dfrac{1 \text{ pm}}{1 \times 10^{-12} \text{ m}} = 2.4 \times 10^2 \text{ or } 240 \text{ pm} \ (1 \text{ Å} = 100 \text{ pm})$

(b) $1.0 \text{ cm} \times \dfrac{1 \text{ m}}{100 \text{ cm}} \times \dfrac{1 \text{ Å}}{1 \times 10^{-10} \text{ m}} \times \dfrac{1 \text{ Cr atom}}{2.4 \text{ Å}} = 4.2 \times 10^7 \text{ Cr atoms}$

2.13   p = protons,   n = neutrons,   e = electrons

(a) ^{40}Ar has 18 p, 22 n, 18 e   (b) ^{55}Mn has 25 p, 30 n, 25 e

(c) ^{65}Zn has 30 p, 35 n, 30 e   (d) ^{79}Se has 34 p, 45 n, 34 e

(e) ^{184}W has 74 p, 110 n, 74 e   (f) ^{235}U has 92 p, 143 n, 92 e

2.15

Symbol	^{39}K	^{55}Mn	^{112}Cd	^{137}Ba	^{207}Pb
Protons	19	25	48	56	82
Neutrons	20	30	64	81	125
Electrons	19	25	48	56	82
Mass no.	39	55	112	137	207

2.17   (a) $^{23}_{11}$Na   (b) $^{51}_{23}$V   (c) $^{4}_{2}$He   (d) $^{37}_{17}$Cl   (e) $^{24}_{12}$Mg

The Periodic Table;   Molecules and Ions

2.19   (a) Ag (metal)   (b) He (nonmetal)   (c) P (nonmetal)   (d) Cd (metal)
         (e) Ca (metal)   (f) Br (nonmetal)   (g) As (metalloid)

2.21   (a) K, alkali metals (metal)   (b) I, halogens (nonmetal)   (c) Mg, alkaline earth metals (metal)   (d) Ar, noble gases (nonmetal)   (e) S, chalcogens (nonmetal)

2.23   An empirical formula shows the simplest ratio of the different atoms in a molecule. A molecular formula shows the exact number and kinds of atoms in a molecule. A structural formula shows how these atoms are arranged.

2.25   (a) 6   (b) 6   (c) 12

2.27   (a) C_2H_6O H—C—O—C—H (with H atoms)   (b) C_2H_6O H—C—C—O—H (with H atoms)

       (c) CH_4O H—C—O—H (with H atoms)   (d) PCl_3 Cl—P—Cl (with Cl)

2.29   CH: C_2H_2, C_6H_6

       CH_2: C_2H_4, C_3H_6, C_4H_8

       NO_2: N_2O_4, NO_2

2.31   (a) Al^{3+} (b) Ca^{2+} (c) S^{2-} (d) I^- (e) Cs^+

2.33   (a) GaF_3, gallium(III) fluoride   (b) LiH, lithium hydride

       (c) AlI_3, aluminum iodide   (d) K_2S, potassium sulfide

2.35   (a) $CaBr_2$ (b) NH_4Cl (c) $Al(C_2H_3O_2)_3$ (d) K_2SO_4 (e) $Mg_3(PO_4)_2$

2.37   Molecular (all elements are nonmetals): (a) B_2H_6 (b) CH_3OH (f) NOCl   (g) NF_3

       Ionic (formed by a cation and an anion, usually contains a metal cation): (c) $LiNO_3$,
       (d) Sc_2O_3, (e) CsBr, (h) Ag_2SO_4

Naming Inorganic Compounds

2.39   (a) ClO_2^- (b) Cl^- (c) ClO_3^- (d) ClO_4^- (e) ClO^-

2.41   (a) aluminum fluoride   (b) iron(II) hydroxide (ferrous hydroxide)
       (c) copper(II) nitrate (cupric nitrate)   (d) barium perchlorate (e) lithium phosphate
       (f) mercury(I) sulfide (mercurous sulfide)   (g) calcium acetate   (h) chromium(III)
       carbonate (chromic carbonate)   (i) potassium chromate   (j) ammonium sulfate

2.43   (a) Cu_2O (b) K_2O_2 (c) $Al(OH)_3$ (d) $Zn(NO_3)_2$ (e) Hg_2Br_2 (f) $Fe_2(CO_3)_3$ (g) NaBrO

2.45   (a) bromic acid   (b) hydrobromic acid   (c) phosphoric acid   (d) HClO   (e) HIO_3
       (f) H_2SO_3

2.47   (a) sulfur hexafluoride   (b) iodine pentafluoride   (c) xenon trioxide   (d) N_2O_4 (e) HCN
       (f) P_4S_6

2.49   (a) $ZnCO_3$, ZnO, CO_2 (b) HF, SiO_2, SiF_4, H_2O (c) SO_2, H_2O, H_2SO_3
       (d) H_3P (or PH_3)   (e) $HClO_4$, Cd, $Cd(ClO_4)_2$ (f) VBr_3

Additional Exercises

2.52 (a) Most of the volume of an atom is empty space in which electrons move. Most alpha particles passed through this space. The path of the massive alpha particle would not be significantly altered by interaction with a "puny" electron.

(b) Most of the mass of an atom is contained in a very small, dense area called the nucleus. The few alpha particles that hit the massive, positively charged gold nuclei were strongly repelled and essentially deflected back in the direction they came from.

2.55 (a) 5 significant figures. $^1H^+$ is a bare proton with mass 1.0073 amu. ^1H is a hydrogen atom, with 1 proton and 1 electron. The mass of the electron is 5.486×10^{-4} or 0.0005486 amu. Thus the mass of the electron is significant in the fourth decimal place or fifth significant figure in the mass of ^1H.

(b) Mass of ^1H =   1.0073 amu   (proton)

 <u>0.0005486 amu</u>   (electron)

 1.0078 amu   (We have not rounded up to 1.0079 since 49 < 50 in the final sum.)

$$\text{Mass \% of electron} = \frac{\text{mass of } e^-}{\text{mass of } ^1H} \times 100 = \frac{5.486 \times 10^{-4} \text{ amu}}{1.0078 \text{ amu}} \times 100 = 0.05444\%$$

2.58 (a) an alkali metal - K   (b) an alkaline earth metal - Ca   (c) a noble gas - Ar
(d) a halogen - Br   (e) a metalloid - Ge   (f) a nonmetal in 1A - H
(g) a metal that forms a 3+ ion - Al   (h) a nonmetal that forms a 2– ion - O
(i) an element that resembles Al - Ga

2.61

Symbol	$^{52}Cr^{3+}$	$^{130}I^-$	$^{107}Ag^+$	$^{119}Sn^{2+}$	$^{75}As^{3-}$
Protons	24	53	47	50	33
Neutrons	28	77	60	69	42
Electrons	21	54	46	48	36
Net Charge	3+	1-	1+	2+	3-

2.64 (a) IO_3^- (b) IO_4^- (c) IO^- (d) HIO   (e) HIO_4 or (H_5IO_6)

2.65 (a) perbromate ion   (b) selenite ion   (c) AsO_4^{3-} (d) $HTeO_4^-$

2.67 (a) potassium nitrate   (b) sodium carbonate   (c) calcium oxide
(d) hydrochloric acid   (e) magnesium sulfate   (f) magnesium hydroxide

3 Stoichiometry: Calculation with Chemical Formulas and Equations

Balancing Chemical Equations

3.1 (a) In balancing chemical equations, the *law of conservation of mass*, that atoms are neither created nor destroyed during the course of a reaction, is observed. This means that the **number** and **kinds** of atoms on both sides of the chemical equation must be the same.

(b) Subscripts in chemical formulas should not be changed when balancing equations because changing the subscript changes the identity of the compound (*law of constant composition*).

(c) gases - (g); liquids - (l); solids - (s); aqueous solutions - (aq)

3.3 Equation (a) best fits the diagram.

Overall, 4 A_2 molecules + 4 B atoms → 4 A_2B molecules

Since 4 is a common factor, this equation reduces to equation (a).

3.5 (a) $2CO(g) + O_2(g) \rightarrow 2CO_2(g)$

(b) $N_2O_5(g) + H_2O(l) \rightarrow 2HNO_3(aq)$

(c) $PCl_5(l) + 4H_2O(l) \rightarrow H_3PO_4(aq) + 5HCl(aq)$

(d) $CH_4(g) + 4Br_2(g) \rightarrow CBr_4(l) + 4HBr(g)$

(e) $2C_5H_{10}O_2(l) + 13O_2(g) \rightarrow 10CO_2(g) + 10H_2O(l)$

(f) $Cr(OH)_3(s) + 3HClO_4(aq) \rightarrow Cr(ClO_4)_3(aq) + 3H_2O(l)$

(g) $(NH_4)_2Cr_2O_7(s) \rightarrow Cr_2O_3(s) + N_2(g) + 4H_2O(l)$

3.7 (a) $CaC_2(s) + 2H_2O(l) \rightarrow Ca(OH)_2(aq) + C_2H_2(g)$

(b) $2KClO_3(s) \overset{\Delta}{\rightarrow} 2KCl(s) + 3O_2(g)$

(c) $Zn(s) + H_2SO_4(aq) \rightarrow H_2(g) + ZnSO_4(aq)$

(d) $PCl_3(l) + 3H_2O(l) \rightarrow H_3PO_3(aq) + 3HCl(aq)$

(e) $3H_2S(g) + 2Fe(OH)_3(s) \rightarrow Fe_2S_3(s) + 6H_2O(g)$

Patterns of Chemical Reactivity

3.9 (a) The products are carbon dioxide and water; $CO_2(g) + H_2O(l)$.

$2C_8H_{18}(l) + 25O_2(g) \rightarrow 16CO_2(g) + 18H_2O(l)$

(b)   Balance the positive and negative charges in the ionic product. Calcium forms Ca^{2+} cations and oxygen forms O^{2-} anions, so the charges are balanced if one cation and one anion combine.

$$2Ca(s) + O_2(g) \rightarrow 2CaO(s)$$

3.11   (a) $C_7H_{16}(l) + 11O_2(g) \rightarrow 7CO_2(g) + 8H_2O(l)$

       (b) $2C_5H_{12}O(l) + 15O_2(g) \rightarrow 10CO_2(g) + 12H_2O(l)$

       (c) $2Rb(s) + 2H_2O(l) \rightarrow 2RbOH(aq) + H_2(g)$

       (d) $Mg(s) + Cl_2(g) \rightarrow MgCl_2(s)$

3.13   (a) $2Al(s) + 3Cl_2(g) \rightarrow 2AlCl_3(s)$ combination

       (b) $C_2H_4(g) + 3O_2(g) \rightarrow 2CO_2(g) + 2H_2O(l)$ combustion

       (c) $6Li(s) + N_2(g) \rightarrow 2Li_3N(s)$ combination

       (d) $PbCO_3(s) \rightarrow PbO(s) + CO_2(g)$ decomposition

       (e) $C_7H_8O_2(l) + 8O_2(g) \rightarrow 7CO_2(g) + 4H_2O(l)$ combustion

Atomic and Molecular Weights

3.15   (a) $^{12}_{6}C$

       (b)   Atomic weights are really average atomic masses, the sum of the mass of each naturally-occurring isotope of an element times its fractional abundance. Each Mg atom will have the mass of one of the naturally-occurring isotopes, while the "atomic weight" is an average value. The naturally-occurring isotopes of Mg, their atomic masses and relative abundances are: ^{24}Mg, 23.985042, 78.99%; ^{25}Mg, 24.985837, 10.00%; ^{26}Mg, 25.982593, 11.01%.

3.17   Average atomic mass (atomic weight) = $\sum$ fractional abundance × mass of isotope
Average atomic mass = 0.6909(62.9298) + 0.3091(64.9278) = 63.5474 = 63.55 amu

3.19   Formula weight (FW) in amu to 1 decimal place (see Sample Exercise 3.5)

       (a) N_2O_5: 2(14.0) + 5(16.0) = 108.0 amu

       (b) $FeCO_3$: 1(55.8) + 1(12.0) + 3(16.0) = 115.8 amu

       (c) $Ca(C_2H_3O_2)_2$: 1(40.1) + 4(12.0) + 6(1.0) + 4(16.0) = 158.1 amu

       (d) $(NH_4)_3PO_4$: 3(14.0) + 12(1.0) + 1(31.0) + 4(16.0) = 149.0 amu

       (e) $NaNO_3$: 1(23.0) + 1(14.0) + 3(16.0) = 85.0 amu

       (f) $CuSO_4$: 1(63.5) + 1(32.1) + 4(16.0) = 159.6 amu

       (g) Si_2Br_6: 2(28.1) + 6(79.9) = 535.6 amu

3.21   Calculate the formula weight (FW), then the mass % oxygen in the compound.

       (a) NO_2: FW = 1(14.0) + 2(16.0) = 46.0 amu

$$\% \ O = \frac{2(16.0) \ amu}{46.0 \ amu} \times 100 = 69.6\%$$

(b) CH_3COOCH_3: FW = 3(12.0) + 6(1.0) + 2(16.0) = 74.0 amu

%O = $\dfrac{2(16.0)\ \text{amu}}{74.0\ \text{amu}}$ × 100 = 43.2%

(c) $Cr(NO_3)_3$: FW = 1(52.0) + 3(14.0) + 9(16.0) = 238.0 amu

%O = $\dfrac{9(16.0)\ \text{amu}}{238.0\ \text{amu}}$ × 100 = 60.5%

(d) $(NH_4)_2CO_3$: FW = 2(14.0) + 8(1.0) + 12.0 + 3(16.0) = 96.0 amu

%O = $\dfrac{3(16.0)\ \text{amu}}{96.0\ \text{amu}}$ × 100 = 50.0%

3.23 (a) C_7H_6O: FW = 7(12.0) + 6(1.0) + 1(16.0) = 106.0 amu

%C = $\dfrac{7(12.0)\ \text{amu}}{106.0\ \text{amu}}$ × 100 = 79.2%

(b) $C_8H_8O_3$: FW = 8(12.0) + 8(1.0) + 3(16.0) = 152.0 amu

%C = $\dfrac{8(12.0)\ \text{amu}}{152.0\ \text{amu}}$ × 100 = 63.2%

(c) $C_7H_{14}O_2$: FW = 7(12.0) + 14(1.0) + 2(16.0) = 130.0 amu

%C = $\dfrac{7(12.0)\ \text{amu}}{130.0\ \text{amu}}$ × 100 = 64.6%

%C = $\dfrac{12.0\ \text{amu}}{76.1\ \text{amu}}$ × 100 = 15.8%

3.25

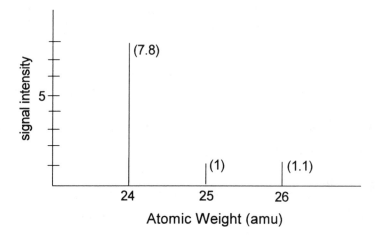

The relative intensities of the peaks in the mass spectrum are the same as the relative abundances of the isotopes. The abundances and peak heights are in the ratio ^{24}Mg: ^{25}Mg: ^{26}Mg as 7.8 : 1.0 : 1.1.

3.27 (a) A Br_2 molecule could consist of two atoms of the same isotope or one atom of each of the two different isotopes. This second possibility is twice as likely as the first. Therefore, the second peak (twice as large as peaks 1 and 3) represents a Br_2 molecule containing different isotopes. The mass numbers of the two isotopes are determined from the masses of the two smaller peaks. Since 157.84 ≈ 158, the first peak represents a ^{79}Br - ^{79}Br molecule. Peak 3, 161.84 ≈ 162, represents a ^{81}Br - ^{81}Br molecule. Peak 2 then contains one atom of each isotope, ^{79}Br - ^{81}Br, with an approximate mass of 160 amu.

(b) The mass of the lighter isotope is 157.84 amu/2 atoms, or 78.92 amu/atom. For the heavier one, 161.84 amu/2 atoms = 80.92 amu/atom.

(c) The relative size of the three peaks in the mass spectrum of Br_2 indicates their relative abundance. The average mass of a Br_2 molecule is
0.2534(157.84) + 0.5000(159.84) + 0.2466(161.84) = 159.83 amu
(Each product has four significant figures and two decimal places, so the answer has two decimal places.)

(d) $$\frac{159.83 \text{ amu}}{\text{avg. } Br_2 \text{ molecule}} \times \frac{1 \; Br_2 \text{ molecule}}{2 \text{ Br atoms}} = 79.915 \text{ amu}$$

(e) Let x = the abundance of ^{79}Br, 1-x = abundance of ^{81}Br. From (b), the masses of the two isotopes are 78.92 amu and 80.92 amu, respectively. From (d), the mass of an average Br atom is 79.915 amu.

$$x(78.92) + (1 - x)(80.92) = 79.915, \; x = 0.5025 = 0.503$$
$$^{79}\text{Br} = 50.3\%, \; ^{81}\text{Br} = 49.7\%$$

The Mole

3.29 (a) A *mole* is the amount of matter that contains as many objects as the number of atoms in exactly 12 g of ^{12}C.

(b) 6.022×10^{23}. This is the number of objects in a mole of anything.

(c) The formula weight of a substance in amu has the same numerical value as the molar mass expressed in grams.

3.31 250 million = $250 \times 10^6 = 2.50 \times 10^8$ people

$$\frac{6.022 \times 10^{23} \text{ ¢}}{2.50 \times 10^8 \text{ people}} \times \frac{\$1}{100 \text{ ¢}} = \frac{\$6.022 \times 10^{21}}{2.50 \times 10^8 \text{ people}} = \$2.41 \times 10^{13}/\text{person}$$

$5.5 trillion = 5.5×10^{12} $\dfrac{\$2.41 \times 10^{13}}{\$5.5 \times 10^{12}} = 4.4$

Each person would receive an amount that is 4.4 times the dollar amount of the national debt.

3.33 (a) molar mass = 14(12.01) + 18(1.008) + 2(14.01) + 5(16.00) = 294.30 g

(b) $1.00 \text{ mg aspartame} \times \dfrac{1 \times 10^{-3} \text{ g}}{1 \text{ mg}} \times \dfrac{1 \text{ mol}}{294.3 \text{ g}} = 3.398 \times 10^{-6}$

$$= 3.40 \times 10^{-6} \text{ mol aspartame}$$

(c) $3.398 \times 10^{-6} \text{ mol aspartame} \times \dfrac{6.022 \times 10^{23} \text{ molecules}}{1 \text{ mol}} = 2.046 \times 10^{18}$

$$= 2.05 \times 10^{18} \text{ aspartame molecules}$$

(d) 2.046×10^{18} aspartame molecules $\times \dfrac{18 \text{ H atoms}}{1 \text{ aspartame molecule}} = 3.68 \times 10^{19}$ H atoms

3.35   (a) $\dfrac{12 \text{ H atoms}}{6 \text{ C atoms}} = \dfrac{2 \text{ H}}{1 \text{ C}} \times 2.03 \times 10^{21}$ C atoms $= 4.06 \times 10^{21}$ H atoms

        (b) $\dfrac{1 \text{ } C_6H_{12}O_6 \text{ molecule}}{6 \text{ C atoms}} \times 2.03 \times 10^{21}$ C atoms $= 3.383 \times 10^{20}$

                                                           $= 3.38 \times 10^{20} \text{ } C_6H_{12}O_6$ molecules

        (c) $3.383 \times 10^{20} \text{ } C_6H_{12}O_6$ molecules $\times \dfrac{1 \text{ mol}}{6.022 \times 10^{23} \text{ molecules}}$

                                                               $= 5.62 \times 10^{-4} \text{ mol } C_6H_{12}O_6$

        (d)   1 mole of $C_6H_{12}O_6$ weighs 180.0 g (Sample Exercise 3.8)

                 $5.618 \times 10^{-4} \text{ mol } C_6H_{12}O_6 \times \dfrac{180.0 \text{ g } C_6H_{12}O_6}{1 \text{ mol}} = 0.101 \text{ g } C_6H_{12}O_6$

3.37   (a)   molar mass $= 24.305 + 2(35.453) = 95.211 = 95.21$ g

                 $0.0750 \text{ g } MgCl_2 \times \dfrac{1 \text{ mol}}{95.21 \text{ g } MgCl_2} \times \dfrac{2 \text{ mol } Cl^-}{1 \text{ mol } MgCl_2} = 1.58 \times 10^{-3} \text{ mol } Cl^-$

        (b)   molar mass $= 2(26.98) + 3(32.07) + 12(16.00) = 342.17 = 342.2$ g

                 $3.50 \times 10^{-3} \text{ mol } Al_2(SO_4)_3 \times \dfrac{342.2 \text{ g } Al_2(SO_4)_3}{1 \text{ mol}} = 1.20 \text{ g } Al_2(SO_4)_3$

        (c)   molar mass $= 8(12.01) + 10(1.008) + 4(14.01) + 2(16.00) = 194.20 = 194.2$ g

                 1.75×10^{20} molecules $\times \dfrac{1 \text{ mol}}{6.022 \times 10^{23} \text{ molecules}} \times \dfrac{194.2 \text{ g } C_8H_{10}N_4O_2}{1 \text{ mol caffeine}}$

                                                      $= 0.0564 \text{ g } C_8H_{10}N_4O_2$

        (d) $\dfrac{0.406 \text{ g cholesterol}}{0.00105 \text{ mol}} = 387$ g cholesterol/mol

3.39   a) $0.0666 \text{ mol } C_3H_8 \times \dfrac{6.022 \times 10^{23} \text{ molecules}}{1 \text{ mol}} = 4.01 \times 10^{22} \text{ } C_3H_8$ molecules

        (b) $50.0 \text{ mg } C_8H_9O_2N \times \dfrac{1 \times 10^{-3} \text{ g}}{1 \text{ mg}} \times \dfrac{1 \text{ mol } C_8H_9O_2N}{151.2 \text{ g } C_8H_9O_2N} \times \dfrac{6.022 \times 10^{23} \text{ molecules}}{1 \text{ mol}}$

                                         $= 1.99 \times 10^{20} \text{ } C_8H_9O_2N$ molecules

        (c) $10.5 \text{ g } C_{12}H_{22}O_{11} \times \dfrac{1 \text{ mol } C_{12}H_{22}O_{11}}{342.3 \text{ g } C_{12}H_{22}O_{11}} \times \dfrac{6.022 \times 10^{23} \text{ molecules}}{1 \text{ mol}}$

                                         $= 1.85 \times 10^{22} \text{ } C_{12}H_{22}O_{11}$ molecules

3.41 $\dfrac{2.05 \times 10^{-6} \text{ g } C_2H_3Cl}{1 \text{ L}} \times \dfrac{1 \text{ mol } C_2H_3Cl}{62.50 \text{ g } C_2H_3Cl} = 3.280 \times 10^{-8} = 3.28 \times 10^{-8} \text{ mol } C_2H_3Cl/L$

       $\dfrac{3.280 \times 10^{-8} \text{ mol } C_2H_3Cl}{1 \text{ L}} \times \dfrac{6.022 \times 10^{23} \text{ molecules}}{1 \text{ mol}} = 1.97 \times 10^{16}$ molecules/L

Empirical Formulas

3.43   (a)   An *empirical formula* gives the relative number and kind of each atom in a compound, but a *molecular formula* gives the actual number of each kind of atom, and thus the molecular weight and molar mass.

       (b)   FW of CH = 12 + 1 = 13. $\dfrac{m}{FW} = \dfrac{104}{13} = 8$

The subscripts in the empirical formula are multiplied by 8; the molecular formula is C_8H_8.

3.45   (a)   Calculate the simplest ratio of moles.

0.104 mol K / 0.052 = 2
0.052 mol C / 0.052 = 1
0.156 mol O / 0.052 = 3

The empirical formula is K_2CO_3.

       (b)   Calculate moles of each element present, then the simplest ratio of moles.

$5.28 \text{ g Sn} \times \dfrac{1 \text{ mol Sn}}{118.7 \text{ g Sn}} = 0.04448 \text{ mol Sn}; \; 0.04448 / 0.04448 = 1$

$3.37 \text{ g F} \times \dfrac{1 \text{ mol F}}{19.00 \text{ g FSn}} = 0.1774 \text{ mol F}; \; 0.1774 / 0.04448 \approx 4$

The integer ratio is 1 Sn : 4 F; the empirical formula is SnF_4.

       (c)   Assume 100 g sample, calculate moles of each element, find the simplest ratio of moles.

$87.5\% \text{ N} = 87.5 \text{ g N} \times \dfrac{1 \text{ mol N}}{14.01 \text{ g}} = 6.25 \text{ mol N}; \; 6.25 / 6.25 = 1$

$12.5\% \text{ H} = 12.5 \text{ g H} \times \dfrac{1 \text{ mol}}{1.008 \text{ g}} = 12.4 \text{ mol H}; \; 12.4 / 6.25 \approx 2$

The empirical formula is NH_2.

3.47   Assume 100 g sample in the following problems.

       (a) $10.4 \text{ g C} \times \dfrac{1 \text{ mol C}}{12.01 \text{ g C}} = 0.866 \text{ mol C}; \; 0.866 / 0.866 = 1$

$27.8 \text{ g S} \times \dfrac{1 \text{ mol S}}{32.07 \text{ g S}} = 0.867 \text{ mol S}; \; 0.867 / 0.866 \approx 1$

$61.7 \text{ g Cl} \times \dfrac{1 \text{ mol Cl}}{35.45 \text{ g Cl}} = 1.74 \text{ mol Cl}; \; 1.74 / 0.866 \approx 2$

The empirical formula is $CSCl_2$.

(b) $21.7 \text{ g C} \times \dfrac{1 \text{ mol C}}{12.01 \text{ g C}} = 1.81 \text{ mol C}; \quad 1.81 / 0.600 \approx 3$

$9.6 \text{ g O} \times \dfrac{1 \text{ mol O}}{16.00 \text{ g O}} = 0.600 \text{ mol O}; \quad 0.600 / 0.600 = 1$

$68.7 \text{ g F} \times \dfrac{1 \text{ mol F}}{19.00 \text{ g F}} = 3.62 \text{ mol F}; \quad 3.62 / 0.600 \approx 6$

The empirical formula is C_3OF_6.

3.49   (a) $FW = 12 + 2(1) = 14. \quad \dfrac{\mathcal{M}}{FW} = \dfrac{84}{14} = 6$

The subscripts in the empirical formula are multiplied by 6. The molecular formula is C_6H_{12}.

(b) $FW = 14.01 + 2(1.008) + 35.45 = 51.48. \quad \dfrac{\mathcal{M}}{FW} = \dfrac{51.5}{51.5} = 1$

The empirical and molecular formulas are NH_2Cl.

3.51   Assume 100 g in the following problems.

(a) $75.69 \text{ g C} \times \dfrac{1 \text{ mol C}}{12.01 \text{ g C}} = 6.30 \text{ mol C}; \; 6.30/0.969 = 6.5$

$8.80 \text{ g H} \times \dfrac{1 \text{ mol H}}{1.008 \text{ g H}} = 8.73 \text{ mol H}; \; 8.73/0.969 = 9.0$

$15.51 \text{ g O} \times \dfrac{1 \text{ mol O}}{16.00 \text{ g O}} = 0.969 \text{ mol O}; \; 0.969/0.969 = 1$

Multiply by 2 to obtain the integer ratio 13:18:2. The empirical formula is $C_{13}H_{18}O_2$, FW = 206 g. Since the empirical formula weight and the molar mass are equal (206 g), the empirical and molecular formulas are $C_{13}H_{18}O_2$.

(b) $59.0 \text{ g C} \times \dfrac{1 \text{ mol C}}{12.01 \text{ g C}} = 4.91 \text{ mol C}; \quad 4.91 / 0.550 \approx 9$

$7.1 \text{ g H} \times \dfrac{1 \text{ mol H}}{1.008 \text{ g H}} = 7.04 \text{ mol H}; \quad 7.04 / 0.550 \approx 13$

$26.2 \text{ g O} \times \dfrac{1 \text{ mol O}}{16.00 \text{ g O}} = 1.64 \text{ mol O}; \quad 6.64 / 0.550 \approx 3$

$7.7 \text{ g N} \times \dfrac{1 \text{ mol N}}{14.01 \text{ g N}} = 0.550 \text{ mol N}; \quad 0.550 / 0.550 = 1$

The empirical formula is $C_9H_{13}O_3N$, FW = 183 amu (or g). Since the molecular weight is approximately 180 amu, the empirical formula and molecular formula are the same, $C_9H_{13}O_3N$.

3.53   (a) $5.86 \times 10^{-3} \text{ g CO}_2 \times \dfrac{1 \text{ mol CO}_2}{44.01 \text{ g CO}_2} \times \dfrac{1 \text{ mol C}}{1 \text{ mol CO}_2} = 1.33 \times 10^{-4} \text{ mol C}.$

$1.37 \times 10^{-3} \text{ g H}_2\text{O} \times \dfrac{1 \text{ mol H}_2\text{O}}{18.02 \text{ g H}_2\text{O}} \times \dfrac{2 \text{ mol H}}{1 \text{ mol H}_2\text{O}} = 1.52 \times 10^{-4} \text{ mol H}.$

Dividing both values by 1.33×10^{-4} gives C:H of 1:1.14. This is not "close enough" to be considered 1:1. No obvious multipliers (2, 3, 4) produce an integer ratio. Testing other multipliers (trial and error!), the correct factor seems to be 7. The empirical formula is C_7H_8.

(b)   Calculate mol C and mol H in the sample.

$$0.2829 \text{ g CO}_2 \times \frac{1 \text{ mol CO}_2}{44.01 \text{ g CO}_2} \times \frac{1 \text{ mol C}}{1 \text{ mol CO}_2} = 0.0064281 = 0.006428 \text{ mol C}$$

$$0.1159 \text{ g H}_2O \times \frac{1 \text{ mol H}_2O}{18.02 \text{ g H}_2O} \times \frac{2 \text{ mol H}}{1 \text{ mol H}_2O} = 0.012863 = 0.01286 \text{ mol H}$$

Calculate g C, g H and get g O by subtraction.

$$0.064281 \text{ mol C} \times \frac{12.01 \text{ g C}}{1 \text{ mol C}} = 0.07720 \text{ g C}$$

$$0.012863 \text{ mol H} \times \frac{1.008 \text{ g H}}{1 \text{ mol H}} = 0.01297 \text{ g H}$$

mass O = 0.1005 g sample - (0.07720 g C + 0.01297 g H) = 0.01033 g O

Calculate mol O and find integer ratio of mol C: mol H: mol O.

$$0.01033 \text{ g O} \times \frac{1 \text{ mol O}}{16.00 \text{ g O}} = 6.456 \times 10^{-4} \text{ mol O}$$

Divide moles by 6.456×10^{-4}.

$$\text{C: } \frac{0.006428}{6.456 \times 10^{-4}} \approx 10; \quad \text{H: } \frac{0.01286}{6.456 \times 10^{-4}} \approx 20; \quad \text{O: } \frac{6.456 \times 10^{-4}}{6.456 \times 10^{-4}} = 1$$

The empirical formula is $C_{10}H_{20}O$.

$$\text{FW} = 10(12) + 20(1) + 16 = 156; \quad \frac{\mathcal{M}}{\text{FW}} = \frac{156}{156} = 1$$

The molecular formula is the same as the empirical formula, $C_{10}H_{20}O$.

3.55   The reaction involved is $MgSO_4 \cdot xH_2O(s) \rightarrow MgSO_4(s) + xH_2O(g)$. First, calculate the number of moles of product $MgSO_4$; this is the same as the number of moles of starting hydrate.

$$2.472 \text{ g MgSO}_4 \times \frac{1 \text{ mol MgSO}_4}{120.4 \text{ g MgSO}_4} \times \frac{1 \text{ mol MgSO}_4 \cdot x \text{ H}_2O}{1 \text{ mol MgSO}_4} = 0.02053 \text{ mol MgSO}_4 \cdot x \text{ H}_2O$$

Thus, $\dfrac{5.061 \text{ g MgSO}_4 \cdot x \text{ H}_2O}{0.02053} = 246.5 \text{ g/mol} = \text{FW of MgSO}_4 \cdot x \text{ H}_2O$.

FW of $MgSO_4 \cdot x H_2O$ = FW of $MgSO_4$ + x(FW of H_2O).

246.5 = 120.4 + x(18.02).   x = 6.998.   The hydrate formula is $MgSO_4 \cdot \underline{7}H_2O$.

Alternatively, we could calculate the number of moles of water represented by weight loss: (5.061 - 2.472) = 2.589 g H_2O lost.

$$2.589 \text{ g } H_2O \times \frac{1 \text{ mol } H_2O}{18.02 \text{ g } H_2O} = 0.1437 \text{ mol } H_2O; \quad \frac{\text{mol } H_2O}{\text{mol } MgSO_4} = \frac{0.1437}{0.02053} = 7.000$$

Again the correct formula is $MgSO_4 \cdot \underline{7}H_2O$.

Calculations Based on Chemical Equations

3.57   The mole ratios implicit in the coefficients of a balanced chemical equation are essential for solving stoichiometry problems. If the equation is not balanced, the mole ratios will be incorrect and lead to erroneous calculated amounts of reactants and/or products.

3.59 $C_6H_{12}O_6(aq) \rightarrow 2C_2H_5OH(aq) + 2CO_2(g)$

(a) $0.300 \text{ mol } C_6H_{12}O_6 \times \dfrac{2 \text{ mol } CO_2}{1 \text{ mol } C_6H_{12}O_6} = 0.600 \text{ mol } CO_2$

(b) $2.00 \text{ g } C_2H_5OH \times \dfrac{1 \text{ mol } C_2H_5OH}{46.07 \text{ g } C_2H_5OH} \times \dfrac{1 \text{ mol } C_6H_{12}O_6}{2 \text{ mol } C_2H_5OH} \times \dfrac{180.2 \text{ g } C_6H_{12}O_6}{1 \text{ mol } C_6H_{12}O_6}$

$$= 3.91 \text{ g } C_6H_{12}O_6$$

(c) $2.00 \text{ g } C_2H_5OH \times \dfrac{1 \text{ mol } C_2H_5OH}{46.07 \text{ g } C_2H_5OH} \times \dfrac{2 \text{ mol } CO_2}{2 \text{ mol } C_2H_5OH} \times \dfrac{44.01 \text{ g } CO_2}{1 \text{ mol } CO_2} = 1.91 \text{ g } CO_2$

3.61   (a) $Al_2S_3(s) + 6H_2O(l) \rightarrow 2Al(OH)_3(s) + 3H_2S(g)$

(b) $10.5 \text{ g } Al_2S_3 \times \dfrac{1 \text{ mol } Al_2S_3}{150.2 \text{ g } Al_2S_3} \times \dfrac{2 \text{ mol } Al(OH)_3}{1 \text{ mol } Al_2S_3} \times \dfrac{78.00 \text{ g } Al(OH)_3}{1 \text{ mol } Al(OH)_3} = 10.9 \text{ g } Al(OH)_3$

3.63   (a) $1.50 \text{ mol } NaN_3 \times \dfrac{3 \text{ mol } N_2}{2 \text{ mol } NaN_3} = 2.25 \text{ mol } N_2$

(b) $5.00 \text{ g } N_2 \times \dfrac{1 \text{ mol } N_2}{28.01 \text{ g } N_2} \times \dfrac{2 \text{ mol } NaN_3}{3 \text{ mol } N_2} \times \dfrac{65.01 \text{ g } NaN_3}{1 \text{ mol } NaN_3} = 7.74 \text{ g } NaN_3$

(c)   First determine how many g N_2 are in 10.0 ft^3, using the density of N_2.

$$\frac{1.25 \text{ g}}{1 \text{ L}} \times \frac{1 \text{ L}}{1000 \text{ cm}^3} \times \frac{(2.54)^3 \text{ cm}^3}{1 \text{ in}^3} \times \frac{(12)^3 \text{ in}^3}{1 \text{ ft}^3} \times 10.0 \text{ ft}^3 = 354.0 = 354 \text{ g } N_2$$

$$354.0 \text{ g } N_2 \times \frac{1 \text{ mol } N_2}{28.01 \text{ g } N_2} \times \frac{2 \text{ mol } NaN_3}{3 \text{ mol } N_2} \times \frac{65.01 \text{ g } NaN_3}{1 \text{ mol } NaN_3} = 548 \text{ g } NaN_3$$

3.65   (a) $1.00 \text{ cm} \times 1.00 \text{ cm} \times 0.550 \text{ mm} \times \dfrac{1 \text{ cm}}{10 \text{ mm}} = 0.0550 \text{ cm}^3 \text{ Al}$

$0.0550 \text{ cm}^3 \text{ Al} \times \dfrac{2.699 \text{ g Al}}{1 \text{ cm}^3} \times \dfrac{1 \text{ mol Al}}{26.98 \text{ g Al}} = 5.502 \times 10^{-3} = 5.50 \times 10^{-3} \text{ mol Al}$

(b) $2Al(s) + 3Br_2(l) \rightarrow 2AlBr_3(s)$

$5.502 \times 10^{-3} \text{ mol Al} \times \dfrac{2 \text{ mol } AlBr_3}{2 \text{ mol Al}} \times \dfrac{266.69 \text{ g } AlBr_3}{1 \text{ mol } AlBr_3} = 1.467 = 1.47 \text{ g } AlBr_3$

Limiting Reactants; Theoretical Yields

3.67 (a) The *limiting reactant* determines the maximum number of product moles resulting from a chemical reaction; any other reactant is an *excess reactant*.

(b) The limiting reactant regulates the amount of products because it is completely used up during the reaction; no more product can be made when one of the reactants is unavailable.

3.69 $N_2 + 3H_2 \rightarrow 2NH_3$. $N_2 =$ 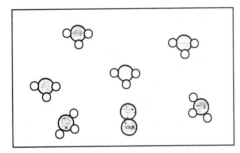 $NH_3 =$

Each N atom (1/2 of an N_2 molecule), reacts with 3 H atoms (1.5 H_2 molecules) to form an NH_3 molecule. Eight N atoms (4 N_2 molecules) require 24 H atoms (12 H_2 molecules) for complete reaction. Only 9 H_2 molecules are available, so H_2 is the limiting reactant. Nine H_2 molecules (18 H atoms) determine that 6 NH_3 molecules are produced. One N_2 molecule is in excess.

3.71 (a) Each bicycle needs 2 wheels, 1 frame and 1 set of handlebars. A total of 5050 wheels corresponds to 2525 pairs of wheels. This is fewer than the number of frames but more than the number of handlebars. The 2455 handlebars determine that 2455 bicycles can be produced.

(b) 3013 frames - 2455 bicycles = 558 frames left over

(2525 pairs of wheels - 2455 bicycles) $\times \dfrac{2\,\text{wheels}}{\text{pair}}$ = 140 wheels left over

(c) The handlebars are the "limiting reactant" in that they determine the number of bicycles that can be produced.

3.73 $3NaHCO_3(aq) + H_3C_6H_5O_7(aq) \rightarrow 3CO_2(g) + 3H_2O(l) + Na_3C_6H_5O_7(aq)$

(a) Abbreviate citric acid as H_3Cit. Follow the approach in Sample Exercise 3.17.

$$1.00\text{ g NaHCO}_3 \times \frac{1\text{ mol NaHCO}_3}{84.01\text{ g NaHCO}_3} = 1.190 \times 10^{-2} = 1.19 \times 10^{-2}\text{ mol NaHCO}_3$$

$$1.00\text{g H}_3\text{C}_6\text{H}_5\text{O}_7 \times \frac{1\text{ mol H}_3\text{Cit}}{192.1\text{ g H}_3\text{Cit}} = 5.206 \times 10^{-3} = 5.21 \times 10^{-3}\text{ mol H}_3\text{Cit}$$

But $NaHCO_3$ and H_3Cit react in a 3:1 ratio, so 5.21×10^{-3} mol H_3Cit require $3(5.21 \times 10^{-3}) = 1.56 \times 10^{-2}$ mol $NaHCO_3$. We have only 1.19×10^{-2} mol $NaHCO_3$, so $NaHCO_3$ is the limiting reactant.

(b) 1.190×10^{-2} mol $NaHCO_3 \times \dfrac{3 \text{ mol } CO_2}{3 \text{ mol } NaHCO_3} \times \dfrac{44.01 \text{ g } CO_2}{1 \text{ mol } CO_2} = 0.524$ g CO_2

(c) 1.190×10^{-2} mol $NaHCO_3 \times \dfrac{1 \text{ mol } H_3Cit}{3 \text{ mol } NaHCO_3} = 3.968 \times 10^{-3}$

                                        $= 3.97 \times 10^{-3}$ mol H_3Cit react

5.206×10^{-3} mol $H_3Cit - 3.968 \times 10^{-3}$ mol react $= 1.238 \times 10^{-3}$

                                        $= 1.24 \times 10^{-3}$ mol H_3Cit remain

1.238×10^{-3} mol $H_3Cit \times \dfrac{192.1 \text{ g } H_3Cit}{\text{mol } H_3Cit} = 0.238$ g H_3Cit remain

3.75 $H_2S(g) + 2NaOH(aq) \rightarrow Na_2S(s) + 2H_2O(l)$

    2.50 g $H_2S \times \dfrac{1 \text{ mol } H_2S}{34.09 \text{ g } H_2S} \times \dfrac{1 \text{ mol } Na_2S}{1 \text{ mol } H_2S} \times \dfrac{78.05 \text{ g } Na_2S}{1 \text{ mol } Na_2S} = 5.72$ g Na_2S

    1.85 g $NaOH \times \dfrac{1 \text{ mol } NaOH}{40.00 \text{ g } NaOH} \times \dfrac{1 \text{ mol } Na_2S}{2 \text{ mol } NaOH} \times \dfrac{78.05 \text{ g } Na_2S}{1 \text{ mol } Na_2S} = 1.80$ g Na_2S

    The lesser amount, 1.80 g Na_2S is formed.

3.77   Strategy: Write balanced equation; determine limiting reactant; calculate amounts of excess reactant remaining and products, based on limiting reactant.

    $H_2SO_4(aq) + Pb(C_2H_3O_2)_2(aq) \rightarrow PbSO_4(s) + 2HC_2H_3O_2(aq)$

    10.0 g $H_2SO_4 \times \dfrac{1 \text{ mol } H_2SO_4}{98.09 \text{ g } H_2SO_4} \times \dfrac{1 \text{ mol } Pb(C_2H_3O_2)_2}{1 \text{ mol } H_2SO_4} \times \dfrac{325.3 \text{ g } Pb(C_2H_3O_2)_2}{1 \text{ mol } Pb(C_2H_3O_2)_2}$

                                             $= 33.2$ g $Pb(C_2H_3O_2)_2$

    10.0 g H_2SO_4 could consume 33.2 g $Pb(C_2H_3O_2)_2$, but we have only 10.0 g $Pb(C_2H_3O_2)_2$, so it is the limiting reactant.

    10.0 g $Pb(C_2H_3O_2)_2 \times \dfrac{1 \text{ mol } Pb(C_2H_3O_2)_2}{325.3 \text{ g } Pb(C_2H_3O_2)_2} \times \dfrac{1 \text{ mol } H_2SO_4}{1 \text{ mol } Pb(C_2H_3O_2)_2} \times \dfrac{98.09 \text{ g } H_2SO_4}{1 \text{ mol } H_2SO_4}$

                                             $= 3.02$ g H_2SO_4

    mass H_2SO_4 remaining $= 10.0$ g initial - 3.02 g reacted $= 6.98$ g $= 7.0$ g

    10.0 g $Pb(C_2H_3O_2)_2 \times \dfrac{1 \text{ mol } Pb(C_2H_3O_2)_2}{325.3 \text{ g } Pb(C_2H_3O_2)_2} \times \dfrac{1 \text{ mol } PbSO_4}{1 \text{ mol } Pb(C_2H_3O_2)_2} \times \dfrac{303.3 \text{ g } PbSO_4}{1 \text{ mol } PbSO_4}$

                                             $= 9.32$ g $PbSO_4$

    10.0 g $Pb(C_2H_3O_2)_2 \times \dfrac{1 \text{ mol } Pb(C_2H_3O_2)_2}{325.3 \text{ g } Pb(C_2H_3O_2)_2} \times \dfrac{2 \text{ mol } HC_2H_3O_2}{1 \text{ mol } Pb(C_2H_3O_2)_2} \times \dfrac{60.05 \text{ g } HC_2H_3O_2}{1 \text{ mol } HC_2H_3O_2}$

                                             $= 3.69$ g $HC_2H_3O_2$

After the reaction is complete there will be no $Pb(C_2H_3O_2)_2$ remaining (limiting reactant), 7.0 g H_2SO_4 (excess reactant), 9.32 g $PbSO_4$ and 3.69 g $HC_2H_3O_2$. The sum of these amounts is 20.0 g; mass is conserved.

3.79   (a)   Compare possible amounts of product from each reactant.

$$30.0 \text{ g } C_6H_6 \times \frac{1 \text{ mol } C_6H_6}{78.11 \text{ g } C_6H_6} \times \frac{1 \text{ mol } C_6H_5Br}{1 \text{ mol } C_6H_6} \times \frac{157.0 \text{ g } C_6H_5Br}{1 \text{ mol } C_6H_5Br} = 60.30$$

$$= 60.3 \text{ g } C_6H_5Br$$

$$65.0 \text{ g } Br_2 \times \frac{1 \text{ mol } Br_2}{159.8 \text{ g } Br_2} \times \frac{1 \text{ mol } C_6H_5Br}{1 \text{ mol } Br_2} \times \frac{157.0 \text{ g } C_6H_5Br}{1 \text{ mol } C_6H_5Br} = 63.9 \text{ g } C_6H_5Br$$

C_6H_6 is the limiting reactant and 60.3 g C_6H_5Br is the theoretical yield.

(b)   % yield = $\dfrac{56.7 \text{ g } C_6H_5Br \text{ actual}}{60.3 \text{ g } C_6H_5Br \text{ theoretical}} \times 100 = 94.0\%$

Additional Exercises

3.81   (a) $C_4H_8O_2(l) + 5O_2(g) \rightarrow 4CO_2(g) + 4H_2O(l)$

        (b) $Cu(OH)_2(s) \rightarrow CuO(s) + H_2O(g)$

        (c) $Zn(s) + Cl_2(g) \rightarrow ZnCl_2(s)$

3.83   FW = 18(12.01) + 27(1.008) + 1(14.01) + 3(16.00) = 305.4 amu

   % C = $\dfrac{18(12.01) \text{ amu}}{305.4 \text{ amu}} \times 100 = 70.8\%$

3.85   (a)   Strategy: volume H_2O → mass H_2O → moles H_2O → molecules H_2O

$$325 \text{ ft} \times 99 \text{ ft} \times 5.5 \text{ ft} \times \frac{12^3 \text{ in}^3}{1 \text{ ft}^3} \times \frac{2.54^3 \text{ cm}^3}{\text{in}^3} \times \frac{1 \text{ mL}}{1 \text{ cm}^3} = 5.011 \times 10^9 = 5.0 \times 10^9 \text{ mL}$$

$$5.011 \times 10^9 \text{ mL} \times \frac{1.0 \text{ g}}{\text{mL}} \times \frac{1 \text{ mol } H_2O}{18.02 \text{ g } H_2O} \times 6.022 \times 10^{23} = 1.7 \times 10^{32} \text{ } H_2O$$
molecules

(b)   Strategy: volume soln → mass soln → mass Sevin (201.2 g/mol)

                                    → moles Sevin → molecules Sevin

0.10 % Sevin = 0.10 g Sevin / 100 g soln

250 mL soln ×

$$\frac{1.0 \text{ g soln}}{\text{mL soln}} \times \frac{0.10 \text{ g Sevin}}{100 \text{ g soln}} \times \frac{1 \text{ mol Sevin}}{201.2 \text{ g Sevin}} \times \frac{6.022 \times 10^{23} \text{ molecules}}{\text{mol}}$$

$$= 7.48 \times 10^{20} = 7.5 \times 10^{20} \text{ molecules}$$

3.88   (a) $0.068 \text{ g } C_5H_5N \times \dfrac{1 \text{ mol } C_5H_5N}{79.1 \text{ g } C_5H_5N} \times \dfrac{6.022 \times 10^{23} \text{ molecules}}{1 \text{ mol}} = 5.18 \times 10^{20}$

$= 5.2 \times 10^{20} \, C_5H_5N \text{ molecules}$

(b) $5.0 \text{ g ZnO} \times \dfrac{1 \text{ mol Zn}}{81.4 \text{ g ZnO}} \times \dfrac{6.022 \times 10^{23} \text{ molecules}}{1 \text{ mol}} = 3.70 \times 10^{22}$

$= 3.7 \times 10^{22} \text{ ZnO formula units}$

There is one C_5H_5N molecule for each $3.70 \times 10^{22}/5.18 \times 10^{20} = 71$ ZnO units

(c) $5.0 \text{ g ZnO} \times \dfrac{48 \text{ m}^2}{1 \text{ g ZnO}} \times \dfrac{1}{5.18 \times 10^{20} \, C_5H_5N \text{ molecules}} = 4.63 \times 10^{-19}$

$= 4.6 \times 10^{-19} \text{ m}^2/\text{molecule}$

$\dfrac{4.63 \times 10^{-19} \text{ m}^2}{C_5H_5N \text{ molecule}} \times \dfrac{(1 \times 10^{10} \text{ Å})^2}{1 \text{ m}^2} = 46 \text{ Å}^2 / C_5H_5N \text{ molecule}$

3.91   (a) $0.7787 \text{ g C} \times \dfrac{1 \text{ mol C}}{12.01 \text{ g C}} = 0.06484 \text{ mol C}$

$0.1176 \text{ g H} \times \dfrac{1 \text{ mol H}}{1.008 \text{ g H}} = 0.1167 \text{ mol H}$

$0.1037 \text{ g O} \times \dfrac{1 \text{ mol C}}{16.00 \text{ g O}} = 0.006481 \text{ mol O}$

Dividing through by the smallest of these values we obtain $C_{10}H_{18}O$.

(b)   The formula weight of $C_{10}H_{18}O$ is 154. Thus, the empirical formula is also the molecular formula.

3.94   Strategy: Because different sample sizes were used to analyze the different elements, calculate mass % of each element in the sample.

i.   Calculate mass % C from g CO_2.

ii.   Calculate mass % Cl from AgCl.

iii. Get mass % H by subtraction.

iv.   Calculate mole ratios and the empirical formulas.

i. $3.52 \text{ g } CO_2 \times \dfrac{1 \text{ mol } CO_2}{44.01 \text{ g } CO_2} \times \dfrac{1 \text{ mol C}}{1 \text{ mol } CO_2} \times \dfrac{12.01 \text{ g C}}{1 \text{ mol C}} = 0.9606 = 0.961 \text{ g C}$

$\dfrac{0.9606 \text{ g C}}{1.50 \text{ g sample}} \times 100 = 64.04 = 64.0\% \text{ C}$

ii. $1.27 \text{ g AgCl} \times \dfrac{1 \text{ mol AgCl}}{143.3 \text{ g AgCl}} \times \dfrac{1 \text{ mol Cl}}{1 \text{ mol AgCl}} \times \dfrac{35.45 \text{ g Cl}}{1 \text{ mol Cl}} = 0.3142 = 0.314 \text{ g Cl}$

$\dfrac{0.3142 \text{ g Cl}}{1.00 \text{ g sample}} \times 100 = 31.42 = 31.4\% \text{ Cl}$

iii. % H = 100.0 - (64.04% C + 31.42% Cl) = 4.54 = 4.5% H

iv.   Assume 100 g sample.

$$64.04 \text{ g C} \times \frac{1 \text{ mol C}}{12.01 \text{ g C}} = 5.33 \text{ mol C}; \; 5.33 / 0.886 = 6.02$$

$$31.42 \text{ g Cl} \times \frac{1 \text{ mol Cl}}{35.45 \text{ g Cl}} = 0.886 \text{ mol Cl}; \; 0.886 / 0.886 = 1.00$$

$$4.54 \text{ g H} \times \frac{1 \text{ mol H}}{1.008 \text{ g H}} = 4.50 \text{ mol H}; \; 4.50 / 0.886 = 5.08$$

The empirical formula is probably C_6H_5Cl.

The subscript for H, 5.08, is relatively far from 5.00, but C_6H_5Cl makes chemical sense. More significant figures in the mass data are required for a more accurate mole ratio.

3.97   **2**$C_{57}H_{110}O_6$ + **163**O_2 → **114**CO_2 + **110**H_2O

molar mass of fat = 57(12.01) + 110(1.008) + 6(16.00) = 891.5

$$1.0 \text{ kg fat} \times \frac{1000 \text{ g}}{1 \text{ kg}} \times \frac{1 \text{ mol fat}}{891.5 \text{ g fat}} \times \frac{110 \text{ mol H}_2\text{O}}{2 \text{ mol fat}} \times \frac{18.02 \text{ g H}_2\text{O}}{1 \text{ mol H}_2\text{O}} \times \frac{1 \text{ kg}}{1000 \text{ g}} = 1.1 \text{ kg H}_2\text{O}$$

3.100   All of the O_2 is produced from $KClO_3$; get g $KClO_3$ from g O_2. All of the H_2O is produced from $KHCO_3$; get g $KHCO_3$ from g H_2O. The g H_2O produced also reveals the g CO_2 from the decomposition of $NaHCO_3$. The remaining CO_2 (13.2 g CO_2 - g CO_2 from $NaHCO_3$) is due to K_2CO_3 and g K_2CO_3 can be derived from it.

$$4.00 \text{ g O}_2 \times \frac{1 \text{ mol O}_2}{32.00 \text{ g O}_2} \times \frac{2 \text{ mol KClO}_3}{3 \text{ mol O}_2} \times \frac{122.6 \text{ g KClO}_3}{1 \text{ mol KClO}_3} = 10.22 = 10.2 \text{ g KClO}_3$$

$$1.80 \text{ H}_2\text{O} \times \frac{1 \text{ mol H}_2\text{O}}{18.02 \text{ g H}_2\text{O}} \times \frac{2 \text{ mol KHCO}_3}{1 \text{ mol H}_2\text{O}} \times \frac{100.1 \text{ g KHCO}_3}{1 \text{ mol KHCO}_3} = 20.00 = 20.0 \text{ g KHCO}_3$$

$$1.80 \text{ g H}_2\text{O} \times \frac{1 \text{ mol H}_2\text{O}}{18.02 \text{ g H}_2\text{O}} \times \frac{2 \text{ mol CO}_2}{1 \text{ mol H}_2\text{O}} \times \frac{44.01 \text{ g CO}_2}{1 \text{ mol CO}_2} = 8.792 = 8.79 \text{ g CO}_2 \text{ from KHCO}_3$$

13.20 g CO_2 total - 8.792 CO_2 from $KHCO_3$ = 4.408 = 4.41 g CO_2 from K_2CO_3

$$4.408 \text{ g CO}_2 \times \frac{1 \text{ mol CO}_2}{44.01 \text{ g CO}_2} \times \frac{1 \text{ mol K}_2\text{CO}_3}{1 \text{ mol CO}_2} \times \frac{138.2 \text{ g K}_2\text{CO}_3}{1 \text{ mol K}_2\text{CO}_3} = 13.84 = 13.8 \text{ g K}_2\text{CO}_3$$

100.0 g mixture - 10.22 g $KClO_3$ - 20.00 g $KHCO_3$ - 13.84 g K_2CO_3 = 56.0 g KCl

Integrative Exercises

3.103   Strategy: volume $\xrightarrow{\text{density}}$ cube mass $CaCO_3$ → moles $CaCO_3$ → moles O → O atoms

$$(1.25)^3 \text{ in}^3 \times \frac{(2.54)^3 \text{ cm}^3}{1 \text{ in}^3} \times \frac{2.71 \text{ g CaCO}_3}{1 \text{ cm}^3} \times \frac{1 \text{ mol CaCO}_3}{100.1 \text{ g CaCO}_3} \times \frac{3 \text{ mol O}}{1 \text{ mol CaCO}_3}$$

$$\times \frac{6.022 \times 10^{23} \text{ O atoms}}{1 \text{ mol O}} = 1.57 \times 10^{24} \text{ O atoms}$$

3.105   Strategy: $m^3 \rightarrow L \xrightarrow{\text{density}} g\ C_8H_{18} \xrightarrow[\text{ratio}]{\text{mole}} g\ CO_2 \rightarrow kg\ CO_2$

$$0.15\ m^3\ C_8H_{18} \times \frac{10^3\ dm^3}{1\ m^3} \times \frac{1\ L}{1\ dm^3} \times \frac{1000\ mL}{1\ L} \times \frac{0.69\ g\ C_8H_{18}}{1\ mL\ C_8H_{18}} = 1.035 \times 10^5$$

$$= 1.0 \times 10^5\ g\ C_8H_{18}$$

$$2C_8H_{18}(l) + 25O_2(g) \rightarrow 16CO_2(g) + 18H_2O(l)$$

$$1.035 \times 10^5\ g\ C_8H_{18} \times \frac{1\ mol\ C_8H_{18}}{114.2\ g\ C_8H_{18}} \times \frac{16\ mol\ CO_2}{2\ mol\ C_8H_{18}} \times \frac{44.01\ g\ CO_2}{1\ mol\ CO_2} \times \frac{1\ kg}{1000\ g}$$

$$= 3.2 \times 10^2\ kg\ CO_2$$

3.107   (a) $S(s) + O_2(g) \rightarrow SO_2(g);\ SO_2(g) + CaO(s) \rightarrow CaSO_3(s)$

(b)

$$\frac{2000\ \text{tons coal}}{\text{day}} \times \frac{2000\ lb}{1\ ton} \times \frac{1\ kg}{2.20\ lb} \times \frac{1000\ g}{1\ kg} \times \frac{0.025\ g\ S}{1\ g\ coal} \times \frac{1\ mol\ S}{32.1\ g\ S}$$

$$\times \frac{1\ mol\ SO_2}{1\ mol\ S} \times \frac{1\ mol\ CaSO_3}{1\ mol\ SO_2} \times \frac{120\ g\ CaSO_3}{1\ mol\ CaSO_3} \times \frac{1\ kg\ CaSO_3}{1000\ g\ CaSO_3}$$

$$= 1.7 \times 10^5\ kg\ CaSO_3/day$$

This corresponds to about 190 tons of $CaSO_3$ per day as a waste product.

4 Aqueous Reactions and Solution Stoichiometry

Electrolytes

4.1   Tap water contains enough dissolved electrolytes to conduct a significant amount of electricity. Thus, water can complete a circuit between an electrical appliance and our body, producing a shock.

4.3   When CH_3OH dissolves, neutral CH_3OH molecules are dispersed throughout the solution. These electrically neutral particles do not carry charge and the solution is nonconducting. When $HC_2H_3O_2$ dissolves, mostly neutral molecules are dispersed throughout the solution. A few of the dissolved molecules ionize to form $H^+(aq)$ and $C_2H_3O_2^-(aq)$. These few ions carry some charge and the solution is weakly conducting.

4.5   (a) $ZnCl_2(aq) \rightarrow Zn^{2+}(aq) + 2Cl^-(aq)$ (b) $HNO_3(aq) \rightarrow H^+(aq) + NO_3^-(aq)$
       (c) $FeSO_4(aq) \rightarrow Fe^{2+}(aq) + SO_4^{2-}(aq)$ (d) $(NH_4)_2CO_3(aq) \rightarrow 2NH_4^+(aq) + CO_3^{2-}(aq)$

4.7   When $HCHO_2$ dissolves in water, neutral $HCHO_2$ molecules, H^+ ions and CHO_2^- ions are all present in the solution. $HCHO_2(aq) \rightleftharpoons H^+(aq) + CHO_2^-(aq)$

Precipitation Reactions and Net Ionic Equations

4.9   Follow the guidelines in Table 4.1.
       (a) $NiCl_2$: soluble   (b) Ag_2S: insoluble
       (c) Cs_3PO_4: soluble (Cs^+ is an alkali metal cation)
       (d) $SrCO_3$: insoluble   (e) $(NH_4)_2SO_4$: soluble

4.11   In each reaction, the precipitate is in bold type.
       (a) $Na_2CO_3(aq) + 2AgNO_3(aq) \rightarrow \mathbf{Ag_2CO_3(s)} + 2NaNO_3(aq)$

       (b)   No precipitate (most sulfates are soluble).

       (c) $FeSO_4(aq) + Pb(NO_3)_2(aq) \rightarrow \mathbf{PbSO_4(s)} + Fe(NO_3)_2(aq)$

4.13   (a) $2Na^+(aq) + CO_3^{2-}(aq) + Mg^{2+}(aq) + SO_4^{2-}(aq) \rightarrow MgCO_3(s) + 2Na^+(aq) + SO_4^{2-}(aq)$

              $Mg^{2+}(aq) + CO_3^{2-}(aq) \rightarrow MgCO_3(s)$

       (b) $Pb^{2+}(aq) + 2NO_3^-(aq) + 2Na^+(aq) + S^{2-}(aq) \rightarrow PbS(s) + 2Na^+(aq) + 2NO_3^-(aq)$

              $Pb^{2+}(aq) + S^{2-}(aq) \rightarrow PbS(s)$

(c) $6NH_4^+(aq) + 2PO_4^{3-}(aq) + 3Ca^{2+}(aq) + 6Cl^-(aq) \rightarrow Ca_3(PO_4)_2(s) + 6NH_4^+(aq)$
$+ 6Cl^-(aq)$

$3Ca^{2+}(aq) + 2PO_4^{3-}(aq) \rightarrow Ca_3(PO_4)_2(s)$

4.15 Br^- and NO_3^- can be ruled out because the Ba^{2+} salts are soluble. (Actually all NO_3^- salts are soluble.) CO_3^{2-} forms insoluble salts with the three cations given; it must be the anion in question.

Acid-Base Reactions

4.17   (a)   A *monoprotic acid* has one ionizable (acidic) H and a *diprotic acid* has two.

(b)   A *strong acid* is completely ionized in aqueous solution whereas only a fraction of *weak acid* molecules are ionized.

(c)   An *acid* is an H^+ donor, a substance that increases the concentration of H^+ in aqueous solution. A *base* is an H^+ acceptor and thus increases the concentration of OH^- in aqueous solution.

4.19   See Table 4.2. (a) strong acid   (b) weak acid   (c) strong base   (d) weak base

4.21   In aqueous solution, HNO_3 exists entirely as H^+ and NO_3^- ions; the single arrow denotes complete ionization.   HCN is only ionized to a small extent; the double arrow denotes a mixture of H^+ ions, CN^- ions and neutral unionized HCN molecules in solution.

4.23   Since the solution does conduct some electricity, but less than an equimolar NaCl solution (a strong electrolyte) the unknown solute must be a weak electrolyte. The weak electrolytes in the list of choices are NH_3 and H_3PO_3; since the solution is acidic, the unknown must be **H_3PO_3.**

4.25   (a) H_2SO_3: weak   (b) C_2H_5OH: non   (c) NH_3: weak

(d) $KClO_3$: strong   (e) $Cu(NO_3)_2$: strong

4.27   (a) $2HBr(aq) + Ca(OH)_2(aq) \rightarrow CaBr_2(aq) + 2H_2O(l)$
$H^+(aq) + OH^-(aq) \rightarrow H_2O(l)$

(b) $Cu(OH)_2(s) + 2HClO_4(aq) \rightarrow Cu(ClO_4)_2(aq) + 2H_2O(l)$
$Cu(OH)_2(s) + 2H^+(aq) \rightarrow 2H_2O(l) + Cu^{2+}(aq)$

(c) $Cr(OH)_3(s) + 3HNO_3(aq) \rightarrow Cr(NO_3)_3(aq) + 3H_2O(l)$
$Cr(OH)_3(s) + 3H^+(aq) \rightarrow 3H_2O(l) + Cr^{3+}(aq)$

4.29   (a) $CdS(s) + H_2SO_4(aq) \rightarrow CdSO_4(aq) + H_2S(g)$
$CdS(s) + 2H^+(aq) \rightarrow H_2S(g) + Cd^{2+}(aq)$

(b) $MgCO_3(s) + 2HClO_4(aq) \rightarrow Mg(ClO_4)_2(aq) + H_2O(l) + CO_2(g)$
$MgCO_3(s) + 2H^+(aq) \rightarrow H_2O(l) + CO_2(g) + Mg^{2+}(aq)$

4.31   (a) $FeO(s) + 2H^+(aq) \rightarrow H_2O(l) + Fe^{2+}(aq)$

(b) $NiO(s) + 2H^+(aq) \rightarrow H_2O(l) + Ni^{2+}(aq)$

Oxidation-Reduction Reactions

4.33 Corrosion was one of the first oxidation-reduction processes to be studied in detail. During corrosion, a metal reacts with some environmental agent, usually oxygen, to form a metal compound. Thus, reaction of a metal with oxygen causes the metal to lose electrons; reaction with oxygen is logically called *oxidation*. Eventually the term oxidation was generalized to mean any process where a substance loses electrons, whether or not the substance is a metal or oxygen is a reactant.

4.35 The most easily oxidized metals are near the bottom of groups on the left side of the chart, especially groups 1A and 2A. The least easily oxidized metals are on the lower right of the transition metals, particularly those near the bottom of groups 8B and 1B.

4.37 (a) +6 (b) +4 (c) +7 (d) +1 (e) 0 (f) -1 (O_2^{2-} is peroxide ion)

4.39 (a) $Ni \rightarrow Ni^{2+}$, Ni is oxidized; $Cl_2 \rightarrow 2Cl^-$, Cl is reduced

(b) $Fe^{2+} \rightarrow Fe$, Fe is reduced; $Al \rightarrow Al^{3+}$, Al is oxidized

(c) $Cl_2 \rightarrow 2Cl^-$, Cl is reduced; $2I^- \rightarrow I_2$, I is oxidized

(d) $S^{2-} \rightarrow SO_4^{2-}$, S is oxidized; $H_2O_2 \rightarrow H_2O$; O is reduced

4.41 (a) $2HCl(aq) + Ni(s) \rightarrow NiCl_2(aq) + H_2(g)$; $Ni(s) + 2H^+(aq) \rightarrow Ni^{2+}(aq) + H_2(g)$

(b) $H_2SO_4(aq) + Fe(s) \rightarrow FeSO_4(aq) + H_2(g)$; $Fe(s) + 2H^+(aq) \rightarrow Fe^{2+}(aq) + H_2(g)$

(c) $2HBr(aq) + Zn(s) \rightarrow ZnBr_2(aq) + H_2(g)$; $Zn(s) + 2H^+(aq) \rightarrow Zn^{2+}(aq) + H_2(g)$

(d) $2HC_2H_3O_2(aq) + Mg(s) \rightarrow Mg(C_2H_3O_2)_2(aq) + H_2(g)$;

$Mg(s) + 2HC_2H_3O_2(aq) \rightarrow Mg^{2+}(aq) + 2C_2H_3O_2^-(aq) + H_2(g)$

4.43 (a) $2Al(s) + 3NiCl_2(aq) \rightarrow 2AlCl_3(aq) + 3Ni(s)$

(b) $Ag(s) + Pb(NO_3)_2(aq) \rightarrow$ no reaction

(c) $2Cr(s) + 3NiSO_4(aq) \rightarrow Cr_2(SO_4)_3(aq) + 3Ni(s)$

(d) $Mn(s) + 2HBr(aq) \rightarrow MnBr_2(aq) + H_2(g)$

(e) $H_2(g) + CuCl_2(aq) \rightarrow Cu(s) + 2HCl(aq)$

4.45 (a) i. $Zn(s) + Cd^{2+}(aq) \rightarrow Cd(s) + Zn^{2+}(aq)$

ii. $Cd(s) + Ni^{2+}(aq) \rightarrow Ni(s) + Cd^{2+}(aq)$

(b) According to Table 4.5, the most active metals are most easily oxidized, and Zn is more active than Ni. Observation (i) indicates that Cd is less active than Zn; observation (ii) indicates that Cd is more active than Ni. Cd is between Zn and Ni on the activity series.

(c) Place an iron strip in $CdCl_2(aq)$. If Cd(s) is deposited, Cd is less active than Fe; if there is no reaction, Cd is more active than Fe. Do the same test with Co if Cd is less active than Fe or with Cr if Cd is more active than Fe.

Solution Composition; Molarity

4.47   Concentration is the **ratio** of the amount of solute present in a certain quantity of solvent or solution. This ratio remains constant regardless of how much solution is present. Thus, concentration is an intensive property. The absolute concentration does depend on the amount of solute present, but once this ratio is established, it doesn't vary with the volume of solution present.

4.49   The second solution is 5 times as concentrated as the first. An equal volume of the more concentrated solution will contain 5 times as much solute (5 times the number of moles and also 5 times the mass) as the 0.50 M solution. Thus, the mass of solute in the 2.50 M solution is 5 × 4.5 g = 22.5 g.

Mathematically:

$$\frac{\dfrac{2.50 \text{ mol solute}}{1 \text{ L solution}}}{\dfrac{0.50 \text{ mol solute}}{1 \text{ L solution}}} = \frac{x \text{ grams solute}}{4.5 \text{ g solute}}$$

$$\frac{2.50 \text{ mol solute}}{0.50 \text{ mol solute}} = \frac{x \text{ g solute}}{4.5 \text{ g solute}}; \quad 5.0(4.5 \text{ g solute}) = 23 \text{ g solute}$$

The result has 2 sig figs; 22.5 rounds to 23 g solute

4.51   (a) $M = \dfrac{\text{mol solute}}{\text{L solution}}; \quad \dfrac{0.0345 \text{ mol NH}_4\text{Cl}}{400 \text{ mL}} \times \dfrac{1000 \text{ mL}}{1 \text{ L}} = 0.0863 \, M \text{ NH}_4\text{Cl}$

(b) $\text{mol} = M \times \text{L}; \quad \dfrac{2.20 \text{ mol HNO}_3}{1 \text{ L}} \times 0.0350 \text{ L} = 0.0770 \text{ mol HNO}_3$

(c) $\text{L} = \dfrac{\text{mol}}{M}; \quad \dfrac{0.125 \text{ mol KOH}}{1.50 \text{ mol KOH/L}} = 0.0833 \text{ L or } 83.3 \text{ mL of } 1.50 \, M \text{ KOH}$

4.53 $M = \dfrac{\text{mol}}{\text{L}}; \quad \text{mol} = \dfrac{g}{\mathcal{M}}$ (𝓜 is the symbol for molar mass in this manual.)

(a) $\dfrac{0.150 \, M \text{ KBr}}{1 \text{ L}} \times 0.250 \text{ L} \times \dfrac{119.0 \text{ g KBr}}{1 \text{ mol KBr}} = 4.46 \text{ g KBr}$

(b) $4.75 \text{ g Ca(NO}_3)_2 \times \dfrac{1 \text{ mol Ca(NO}_3)_2}{164.1 \text{ g Ca(NO}_3)_2} \times \dfrac{1}{0.200 \text{ L}} = 0.145 \, M \text{ Ca(NO}_3)_2$

(c) $5.00 \text{ g Na}_3\text{PO}_4 \times \dfrac{1 \text{ mol Na}_3\text{PO}_4}{163.9 \text{ g Na}_3\text{PO}_4} \times \dfrac{1 \text{ L}}{1.50 \text{ mol Na}_3\text{PO}_4} \times \dfrac{1000 \text{ mL}}{1 \text{ L}}$

$= 20.3 \text{ mL solution}$

4.55 $\text{KCl} \rightarrow \text{K}^+ + \text{Cl}^-; \; 0.20 \, M \text{ KCl} = 0.20 \, M \text{ K}^+$

$\text{K}_2\text{CrO}_4 \rightarrow \textbf{2} \text{ K}^+ + \text{CrO}_4{}^{2-}; \; 0.15 \, M \text{ K}_2\text{CrO}_4 = 0.30 \, M \text{ K}^+$

$\text{K}_3\text{PO}_4 \rightarrow \textbf{3} \text{ K}^+ + \text{PO}_4{}^{3-}; \; 0.080 \, M \text{ K}_3\text{PO}_4 = 0.24 \, M \text{ K}^+$

$0.15 \, M \text{ K}_2\text{CrO}_4$ has the highest K^+ concentration.

4.57   (a)   0.14 M Na^+, 0.14 M OH^-

       (b)   0.25 M Ca^{2+}, 0.50 M Br^-

       (c)   0.25 M (CH_3OH is a molecular solute)

       (d) $M_2 = M_1V_1/V_2$, where V_2 is the total solution volume.

$$K^+: \frac{0.20\ M \times 0.050\ L}{0.075\ L} = 0.133 = 0.13\ M$$

ClO_3^-: concentration ClO_3^- = concentration K^+ = 0.13 M

$$SO_4^{2-}: \frac{0.20\ M \times 0.0250\ L}{0.075\ L} = 0.0667 = 0.067\ M\ SO_4^{2-}$$

Na^+: concentration Na^+ = 2 × concentration SO_4^{2-} = 0.13 M

4.59   (a) $V_1 = M_2V_2/M_1$; $\dfrac{0.100\ M\ NH_3 \times 100.0\ mL}{14.8\ M\ NH_3} = 0.6757 = 0.676\ mL\ 14.8\ M\ NH_3$

       (b) $M_2 = M_1V_1/V_2$; $\dfrac{14.8\ M\ NH_3 \times 10.0\ mL}{250\ mL} = 0.592\ M\ NH_3$

4.61   (a)   The number of moles of sucrose needed is

$$\frac{0.150\ mol}{1\ L} \times 0.125\ L = 0.01875 = 0.0188\ mol$$

Weigh out 0.01875 mol $C_{12}H_{22}O_{11} \times \dfrac{342.3\ g\ C_{12}H_{22}O_{11}}{1\ mol\ C_{12}H_{22}O_{11}} = 6.42\ g\ C_{12}H_{22}O_{11}$

Add this amount of solid to a 125 mL volumetric flask, dissolve in a small volume of water, and add water to the mark on the neck of the flask. Agitate thoroughly to ensure total mixing.

       (b)   Calculate the moles of solute present in the final 400.0 mL of 0.100 M $C_{12}H_{22}O_{11}$ solution:

moles $C_{12}H_{22}O_{11} = M \times L = \dfrac{0.100\ mol\ C_{12}H_{22}O_{11}}{1\ L} \times 0.4000\ L = 0.0400\ mol\ C_{12}H_{22}O_{11}$

Calculate the volume of 1.50 M glucose solution that would contain 0.04000 mol $C_{12}H_{22}O_{11}$:

L = moles/M; 0.04000 mol $C_{12}H_{22}O_{11} \times \dfrac{1\ L}{1.50\ mol\ C_{12}H_{22}O_{11}} = 0.02667 = 0.0267\ L$

0.02667 L × $\dfrac{1000\ mL}{1\ L}$ = 26.7 mL

Thoroughly rinse, clean and fill a 50 mL buret with the 1.50 M $C_{12}H_{22}O_{11}$. Dispense 26.7 mL of this solution into a 400 mL volumetric container, add water to the mark and mix thoroughly. (26.7 mL is a difficult volume to measure with a pipette.)

4.63   Calculate the mass of acetic acid, $HC_2H_3O_2$, present in 10.0 mL of the pure liquid.

$$10.00 \text{ mL acetic acid} \times \frac{1.049 \text{ g acetic acid}}{1 \text{ mL acetic acid}} = 10.49 \text{ g acetic acid}$$

$$10.49 \text{ g } HC_2H_3O_2 \times \frac{1 \text{ mol } HC_2H_3O_2}{60.05 \text{ g } HC_2H_3O_2} = 0.17469 = 0.1747 \text{ mol } HC_2H_3O_2$$

$$M = \text{mol/L} = \frac{0.17469 \text{ mol } HC_2H_3O_2}{0.1000 \text{ L solution}} = 1.747 \ M \ HC_2H_3O_2$$

Solution Stoichiometry; Titrations

4.65   Strategy: $M \times L = $ mol $AgNO_3 = $ mol Ag^+; balanced equation gives ratio mol NaCl/mol $AgNO_3$; mol NaCl → g NaCl

$$\frac{0.100 \text{ mol } AgNO_3}{1 \text{ L}} \times 0.0200 \text{ L} = 2.00 \times 10^{-3} \text{ mol } AgNO_3(aq)$$

$$AgNO_3(aq) + NaCl(aq) \rightarrow AgCl(s) + NaNO_3(aq)$$

$$\text{mol NaCl} = \text{mol } AgNO_3 = 2.00 \times 10^{-3} \text{ mol NaCl}$$

$$2.00 \times 10^{-3} \text{ mol NaCl} \times \frac{58.44 \text{ g NaCl}}{1 \text{ mol NaCl}} = 0.117 \text{ g NaCl}$$

4.67   (a)   Write the balanced equation for the reaction in question:
$$HClO_4(aq) + NaOH(aq) \rightarrow NaClO_4(aq) + H_2O(l)$$

Calculate the moles of the known substance, in this case NaOH.

$$\text{moles NaOH} = M \times L = \frac{0.0875 \text{ mol NaOH}}{1 \text{ L}} \times 0.0500 \text{ L} = 0.004375$$
$$= 0.00438 \text{ mol NaOH}$$

Apply the mole ratio (mol unknown/mol known) from the chemical equation.

$$0.004375 \text{ mol NaOH} \times \frac{1 \text{ mol } HClO_4}{1 \text{ mol NaOH}} = 0.004375 \text{ mol } HClO_4$$

Calculate the desired quantity of unknown, in this case the volume of 0.115 M $HClO_4$ solution.

$$L = \text{mol}/M; \quad L = 0.004375 \text{ mol } HClO_4 \times \frac{1 \text{ L}}{0.115 \text{ mol } HClO_4} = 0.0380 \text{ L} = 38.0 \text{ mL}$$

(b)   Following the procedure outlined in part (a):
$$2HCl(aq) + Mg(OH)_2(s) \rightarrow MgCl_2(aq) + 2H_2O(l)$$

$$2.87 \text{ g } Mg(OH)_2 \times \frac{1 \text{ mol } Mg(OH)_2}{58.33 \text{ g } Mg(OH)_2} = 0.04920 = 0.04920 \text{ mol } Mg(OH)_2$$

$$0.0492 \text{ mol } Mg(OH)_2 \times \frac{2 \text{ mol HCl}}{1 \text{ mol } Mg(OH)_2} = 0.0984 \text{ mol HCl}$$

$$L = \text{mol}/M = 0.09840 \text{ mol HCl} \times \frac{1 \text{ L HCl}}{0.128 \text{ mol HCl}} = 0.769 \text{ L} = 769 \text{ mL}$$

(c) $AgNO_3(aq) + KCl(aq) \rightarrow AgCl(s) + KNO_3(aq)$

$$785 \text{ mg KCl} \times \frac{1 \times 10^{-3} \text{ g}}{1 \text{ mg}} \times \frac{1 \text{ mol KCl}}{74.55 \text{ g KCl}} \times \frac{1 \text{ mol AgNO}_3}{1 \text{ mol KCl}} = 0.01053$$

$$= 0.0105 \text{ mol AgNO}_3$$

$$M = \text{mol/L} = \frac{0.01053 \text{ mol AgNO}_3}{0.0258 \text{ L}} = 0.408 \ M \text{ AgNO}_3$$

(d) $HCl(aq) + KOH(aq) \rightarrow KCl(aq) + H_2O(l)$

$$\frac{0.108 \text{ mol HCl}}{1 \text{ L}} \times 0.0453 \text{ L} \times \frac{1 \text{ mol KOH}}{1 \text{ mol HCl}} \times \frac{56.11 \text{ g KOH}}{1 \text{ mol KOH}} = 0.275 \text{ g KOH}$$

4.69   See Exercise 4.67 (a) for a more detailed approach.

$$\frac{6.0 \text{ mol H}_2\text{SO}_4}{1 \text{ L}} \times 0.035 \text{ L} \times \frac{2 \text{ mol NaHCO}_3}{1 \text{ mol H}_2\text{SO}_4} \times \frac{84.01 \text{ g NaHCO}_3}{1 \text{ mol NaHCO}_3} = 35 \text{ g NaHCO}_3$$

4.71   The neutralization reaction here is:

$$2HBr(aq) + Ca(OH)_2(aq) \rightarrow CaBr_2(aq) + 2H_2O(l)$$

$$0.0488 \text{ L HBr soln} \times \frac{5.00 \times 10^{-2} \text{ mol HBr}}{1 \text{ L soln}} \times \frac{1 \text{ mol Ca(OH)}_2}{2 \text{ mol HBr}} \times \frac{1}{0.100 \text{ L of Ca(OH)}_2}$$

$$= 1.220 \times 10^{-2} = 1.22 \times 10^{-2} \ M \text{ Ca(OH)}_2$$

From the molarity of the saturated solution, we can calculate the gram solubility of $Ca(OH)_2$ in 100 mL of H_2O.

$$0.100 \text{ L soln} \times \frac{1.220 \times 10^{-2} \text{ mol Ca(OH)}_2}{1 \text{ L soln}} \times \frac{74.10 \text{ g Ca(OH)}_2}{1 \text{ mol Ca(OH)}_2}$$

$$= 0.0904 \text{ g Ca(OH)}_2 \text{ in 100 mL soln}$$

4.73   (a) $NiSO_4(aq) + 2KOH(aq) \rightarrow Ni(OH)_2(s) + K_2SO_4(aq)$

         (b)   The precipitate is $Ni(OH)_2$.

         (c)   Strategy: compare mol of each reactant; mol = $M \times L$

                 0.200 M KOH × 0.1000 L KOH = 0.0200 mol KOH
                 0.150 M $NiSO_4$ × 0.2000 L KOH = 0.0300 mol $NiSO_4$

                 1 mol $NiSO_4$ requires 2 mol KOH, so 0.0300 mol $NiSO_4$ requires 0.0600 mol KOH. Since only 0.0200 mol KOH is available, KOH is the limiting reactant.

         (d)   The amount of the limiting reactant (KOH) determines amount of product, in this case $Ni(OH)_2$.

$$0.0200 \text{ mol KOH} \times \frac{1 \text{ mol Ni(OH)}_2}{2 \text{ mol KOH}} \times \frac{92.71 \text{ g Ni(OH)}_2}{1 \text{ mol Ni(OH)}_2} = 0.927 \text{ g Ni(OH)}_2$$

(e)   Limiting reactant: OH^-: no excess OH^- remains in solution.

Excess reactant: Ni^{2+}: M Ni^{2+} remaining = mol Ni^{2+} remaining/L solution

0.0300 mol Ni^{2+} initial - 0.0100 mol Ni^{2+} reacted = 0.0200 mol Ni^{2+} remaining

0.0200 mol Ni^{2+}/0.3000 L = 0.0667 M Ni^{2+}(aq)

Spectators: SO_4^{2-}, K^+. These ions do not react, so the only change in their concentration is dilution. The final volume of the solution is 0.3000 L.

$M_2 = M_1 V_1 / V_2$: 0.200 M K^+ × 0.1000 L / 0.3000 L = 0.0667 M K^+(aq)

0.150 M SO_4^{2-} × 0.2000 L/0.3000 L = 0.100 M SO_4^{2-}(aq)

Additional Exercises

4.75   When an ionic compound dissolves in water, water molecules surround and separate ions from the solid lattice and disperse them into the solution. The negative (O) ends of water molecules point toward cations and the positive (H) ends of water molecules point toward anions.

4.77   The two precipitates formed are due to AgCl(s) and $SrSO_4$(s). Since no precipitate forms on addition of hydroxide ion to the remaining solution, the other two possibilities, Ni^{2+} and Mn^{2+}, are absent.

4.79   (a) $Al(OH)_3(s) + 3H^+(aq) \rightarrow Al^{3+}(aq) + 3H_2O(l)$

(b) $Mg(OH)_2(s) + 2H^+(aq) \rightarrow Mg^{2+}(aq) + 2H_2O(l)$

(c) $MgCO_3(s) + 2H^+(aq) \rightarrow Mg^{2+}(aq) + H_2O(l) + CO_2(g)$

(d) $NaAl(CO_3)(OH)_2(s) + 4H^+(aq) \rightarrow Na^+(aq) + Al^{3+}(aq) + 3H_2O(l) + CO_2(g)$

(e) $CaCO_3(s) + 2H^+(aq) \rightarrow Ca^{2+}(aq) + H_2O(l) + CO_2(g)$

[In (c), (d) and (e), one could also write the equation for formation of bicarbonate, e.g.,

$MgCO_3(s) + H^+(aq) \rightarrow Mg^{2+} + HCO_3^-(aq)$.]

4.82   A metal on Table 4.5 is able to displace the metal cations below it from their compounds. That is, zinc will reduce the cations below it to their metals.

(a) $Zn(s) + Na^+(aq) \rightarrow$ no reaction

(b) $Zn(s) + Pb^{2+}(aq) \rightarrow Zn^{2+}(aq) + Pb(s)$

(c) $Zn(s) + Mg^{2+}(aq) \rightarrow$ no reaction

(d) $Zn(s) + Fe^{2+}(aq) \rightarrow Zn^{2+}(aq) + Fe(s)$

(e) $Zn(s) + Cu^{2+}(aq) \rightarrow Zn^{2+}(aq) + Cu(s)$

(f) $Zn(s) + Al^{3+}(aq) \rightarrow$ no reaction

4.85   (a) $0.0500 \text{ L soln} \times \dfrac{0.200 \text{ mol NaCl}}{1 \text{ L soln}} = 1.00 \times 10^{-2} \text{ mol NaCl}$

$0.1000 \text{ L soln} \times \dfrac{0.100 \text{ mol NaCl}}{1 \text{ L soln}} = 1.00 \times 10^{-2} \text{ mol NaCl}$

Total moles NaCl = 2.00×10^{-2}, total volume = 0.0500 L + 0.1000 L = 0.1500 L

$$\text{Molarity} = \frac{2.00 \times 10^{-2}\,\text{mol}}{0.150\,\text{L}} = 0.133\ M$$

(b) $0.0245\,\text{L soln} \times \dfrac{1.50\,\text{mol NaOH}}{1\,\text{L soln}} = 0.03675 = 0.0368\ \text{mol NaOH}$

$0.0250\,\text{L soln} \times \dfrac{0.850\,\text{mol NaOH}}{1\,\text{L soln}} = 0.017425 = 0.0174\ \text{mol NaOH}$

Total moles NaOH = 0.054175 = 0.0542, total volume = 0.0450 L

$$\text{Molarity} = \frac{0.054175\,\text{mol NaOH}}{0.0450\,\text{L}} = 1.20\ M$$

4.88 Na^+ must replace the total + charge due to Ca^{2+} and Mg^{2+}. Think of this as moles of charge rather than moles of particles.

$$\frac{0.010\,\text{mol Ca}^{2+}}{1\,\text{L water}} \times 1.0 \times 10^3\,\text{L} \times \frac{2\,\text{mol + charge}}{1\,\text{mol Ca}^{2+}} = 20\ \text{mol of + charge}$$

$$\frac{0.0050\,\text{mol Mg}^{2+}}{1\,\text{L water}} \times 1.0 \times 10^3\,\text{L} \times \frac{2\,\text{mol + charge}}{1\,\text{mol Mg}^{2+}} = 10\ \text{mol of + charge}$$

30 moles of + charge must be replaced; 30 mol Na^+ are needed.

4.90   Strategy: mol MnO_4^- = $M \times$ L $\rightarrow$ mol ratio $\rightarrow$ mol H_2O_2 $\rightarrow$ M H_2O_2

$2MnO_4^-(aq) + 5H_2O_2(aq) + 6H^+ \rightarrow 2Mn^{2+}(aq) + 5O_2(aq) + 8H_2O(l)$

$$\frac{0.103\,\text{mol MnO}_4^-}{\text{L}} \times 0.0152\,\text{L MnO}_4^- \times \frac{5\,\text{mol H}_2\text{O}_2}{2\,\text{mol MnO}_4^-} \times \frac{1}{0.0100\,\text{L H}_2\text{O}_2}$$

$$= 0.3914\ \text{mol H}_2\text{O}_2\,/\,\text{L} = 0.391\ M\ \text{H}_2\text{O}_2$$

Integrative Exercises

4.92   Strategy: $M \times$ L = mol Na_3PO_4 $\rightarrow$ mol Na^+ $\rightarrow$ Na^+ ions

$$\frac{0.0100\,\text{mol Na}_3\text{PO}_4}{1\,\text{L solution}} \times 1.00\,\text{mL} \times \frac{1\,\text{L}}{1000\,\text{mL}} \times \frac{3\,\text{mol Na}^+}{1\,\text{mol Na}_3\text{PO}_4} \times \frac{6.022 \times 10^{23}\,\text{Na}^+\,\text{ions}}{1\,\text{mol Na}^+}$$

4.95   (a) $Na_2SO_4(aq) + Pb(NO_3)_2(s) \rightarrow PbSO_4(s) + 2NaNO_3(aq)$

(b)   Calculate mol of each reactant and compare.

$$1.50\,\text{g Pb(NO}_3)_2 \times \frac{1\,\text{mol Pb(NO}_3)_2}{331.2\,\text{g Pb(NO}_3)_2} = 0.004529 = 4.53 \times 10^{-3}\ \text{mol Pb(NO}_3)_2$$

$0.100\ M\ \text{Na}_2\text{SO}_4 \times 0.125\,\text{L} = 0.0125\ \text{mol Na}_2\text{SO}_4$

Since the reactants combine in a 1:1 mol ratio, $Pb(NO_3)_2$ is the limiting reactant.

(c) $Pb(NO_3)_2$ is the limiting reactant, so no Pb^{2+} remains in solution. The remaining ions are: SO_4^{2-} (excess reactant), Na^+ and NO_3^- (spectators).

SO_4^{2-}: 0.0125 mol SO_4^{2-} initial - 0.00453 mol SO_4^{2-} reacted
$$= 0.00797 = 0.0080 \text{ mol } SO_4^{2-} \text{ remain}$$
0.00797 mol $SO_4^{2-}/ 0.125$ L soln $= 0.064$ M SO_4^{2-}

Na^+:   Since the total volume of solution is the volume of $Na_2SO_4(aq)$ added, the concentration of Na^+ is unchanged.
0.100 M Na_2SO_4 × (2 mol Na^+ / 1 mol Na_2SO_4) = 0.200 M Na^+

NO_3^{2-}: 4.53×10^{-3} mol $Pb(NO_3)_2$ × 2 mol NO_3^- / 1 mol $Pb(NO_3)_2$
$$= 9.06 \times 10^{-3} \text{ mol } NO_3^-$$
9.06×10^{-3} mol NO_3^- / 0.125 L = 0.0725 M NO_3^-

4.98   (a) $\mathbf{As}O_4^{3-}$; +5

(b) $Ag_3\mathbf{P}O_4$ is silver phosphate; $Ag_3\mathbf{As}O_4$ is silver arsenate

(c) 0.0250 L soln $\times \dfrac{0.102 \text{ mol } Ag^+}{1 \text{ L soln}} \times \dfrac{1 \text{ mol } Ag_3AsO_4}{3 \text{ mol } Ag^+} \times \dfrac{1 \text{ mol As}}{1 \text{ mol } Ag_3AsO_4} \times \dfrac{74.92 \text{ g As}}{1 \text{ mol As}}$

$$= 0.06368 = 0.0637 \text{ g As}$$

mass percent $= \dfrac{0.06368 \text{ g As}}{1.22 \text{ g sample}} \times 100 = 5.22\%$ As

5 Thermochemistry

Nature of Energy

5.1   An object can possess energy by virtue of its motion or position. Kinetic energy, the energy of motion, depends on the mass of the object and its velocity. Potential energy, stored energy, depends on the position of the object relative to the body with which it interacts.

5.3   (a)   Since $1\ J = 1\ kg \cdot m^2/s^2$, convert g → kg to obtain E_k in joules.

$$E_k = 1/2\ mv^2 = 1/2\ \times 45\ g\ \times \frac{1\ kg}{1000\ g}\ \times \left(\frac{61\ m}{1\ s}\right)^2 = \frac{84\ kg \cdot m^2}{1\ s^2} = 84\ J$$

(b) $83.72\ J\ \times \dfrac{1\ cal}{4.184\ J} = 20\ cal$

(c)   As the ball hits the tree, its speed (and hence its kinetic energy) drops to zero. Most of the kinetic energy is transferred to the potential energy of a slightly deformed golf ball, some is absorbed by the tree and some is released as heat. As the ball bounces off the tree, its potential energy is reconverted to kinetic energy.

5.5   Find: J/Btu

Given: heat capacity of water = 1 Btu/lb•°F

Know: heat capacity of water = 4.184 J/g•°C

Strategy: $\dfrac{J}{g \cdot {}^\circ C} \rightarrow \dfrac{J}{lb \cdot {}^\circ F} \rightarrow \dfrac{J}{Btu}$

This strategy requires changing °F to °C. Since this involves the magnitude of a degree on each scale, rather than a specific temperature, the 32 in the temperature relationship is not needed.

100 °C = 180 °F; 5 °C = 9 °F

$$\frac{4.184\ J}{g \cdot {}^\circ C}\ \times \frac{453.6\ g}{lb}\ \times \frac{5\ {}^\circ C}{9\ {}^\circ F}\ \times \frac{1\ lb \cdot {}^\circ F}{1\ Btu} = 1054\ J/Btu$$

5.7   (a)   In thermodynamics, the *system* is the well-defined part of the universe whose energy changes are being studied.

(b)   A closed system can exchange heat but not mass with its surroundings.

5.9   (a)   *Work* is a force applied over a distance.

         (b)   The amount of work done is the magnitude of the force times the distance over which it is applied. $w = F \times d.$

5.11   (a)   Gravity; work is done because the force of gravity is opposed and the pencil is lifted.

         (b)   Mechanical force; work is done because the force of the coiled spring is opposed as the spring is compressed over a distance.

The First Law of Thermodynamics

5.13   (a)   In any chemical or physical change, energy can be neither created nor destroyed, but it can be changed in form.

         (b)   The total *internal energy* (E) of a system is the sum of all the kinetic and potential energies of the system components.

         (c)   The internal energy of a system increases when work is done on the system by the surroundings and/or when heat is transferred to the system from the surroundings (the system is heated).

5.15   In each case, evaluate q and w in the expression $\Delta E = q + w$. For an exothermic process, q is negative; for an endothermic process, q is positive.

         (a)   q is negative because the system loses heat and w is negative because the system does work. $\Delta E = -113 \text{ kJ} - 39 \text{ kJ} = -152 \text{ kJ}$. The process is exothermic.

         (b) $\Delta E = +1.62 \text{ kJ} - 847 \text{ J} = +1.62 \text{ kJ} - 0.847 \text{ kJ} = +0.746 = +0.75 \text{ kJ}$. The process is endothermic.

         (c)   q is positive because the system gains heat and w is negative because the system does work. $\Delta E = +77.5 \text{ kJ} - 63.5 \text{ kJ} = +14.0 \text{ kJ}$. The process is endothermic.

5.17   (a) 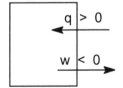   (b) 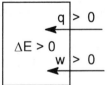   (c)

         ΔE depends on the relative magnitudes of q and w.

         If $\Delta E < 0$, then w must be negative and have a larger magnitude than q.

5.19   (a)   A *state function* is a property of a system that depends only on the physical state (pressure, temperature, etc.) of the system, not on the route used by the system to get to the current state.

         (b)   Internal energy and enthalpy <u>are</u> state functions; work <u>is not</u> a state function.

(c)   Temperature is a state function; regardless of how hot or cold the sample has been, the temperature depends only on its present condition.

Enthalpy

5.21   (a)   For the many laboratory and real world processes that occur at constant atmospheric pressure, the enthalpy change is a meaningful measure of the energy change associated with the process. At constant pressure, most of the energy change is transferred as heat ($\Delta H = q_p$), even if gases are involved in the process.

       (b)   Only under conditions of constant pressure is ΔH for a process equal to the heat transferred during the process.

       (c)   If ΔH is negative, the enthalpy of the system decreases and the process is exothermic.

5.23   (a) $HC_2H_3O_2(l) + 2O_2(g) \rightarrow 2H_2O(l) + 2CO_2(g)$ (b)

                 $\Delta H = -871.7$ kJ

$$HC_2H_3O_2(l) + 2\,O_2(g)$$

$$\Delta H = -871.7 \text{ kJ} \downarrow$$

$$2\,H_2O(l) + 2\,CO_2(g)$$

5.25   Since ΔH is negative, the reactants, $2Cl(g)$ have the higher enthalpy.

5.27   (a)   Exothermic (ΔH is negative)

       (b) $2.4 \text{ g Mg} \times \dfrac{1 \text{ mol Mg}}{24.305 \text{ g Mg}} \times \dfrac{-1204 \text{ kJ}}{2 \text{ mol Mg}} = -59$ kJ heat transferred

       (c) $-96.0 \text{ kJ} \times \dfrac{2 \text{ mol MgO}}{-1204 \text{ kJ}} \times \dfrac{40.30 \text{ g MgO}}{1 \text{ mol Mg}} = 6.43$ g MgO produced

       (d) $2MgO(s) \rightarrow 2Mg(s) + O_2(g)$ $\Delta H = +1204$ kJ

               This is the reverse of the reaction given above, so the sign of ΔH is reversed.

               $7.50 \text{ g MgO} \times \dfrac{1 \text{ mol MgO}}{40.30 \text{ g MgO}} \times \dfrac{1204 \text{ kJ}}{2 \text{ mol MgO}} = +112$ kJ heat absorbed

5.29   (a) $0.200 \text{ mol AgCl} \times \dfrac{-65.5 \text{ kJ}}{1 \text{ mol AgCl}} = -13.1$ kJ

       (b) $2.50 \text{ g AgCl} \times \dfrac{1 \text{ mol AgCl}}{143.3 \text{ g AgCl}} \times \dfrac{-65.5 \text{ kJ}}{1 \text{ mol AgCl}} = -1.14$ kJ

       (c) $0.350 \text{ mmol AgCl} \times \dfrac{1 \times 10^{-3} \text{ mol}}{1 \text{ mmol}} \times \dfrac{+65.5 \text{ kJ}}{1 \text{ mol AgCl}} = +0.0229 \text{ kJ} = +22.9$ J

                                                        (sign of ΔH reversed)

5.31　At constant pressure, $\Delta E = \Delta H - P\Delta V$. In order to calculate ΔE, more information about the conditions of the reaction must be known. For an ideal gas at constant pressure and temperature, $P\Delta V = RT\Delta n$. The values of either P and ΔV or T and Δn must be known to calculate ΔE from ΔH.

5.33　$q = -89$ kJ (heat is given off by the system), $w = -36$ kJ (work is done by the system).

　　　$\Delta E = q + w = -89$ kJ $- 36$ kJ $= -125$ kJ. $\Delta H = q = -89$ kJ (at constant pressure).

5.35　(a)　　$CO_2(g) + 2H_2O(l) \rightarrow CH_3OH(l) + 3/2\ O_2(g)$　　　$\Delta H = +726.5$ kJ

　　　(b)　　$2CH_3OH(l) + 3O_2(g) \rightarrow 2CO_2(g) + 4H_2O(l)$　　$\Delta H = 2(-726.5)$ kJ $= -1453$ kJ

　　　(c)　　The exothermic forward reaction is more likely to be thermodynamically favored.

　　　(d)　　Vaporization (liquid $\rightarrow$ gas) is endothermic. If the product were $H_2O(g)$, the reaction would be more endothermic and would have a smaller negative ΔH. (Depending on temperature, the enthalpy of vaporization for 2 mol H_2O is about +88 kJ, not large enough to cause the overall reaction to be endothermic.)

Calorimetry

The specific heat of water to four significant figures, **4.184 J/g•K**, will be used in many of the following exercises; temperature units of K and °C will be used interchangeably.

5.37　(a)　$\dfrac{4.184\ J}{1\ g \cdot K}$ or $\dfrac{4.184\ J}{1\ g \cdot °C}$　　(b)　$\dfrac{185\ g\ H_2O \times 4.184\ J}{1\ g \cdot °C} = 774$ J/°C

　　　(c)　10.00 kg $H_2O \times \dfrac{1000\ g}{1\ kg} \times \dfrac{4.184\ J}{1\ g \cdot °C} \times \dfrac{1\ kJ}{1000\ J} \times (46.2°C - 24.6°C) = 904$ kJ

5.39　1.42 kg Cu $\times \dfrac{1000\ g}{1\ kg} \times \dfrac{0.385\ J}{g \cdot K} \times (88.5°C - 25.0°C) = 3.47 \times 10^4$ J (or 34.7 kJ)

5.41　Since the temperature of the water increases, the dissolving process is exothermic and the sign of ΔH is negative. The heat lost by the NaOH(s) dissolving equals the heat gained by the solution.

　　　Calculate the heat gained by the solution. The temperature change is $37.8 - 21.6 = 16.2°C$. The total mass of solution is (100.0 g H_2O + 6.50 g NaOH) = 106.5 g.

　　　106.5 g solution $\times \dfrac{4.184\ J}{1\ g \cdot °C} \times 16.2°C \times \dfrac{1\ kJ}{1000\ J} = 7.219 = 7.22$ kJ

　　　This is the amount of heat lost when 6.50 g of NaOH dissolves.

　　　The heat loss per mole NaOH is

　　　$\dfrac{-7.219\ kJ}{6.50\ g\ NaOH} \times \dfrac{40.00\ g\ NaOH}{1\ mol\ NaOH} = -44.4$ kJ/mol　　$\Delta H = q_p = -44.4$ kJ/mol NaOH

5.43 $q_{bomb} = -q_{rxn}$; $\Delta T = 30.57°C - 23.44°C = 7.13°C$

$q_{bomb} = \dfrac{7.854 \text{ kJ}}{1°C} \times 7.13°C = 56.00 = 56.0 \text{ kJ}$

At constant volume, $q_v = \Delta E$. ΔE and ΔH are very similar.

$\Delta E_{rxn} = q_{rxn} = -q_{bomb} = \dfrac{-56.0 \text{ kJ}}{2.20 \text{ g } C_6H_4O_2} = -25.454 = -25.5 \text{ kJ/g } C_6H_4O_2$

$\Delta E_{rxn} = \dfrac{-25.454 \text{ kJ}}{1 \text{ g } C_6H_4O_2} \times \dfrac{108.1 \text{ g } C_6H_4O_2}{1 \text{ mol } C_6H_4O_2} = -2.75 \times 10^3 \text{ kJ/mol } C_6H_4O_2$

5.45 (a) $C_{total} = 2.500 \text{ g glucose} \times \dfrac{15.57 \text{ kJ}}{1 \text{ g glucose}} \times \dfrac{1}{2.70°C} = 14.42 = 14.4 \text{ kJ/°C}$

(b) $C_{H_2O} = 2.700 \text{ kg } H_2O \times \dfrac{4.184 \text{ kJ}}{1 \text{ kg} \cdot °C} = 11.30 \text{ kJ/°C}$

$C_{empty \ calorimeter} = \dfrac{14.42 \text{ kJ}}{1°C} - \dfrac{11.30 \text{ kJ}}{1°C} = 3.12 = 3.1 \text{ kJ/°C}$

(c) $q = 2.500 \text{ g glucose} \times \dfrac{15.57 \text{ kJ}}{1 \text{ g glucose}} = 38.93 \text{ kJ produced}$

$C_{H_2O} = 2.000 \text{ kg } H_2O \times \dfrac{4.184 \text{ kJ}}{1 \text{ kg} \cdot °C} = 8.368 \text{ kJ/°C}$

$C_{total} = \dfrac{8.368 \text{ kJ}}{1°C} + \dfrac{3.12 \text{ kJ}}{1°C} = 11.49 = 11.5 \text{ kJ/°C}$

$38.98 \text{ kJ} = \dfrac{11.49 \text{ kJ}}{°C} \times \Delta T$; $\Delta T = 3.39°C$

Hess's Law

5.47 If a reaction can be described as a series of steps, ΔH for the reaction is the sum of the enthalpy changes for each step. As long as we can describe a route where ΔH for each step is known, ΔH for any process can be calculated.

5.49 (a)

A → B	$\Delta H = +30 \text{ kJ}$
B → C	$\Delta H = +60 \text{ kJ}$
A → C	$\Delta H = +90 \text{ kJ}$

(b)

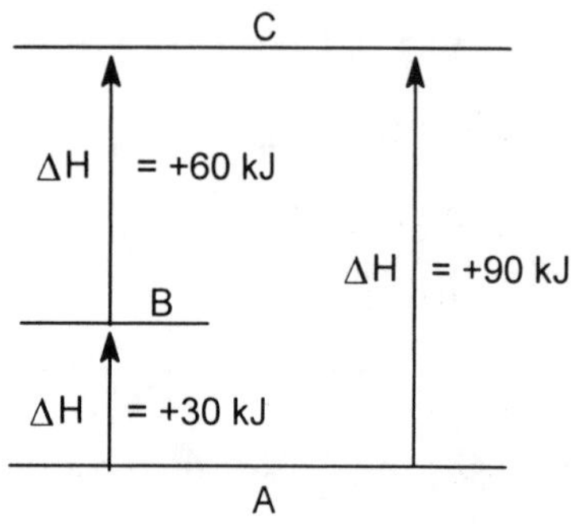

The process of A forming C can be described as A forming B and B forming C.

5.51
$$P_4O_6(s) \rightarrow P_4(s) + 3O_2(g) \qquad \Delta H = 1640.1 \text{ kJ}$$
$$P_4(s) + 5O_2(g) \rightarrow P_4O_{10}(s) \qquad \Delta H = -2940.1 \text{ kJ}$$

$$P_4O_6(s) + 2O_2(g) \rightarrow P_4O_{10}(s) \qquad \Delta H = -1300.0 \text{ kJ}$$

5.53
$$C_2H_4(g) \rightarrow 2H_2(g) + 2C(s) \qquad \Delta H = -52.3 \text{ kJ}$$
$$2C(s) + 4F_2(g) \rightarrow 2CF_4(g) \qquad \Delta H = 2(-680 \text{ kJ})$$
$$2H_2(g) + 2F_2(g) \rightarrow 4HF(g) \qquad \Delta H = 2(-537 \text{ kJ})$$

$$C_2H_4(g) + 6F_2(g) \rightarrow 2CF_4(g) + 4HF(g) \qquad \Delta H = -2.49 \times 10^3 \text{ kJ}$$

Enthalpies of Formation

5.55 (a) *Standard conditions* for enthalpy changes are usually P = 1 atm and T = 298 K. For the purpose of comparison, standard enthalpy changes, $\Delta H°$, are tabulated for reactions at these conditions.

(b) *Enthalpy of formation* , ΔH_f, is the enthalpy change that occurs when a compound is formed from its component elements.

(c) Standard enthalpy of formation, $\Delta H°_f$ is the enthalpy change that accompanies formation of one mole of a substance from elements in their standard states.

5.57 (a) $1/2 \ N_2(g) + 3/2 \ H_2(g) \rightarrow NH_3(g)$ $\Delta H°_f = -80.29 \text{ kJ}$

(b) $1/8 \ S_8(s) + O_2(g) \rightarrow SO_2(g)$ $\Delta H°_f = -269.9 \text{ kJ}$

(c) $Rb(s) + 1/2 \ Cl_2(g) + 3/2 \ O_2(g) \rightarrow RbClO_3(s)$ $\Delta H°_f = -392.4 \text{ kJ}$

(d) $N_2(g) + 2H_2(g) + 3/2 \ O_2(g) \rightarrow NH_4NO_3(s)$ $\Delta H°_f = -365.6 \text{ kJ}$

5.59 $\Delta H°_{rxn} = \Delta H°_f \ Al_2O_3(s) + 2\Delta H°_f \ Fe(s) - \Delta H°_f \ Fe_2O_3 - 2\Delta H°_f \ Al(s)$

$\Delta H°_{rxn} = (-1669.8 \text{ kJ}) + 2(0) - (-822.16 \text{ kJ}) - 2(0) = -847.6 \text{ kJ}$

5.61 (a) $\Delta H°_{rxn} = 2\Delta H°_f \ SO_3(g) - 2\Delta H°_f \ SO_2(g) - \Delta H°_f \ O_2(g)$

$\qquad = 2(-395.2 \text{ kJ}) - 2(-296.9 \text{ kJ}) - 0 = -196.6 \text{ kJ}$

(b) $\Delta H°_{rxn} = \Delta H°_f \ MgO(s) + \Delta H°_f \ H_2O(l) - \Delta H°_f \ Mg(OH)_2(s)$

$\qquad = -601.8 \text{ kJ} + (-285.83 \text{ kJ}) - (-924.7 \text{ kJ}) = 37.1 \text{ kJ}$

(c) $\Delta H°_{rxn} = 2\Delta H°_f \ Fe_2O_3(s) - 4\Delta H°_f \ FeO(s) - \Delta H°_f \ O_2(g)$

$\qquad = 2(-822.16 \text{ kJ}) - 4(-271.9 \text{ kJ}) - 0 = -556.7 \text{ kJ}$

(d) $\Delta H°_{rxn} = \Delta H°_f \ SiO_2(s) + 4\Delta H°_f \ HCl(g) - \Delta H°_f \ SiCl_4(l) - 2 \ \Delta H°_f \ H_2O(l)$

$\qquad = -910.9 \text{ kJ} + 4(-92.30 \text{ kJ}) - (-640.1 \text{ kJ}) - 2(-285.83 \text{ kJ}) = -68.3 \text{ kJ}$

5.63 $\Delta H^{\circ}_{rxn} = 3\Delta H^{\circ}_{f}\ CO_2 + 3\Delta H^{\circ}_{f}\ H_2O(l) - \Delta H^{\circ}_{f}\ C_3H_6O(l)$

       $-1790\ kJ = 3(-393.5\ kJ) + 3(-285.83\ kJ) - \Delta H^{\circ}_{f}\ C_3H_6O(l)$

       $\Delta H^{\circ}_{f}\ C_3H_6O(l) = -248\ kJ$

5.65 $Mg(s) + 1/2\ O_2(g) \rightarrow MgO(s)$ $\Delta H^{\circ} = 1/2(-1203.6\ kJ)$

         $MgO(s) + H_2O(l) \rightarrow Mg(OH)_2(s)$ $\Delta H^{\circ} = -(37.1\ kJ)$

          $H_2(g) + 1/2\ O_2(g) \rightarrow H_2O(l)$ $\Delta H^{\circ} = 1/2(-571.7\ kJ)$

         $Mg(s) + O_2(g) + H_2(g) \rightarrow Mg(OH)_2(s)$ $\Delta H^{\circ}_{f} = -924.8\ kJ$

5.67   (a) $C_8H_{18}(l) + 25/2\ O_2(g) \rightarrow 8CO_2(g) + 9H_2O(g)$ $\Delta H^{\circ} = -5069\ kJ$

     (b) $8C(s,\ gr) + 9H_2(g) \rightarrow C_8H_{18}(l)$ $\Delta H^{\circ}_{f} = ?$

     (c) $\Delta H^{\circ}_{rxn} = 8\Delta H^{\circ}_{f}\ CO_2(g) + 9\Delta H^{\circ}_{f}\ H_2O(g) - \Delta H^{\circ}_{f}\ C_8H_{18}(l) - 25/2\ \Delta H^{\circ}_{f}\ O_2(g)$

             $-5069\ kJ = 8(-393.5\ kJ) + 9(-241.82\ kJ) - \Delta H^{\circ}_{f}\ C_8H_{18}(l) - 25/2(0)$

             $\Delta H^{\circ}_{f}\ C_8H_{18}(l) = 8(-393.5\ kJ) + 9(-241.82\ kJ) + 5069\ kJ = -255\ kJ$

Foods and Fuels

5.69   (a)   *Fuel value* is the amount of heat produced when 1 gram of a substance (fuel) is combusted.

     (b)   Glucose, $C_6H_{12}O_6$, is referred to as *blood sugar*. It is important because glucose is the fuel that is carried by blood to cells and combusted to produce energy in the body.

     (c)   The fuel value of fats is 9 kcal/g and of carbohydrates is 4 kcal/g. Therefore, 5 g of fat produce 45 kcal, while 9 g of carbohydrates produce 36 kcal; 5 g of fat are a greater energy source.

5.71   Calculate the Cal (kcal) due to each nutritional component of the Campbell's® soup, then sum.

    $9\ g\ carbohydrates \times \dfrac{17\ kJ}{1\ g\ carbohydrate} = 153\ or\ 2 \times 10^2\ kJ$

    $1\ g\ protein \times \dfrac{17\ kJ}{1\ g\ protein} = 17\ or\ 0.2 \times 10^2\ kJ$

    $7\ g\ fat \times \dfrac{38\ kJ}{1\ g\ fat} = 266\ or\ 3 \times 10^2\ kJ$

    total energy = 153 kJ + 17 kJ + 266 kJ = 436 or 4×10^2 kJ

    $436\ kJ \times \dfrac{1\ kcal}{4.184\ kJ} \times \dfrac{1\ Cal}{1kcal} = 104\ or\ 1 \times 10^2\ Cal/serving$

5.73 $16.0 \text{ g } C_6H_{12}O_6 \times \dfrac{1 \text{ mol } C_6H_{15}O_6}{180.2 \text{ g } C_6H_{12}O_6} \times \dfrac{2812 \text{ kJ}}{\text{mol } C_6H_{12}O_6} \times \dfrac{1 \text{ Cal}}{4.184 \text{ kJ}} = 59.7 \text{ Cal}$

5.75 Propyne: $C_3H_4(g) + 4O_2(g) \rightarrow 3CO_2(g) + 2H_2O(g)$

    (a) $\Delta H = 3(-393.5 \text{ kJ}) + 2(-241.82 \text{ kJ}) - (185.4 \text{ kJ}) - 4(0) = -1849.5 = -1850 \text{ kJ/mol } C_3H_4$

    (b) $\dfrac{-1849.5 \text{ kJ}}{1 \text{ mol } C_3H_4} \times \dfrac{1 \text{ mol } C_3H_4}{40.065 \text{ g } C_3H_4} \times \dfrac{1000 \text{ g } C_3H_4}{1 \text{ kg } C_3H_4} = -4.616 \times 10^4 \text{ kJ/kg } C_3H_4$

Propylene: $C_3H_6(g) + 9/2 \, O_2(g) \rightarrow 3CO_2(g) + 3H_2O(g)$

    (a) $\Delta H = 3(-393.5 \text{ kJ}) + 3(-241.82 \text{ kJ}) - (20.4 \text{ kJ}) - 9/2(0) = -1926.4 = -1926 \text{ kJ/mol } C_3H_6$

    (b) $\dfrac{-1926.4 \text{ kJ}}{1 \text{ mol } C_3H_6} \times \dfrac{1 \text{ mol } C_3H_6}{42.080 \text{ g } C_3H_6} \times \dfrac{1000 \text{ g } C_3H_6}{1 \text{ kg } C_3H_6} = -4.578 \times 10^4 \text{ kJ/kg } C_3H_6$

Propane: $C_3H_8(g) + 5O_2(g) \rightarrow 3CO_2(g) + 4H_2O(g)$

    (a) $\Delta H = 3(-393.5 \text{ kJ}) + 4(-241.82 \text{ kJ}) - (-103.8 \text{ kJ}) - 5(0) = -2044.0 = -2044 \text{ kJ/mol } C_3H_8$

    (b) $\dfrac{-2044.0 \text{ kJ}}{1 \text{ mol } C_3H_8} \times \dfrac{1 \text{ mol } C_3H_8}{44.096 \text{ g } C_3H_8} \times \dfrac{1000 \text{ g } C_3H_8}{1 \text{ kg } C_3H_8} = -4.635 \times 10^4 \text{ kJ/kg } C_3H_8$

    (c)   These three substances yield nearly identical quantities of heat per unit mass, but propane is marginally higher than the other two.

Additional Exercises

5.77   (a)   mi/hr $\rightarrow$ m/s

        $1050 \, \dfrac{\text{mi}}{\text{hr}} \times \dfrac{1.6093 \text{ km}}{1 \text{ mi}} \times \dfrac{1000 \text{ m}}{1 \text{ km}} \times \dfrac{1 \text{ hr}}{3600 \text{ s}} = 469.38 = 469.4 \text{ m/s}$

    (b)   Find the mass of one N_2 molecule in kg.

        $\dfrac{28.0134 \text{ g } N_2}{1 \text{ mol}} \times \dfrac{1 \text{ mol}}{6.022 \times 10^{23} \text{ molecules}} \times \dfrac{1 \text{ kg}}{1000 \text{ g}} = 4.6518 \times 10^{-26}$

        $= 4.652 \times 10^{-26} \text{ kg}$

        $E_k = 1/2 \, mv^2 = 1/2 \times 4.6518 \times 10^{-26} \text{ kg} \times (469.38 \text{ m/s})^2$

        $= 5.1244 \times 10^{-21} \, \dfrac{\text{kg} \cdot \text{m}^2}{\text{s}^2} = 5.124 \times 10^{-21} \text{ J}$

    (c) $\dfrac{5.1244 \times 10^{21} \text{ J}}{\text{molecule}} \times \dfrac{6.022 \times 10^{23} \text{ molecules}}{1 \text{ mol}} = 3086 \text{ J/mol} = 3.086 \text{ kJ/mol}$

5.80 $w = \Delta E - q$; $\Delta E = +5.75 \text{ kJ}$, $q = +8.34 \text{ kJ}$; $w = 5.75 \text{ kJ} - 8.34 \text{ kJ} = -2.59 \text{ kJ}$

The negative sign for w indicates that work is done by the system on the surroundings.

5.83 (a) $q = 0$, $w > 0$ (work done to system), $\Delta E > 0$

(b) Since the system (the gas) is losing heat, the sign of q is negative. The magnitude of ΔE is the same in both cases, so w will have a larger positive value.

(c) The changes in state described in parts (a) and (b) are identical and ΔE is the same in both cases. The distribution of energy transferred as either work or heat is different in the two scenarios. In part (b), more work is required to compress the gas because some heat is lost to the surroundings.

5.86 Find the heat capacity of 1000 gal H_2O.

$$C_{H_2O} = 1000 \text{ gal } H_2O \times \frac{4 \text{ qt}}{1 \text{ gal}} \times \frac{1 \text{ L}}{1.057 \text{ qt}} \times \frac{1 \times 10^3 \text{ cm}^3}{1 \text{ L}} \times \frac{1 \text{ g}}{1 \text{ cm}^3} \times \frac{4.184 \text{ J}}{1 \text{ g} \cdot {}^\circ C}$$

$= 1.58 \times 10^7 \text{ J/}^\circ C = 1.58 \times 10^4 \text{ kJ/}^\circ C$; then,

$$\frac{1.58 \times 10^7 \text{ J}}{1 {}^\circ C} \times \frac{1 {}^\circ C \cdot g}{0.85 \text{ J}} \times \frac{1 \text{ kg}}{1 \times 10^3 \text{ g}} \times \frac{1 \text{ brick}}{1.8 \text{ kg}} = 1.0 \times 10^4 \text{ or } 10,000 \text{ bricks}$$

5.90 (a) For comparison, balance the equations so that 1 mole of CH_4 is burned in each.

$CH_4(g) + O_2(g) \rightarrow C(s) + 2H_2O(l)$ $\Delta H^\circ = -496.9 \text{ kJ}$

$CH_4(g) + 3/2\, O_2(g) \rightarrow CO(g) + 2H_2O(l)$ $\Delta H^\circ = -607.4 \text{ kJ}$

$CH_4(g) + 2O_2(g) \rightarrow CO_2(g) + 2H_2O(l)$ $\Delta H^\circ = -890.4 \text{ kJ}$

(b) $\Delta H^\circ_{rxn} = \Delta H^\circ_f\, C(s) + 2\Delta H^\circ_f\, H_2O(l) - \Delta H^\circ_f\, CH_4(g) - \Delta H^\circ_f\, O_2(g)$

        $= 0 + 2(-285.83 \text{ kJ}) - (-74.8) - 0 = -496.9 \text{ kJ}$

$\Delta H^\circ_{rxn} = \Delta H^\circ_f\, CO(g) + 2\Delta H^\circ_f\, H_2O(l) - \Delta H^\circ_f\, CH_4(g) - 3/2\, \Delta H^\circ_f\, O_2(g)$

        $= (-110.5 \text{ kJ}) + 2(-285.83 \text{ kJ}) - (-74.8 \text{ kJ}) - 3/2(0) = -607.4 \text{ kJ}$

$\Delta H^\circ_{rxn} = \Delta H^\circ_f\, CO_2(g) + 2\Delta H^\circ_f\, H_2O(l) - \Delta H^\circ_f\, CH_4(g) - 2\Delta H^\circ_f\, O_2(g)$

        $= -393.5 \text{ kJ} + 2(-285.83 \text{ kJ}) - (-74.8 \text{ kJ}) - 2(0) = -890.4 \text{ kJ}$

(c) Assuming that $O_2(g)$ is present in excess, the reaction that produces $CO_2(g)$ represents the most negative ΔH per mole of CH_4 burned. More of the potential energy of the reactants is released as heat during the reaction to give products of lower potential energy. The reaction that produces $CO_2(g)$ is the most "downhill" in enthalpy.

5.93 (a) $C_6H_{12}O_6(s) + 6O_2(g) \rightarrow 6CO_2(g) + 6H_2O(l)$

$\Delta H^\circ_{rxn} = 6\Delta H^\circ_f\, CO_2(g) + 6\Delta H^\circ_f\, H_2O(l) - \Delta H^\circ_f\, C_6H_{12}O_6(s) - 6\Delta H^\circ_f\, O_2(g)$

        $= 6(-393.5 \text{ kJ}) + 6(-285.83 \text{ kJ}) - (-1260 \text{ kJ}) - 6(0)$

        $= -2816 \text{ kJ/mol } C_6H_{12}O_6$

$C_{12}H_{22}O_{11}(s) + 12O_2(g) \rightarrow 12CO_2(g) + 11H_2O(l)$

$\Delta H^\circ_{rxn} = 12\Delta H^\circ_f\, CO_2(g) + 11\Delta H^\circ_f\, H_2O(l) - \Delta H^\circ_f\, C_{12}H_{22}O_{11}(s) - 12\Delta H^\circ_f\, O_2(g)$

        $= 12(-393.5 \text{ kJ}) + 11(-285.83 \text{ kJ}) - (-2221 \text{ kJ}) - 12(0)$

        $= -5645 \text{ kJ/mol } C_{12}H_{22}O_{11}$

(b) $\dfrac{-2816 \text{ kJ}}{1 \text{ mol } C_6H_{12}O_6} \times \dfrac{1 \text{ mol } C_6H_{12}O_6}{180.2 \text{ g } C_6H_{12}O_6} = -\dfrac{15.63 \text{ kJ}}{1 \text{ g } C_6H_{12}O_6} \rightarrow 16 \text{ kJ/g } C_6H_{12}O_6$

(fuel value)

$\dfrac{-5645 \text{ kJ}}{1 \text{ mol } C_{12}H_{22}O_{11}} \times \dfrac{1 \text{ mol } C_{12}H_{22}O_{11}}{342.3 \text{ g } C_{12}H_{22}O_{11}} = -\dfrac{16.49 \text{ kJ}}{1 \text{ g } C_{12}H_{22}O_{11}} \rightarrow 16 \text{ kJ/g } C_{12}H_{22}O_{11}$

(fuel value)

(c)   The average fuel value of carbohydrates (Section 5.8) is 17 kJ/g. These two carbohydrates have fuel values (16 kJ/g) slightly lower but in line with this average. (More complex carbohydrates supply more energy and raise the average value.)

Integrative Exercises

5.96   (a) $CH_4(g) + 2O_2(g) \rightarrow CO_2(g) + 2H_2O(l)$

$\Delta H^\circ = \Delta H^\circ_f \ CO_2(g) + 2\Delta H^\circ_f \ H_2O(l) - \Delta H^\circ_f \ CH_4(g) - 2\Delta H^\circ_f \ O_2(g)$

$= -393.5 \text{ kJ} + 2(-285.83 \text{ kJ}) - (-74.8 \text{ kJ}) - 2(0) = -890.36 = -890.4 \text{ kJ/mol } CH_4$

$\dfrac{-890.36 \text{ kJ}}{\text{mol } CH_4} \times \dfrac{1000 \text{ J}}{1 \text{ kJ}} \times \dfrac{1 \text{ mol}}{6.022 \times 10^{23} \text{ molecules } CH_4} = 1.4785 \times 10^{-18}$

$= 1.479 \times 10^{-18}$ J/molecule

(b) $1 \text{ eV} = 96.485 \text{ kJ/mol}$

$8 \text{ keV} \times \dfrac{1000 \text{ eV}}{1 \text{ keV}} \times \dfrac{96.485 \text{ kJ}}{\text{eV} \cdot \text{mol}} \times \dfrac{1 \text{ mol}}{6.022 \times 10^{23}} \times \dfrac{1000 \text{ J}}{\text{kJ}} = 1.282 \times 10^{-15}$

$= 1 \times 10^{-15}$ J/X-ray

The X-ray has approximately 1000 times more energy than is produced by the combustion of 1 molecule of $CH_4(g)$.

5.100   (a)   mol Cu = M × L = 1.00 M × 0.0500 L = 0.0500 mol

g = mol × $\mathscr{M}$ = 0.0500 × 63.546 = 3.1773 = 3.18 g Cu

(b)   The precipitate is copper(II) hydroxide, $Cu(OH)_2$.

(c) $CuSO_4(aq) + 2KOH(aq) \rightarrow Cu(OH)_2(s) + K_2SO_4(aq)$, complete

$Cu^{2+}(aq) + 2OH^-(aq) \rightarrow Cu(OH)_2(s)$, net ionic

(d)   The temperature of the calorimeter rises, so the reaction is exothermic and the sign of q is negative.

$q = -6.2°C \times 100 \text{ g} \times \dfrac{4.184 \text{ J}}{1 \text{ g} \cdot °C} = -2.6 \times 10^3 \text{ J} = -2.6 \text{ kJ}$

The reaction as carried out involves only 0.050 mol of $CuSO_4$ and the stoichiometrically equivalent amount of KOH. On a molar basis,

$\Delta H = \dfrac{-2.6 \text{ kJ}}{0.050 \text{ mol}} = -52 \text{ kJ}$ for the reaction as written in part (c)

6 Electronic Structure of Atoms

Radiant Energy

6.1 (a) meters (m)   (b) 1/seconds (s^{-1})   (c) meters/second ($m \cdot s^{-1}$ or m/s)

6.3 (a)   True.

(b)   False. The frequency of radiation decreases as the wavelength increases.

(c)   True.

(d)   False. Electromagnetic radiation and sound waves travel at different speeds.

6.5 Wavelength of (a) gamma rays < (d) yellow (visible) light < (e) red (visible) light <
(b) 93.1 MHz FM (radio) waves < (c) 680 kHz or 0.680 MHz AM (radio) waves

6.7 (a) $\nu = c/\lambda$; $\dfrac{2.998 \times 10^8 \text{ m}}{\text{s}} \times \dfrac{1}{0.589 \text{ pm}} \times \dfrac{1 \text{ pm}}{1 \times 10^{-12} \text{ m}} = 5.09 \times 10^{20} \text{ s}^{-1}$

(b) $\lambda = c/\nu$; $\dfrac{2.998 \times 10^8 \text{ m}}{\text{s}} \times \dfrac{1 \text{ s}}{5.11 \times 10^{11}} = 5.87 \times 10^{-4} \text{ m}$ (587 μm)

(c)   No. The radiation in (a) is gamma rays and in (b) is infrared. Neither is visible to humans.

(d) $6.54 \text{ s} \times \dfrac{2.998 \times 10^8 \text{ m}}{\text{s}} = 1.96 \times 10^9 \text{ m}$

6.9 $\nu = c/\lambda$; $\dfrac{2.998 \times 10^8 \text{ m}}{1 \text{ s}} \times \dfrac{1}{436 \text{ nm}} \times \dfrac{1 \text{ nm}}{1 \times 10^{-9} \text{ m}} = 6.88 \times 10^{14} \text{ s}^{-1}$
The color is blue.

Quantized Energy and Photons

6.11 (a)   *Quantization* means that energy can only be absorbed or emitted in specific amounts or multiples of these amounts. This minimum amount of energy is called a quantum and is equal to a constant times the frequency of the radiation absorbed or emitted. **E = h**ν.

(b)   In everyday activities, we deal with macroscopic objects such as our bodies or our cars, which gain and lose total amounts of energy much larger than a single quantum, hν. The gain or loss of the relatively minuscule quantum of energy is unnoticed.

6.13   (a) $E = h\nu = hc/\lambda = 6.626 \times 10^{-34} \text{ J} \bullet \text{s} \times \dfrac{2.998 \times 10^8 \text{ m}}{1 \text{ s}} \times \dfrac{1}{812 \text{ nm}} \times \dfrac{1 \text{ nm}}{1 \times 10^{-9} \text{ m}}$

$$= 2.45 \times 10^{-19} \text{ J}$$

       (b) $E = h\nu = 6.626 \times 10^{-34} \text{ J} \bullet \text{s} \times \dfrac{5.72 \times 10^{13}}{1 \text{ s}} = 3.79 \times 10^{-20} \text{ J}$

       (c) $\lambda = hc/E = 6.626 \times 10^{-34} \text{ J} \bullet \text{s} \times \dfrac{2.998 \times 10^8 \text{ m}}{1 \text{ s}} \times \dfrac{1}{5.44 \times 10^{-18} \text{ J}} = 3.65 \times 10^{-8} \text{ m}$

$$= 36.5 \text{ nm}$$

This radiation is in the ultraviolet region.

6.15   (a) $E = hc/\lambda = 6.626 \times 10^{-34} \text{ J} \bullet \text{s} \times \dfrac{2.998 \times 10^8 \text{ m}}{1 \text{ s}} \times \dfrac{1}{3.3 \text{ μm}} \times \dfrac{1 \text{ μm}}{1 \times 10^{-6} \text{ m}}$

$$= 6.0 \times 10^{-20} \text{ J}$$

            $E = hc/\lambda = 6.626 \times 10^{-34} \text{ J} \bullet \text{s} \times \dfrac{2.998 \times 10^8 \text{ m}}{1 \text{ s}} \times \dfrac{1}{0.154 \text{ nm}} \times \dfrac{1 \text{ nm}}{1 \times 10^{-9} \text{ m}}$

$$= 1.29 \times 10^{-15} \text{ J}$$

       (b)   The 3.3 μm photon is in the infrared and the 0.154 nm (1.54×10^{-10} m) photon is in the X-ray region; the X-ray photon has the greater energy.

6.17 $E_{photon} = hc/\lambda = \dfrac{6.626 \times 10^{-34} \text{ J} \bullet \text{s}}{987 \times 10^{-9} \text{ m}} \times \dfrac{2.998 \times 10^8 \text{ m}}{1 \text{ s}} = 2.0126 \times 10^{-19} = 2.01 \times 10^{-19} \text{ J/photon}$

$\dfrac{0.52 \text{ J}}{32 \text{ s}} \times \dfrac{1 \text{ photon}}{2.0126 \times 10^{-19} \text{ J}} = 8.1 \times 10^{16} \text{ photons/s}$

6.19 $\dfrac{495 \times 10^3 \text{ J}}{\text{mol O}_2} \times \dfrac{1 \text{ mol}}{6.022 \times 10^{23} \text{ photons}} = 8.220 \times 10^{-19} = 8.22 \times 10^{-19} \text{ J/photon}$

$\lambda = hc/E = \dfrac{6.626 \times 10^{-34} \text{ J} \bullet \text{s}}{8.220 \times 10^{-19} \text{ J}} \times \dfrac{2.998 \times 10^8 \text{ m}}{1 \text{ s}} = 2.42 \times 10^{-7} \text{ m} = 242 \text{ nm}$

According to Figure 6.4, this is ultraviolet radiation.

6.21   (a) $E = h\nu = 6.626 \times 10^{-34} \text{ J} \bullet \text{s} \times 1.09 \times 10^{15} \text{ s}^{-1} = 7.22 \times 10^{-19} \text{ J}$

       (b) $\lambda = c/\nu = \dfrac{2.998 \times 10^8 \text{ m}}{1 \text{ s}} \times \dfrac{1 \text{ s}}{1.09 \times 10^{15}} = 2.75 \times 10^{-7} \text{ m} = 275 \text{ nm}$

       (c) $E_{120} = hc/\lambda = 6.626 \times 10^{-34} \text{ J} \bullet \text{s} \times \dfrac{2.998 \times 10^8 \text{ m}}{1 \text{ s}} \times \dfrac{1}{120 \text{ nm}} \times \dfrac{1 \text{ nm}}{1 \times 10^{-9} \text{ m}}$

$$= 1.655 \times 10^{-18} = 1.66 \times 10^{-18} \text{ J}$$

The excess energy of the 120 nm photon is converted into the kinetic energy of the emitted electron.

$E_k = E_{120} - E_{min} = 16.55 \times 10^{-19} \text{ J} - 7.22 \times 10^{-19} \text{ J} = 9.3 \times 10^{-19} \text{ J/electron}$

Bohr's Model; Matter Waves

6.23   When applied to atoms, the notion of quantized energies means that only certain energies can be gained or lost, only certain values of ΔE are allowed. The allowed values of ΔE are represented by the lines in the emission spectra of excited atoms.

6.25   An isolated electron is assigned an energy of zero; the closer the electron comes to the nucleus, the more negative its energy. Thus, as an electron moves closer to the nucleus, the energy of the electron decreases and the excess energy is emitted. Conversely, as an electron moves further from the nucleus, the energy of the electron increases and energy must be absorbed.

     (a)   As the principle quantum number decreases, the electron moves toward the nucleus and energy is **emitted**.

     (b)   An increase in the radius of the orbit means the electron moves away from the nucleus; energy is **absorbed**.

     (c)   An isolated electron is assigned an energy of zero. As the electron moves to the $n = 3$ state closer to the H^+ nucleus, its energy becomes more negative (decreases) and energy is **emitted**.

6.27   (a) $\Delta E = R_H \left[\dfrac{1}{n_i^2} - \dfrac{1}{n_f^2} \right] = 2.18 \times 10^{-18}$ J $(1/25 - 1/1) = -2.093 \times 10^{-18} = -2.09 \times 10^{-18}$ J

$$\nu = E/h = \frac{2.093 \times 10^{-18} \text{ J}}{6.626 \times 10^{-34} \text{ J} \cdot \text{s}} = 3.158 \times 10^{15} = 3.16 \times 10^{15} \text{ s}^{-1}$$

$$\lambda = c/\nu = \frac{2.998 \times 10^8 \text{ m}}{1 \text{ s}} \times \frac{1 \text{ s}}{3.158 \times 10^{15}} = 9.49 \times 10^{-8} \text{ m}$$

Since the sign of ΔE is negative, radiation is emitted.

     (b) $\Delta E = 2.18 \times 10^{-18}$ J$(1/36 - 1/4) = -4.844 \times 10^{-19} = -4.84 \times 10^{-19}$ J

$$\nu = \frac{4.844 \times 10^{-19} \text{ J}}{6.626 \times 10^{-34} \text{ J} \cdot \text{s}} = 7.311 \times 10^{14} = 7.31 \times 10^{14} \text{ s}^{-1}; \quad \lambda = \frac{2.998 \times 10^8 \text{ m/s}}{7.311 \times 10^{14}/\text{s}}$$

$\lambda = 4.10 \times 10^{-7}$ m. Visible radiation is emitted.

     (c) $\Delta E = 2.18 \times 10^{-18}$ J$(1/16 - 1/25) = 4.095 \times 10^{-20} = 4.91 \times 10^{-20}$ J

$$\nu = \frac{4.095 \times 10^{-20} \text{ J}}{6.626 \times 10^{-34} \text{ J} \cdot \text{s}} = 7.403 \times 10^{13} = 7.40 \times 10^{13} \text{ s}^{-1}; \quad \lambda = \frac{2.998 \times 10^8 \text{ m/s}}{7.403 \times 10^{13}/\text{s}}$$

$\lambda = 4.05 \times 10^{-6}$ m. Radiation is absorbed.

6.29   (a)   Only lines with $n_f = 2$ represent ΔE values and wavelengths that lie in the visible portion of the spectrum. Lines with $n_f = 1$ have larger ΔE values and shorter wavelengths that lie in the ultraviolet. Lines with $n_f > 2$ have smaller ΔE values and lie in the lower energy longer wavelength regions of the electromagnetic spectrum.

(b) $n_i = 3$, $n_f = 2$; $\Delta E = R_H \left[\dfrac{1}{n_i^2} - \dfrac{1}{n_f^2} \right] = 2.18 \times 10^{-18}$ J (1/9 − 1/4)

$$\lambda = hc/E = \dfrac{6.626 \times 10^{-34} \text{ J} \bullet \text{s} \times 2.998 \times 10^8 \text{ m/s}}{2.18 \times 10^{-18} \text{ J (1/9} - \text{1/4)}} = 6.56 \times 10^{-7} \text{ m}$$

This is the yellow line at 656 nm.

$$n_i = 4, n_f = 2; \ \lambda = hc/E = \dfrac{6.626 \times 10^{-34} \text{ J} \bullet \text{s} \times 2.998 \times 10^8 \text{ m/s}}{2.18 \times 10^{-18} \text{ J (1/16} - \text{1/4)}} = 4.86 \times 10^{-7} \text{ m}$$

This is the blue-green (cyan) line at 486 nm.

$$n_i = 5, n_f = 2; \ \lambda = hc/E = \dfrac{6.626 \times 10^{-34} \text{ J} \bullet \text{s} \times 2.998 \times 10^8 \text{ m/s}}{2.18 \times 10^{-18} \text{ J (1/25} - \text{1/4)}} = 4.34 \times 10^{-7} \text{ m}$$

This is the blue line at 434 nm.

6.31   (a) $93.8 \text{ nm} \times \dfrac{1 \times 10^{-9} \text{ m}}{1 \text{ nm}} = 9.38 \times 10^{-8}$ m;   this line is in the ultraviolet region.

       (b)   Only lines with $n_f = 1$ have a large enough ΔE to lie in the ultraviolet region. Solve Equation 6.6 for n_i, recalling that ΔE is negative for emission.

$$- hc/\lambda = R_H \left[\dfrac{1}{n_i^2} - \dfrac{1}{n_f^2} \right]; \ \ - \dfrac{hc}{\lambda \times R_H} = \left[\dfrac{1}{n_i^2} - 1 \right]; \ \ \dfrac{1}{n_i^2} = 1 - \dfrac{hc}{\lambda \times R_H}$$

$$n_i^2 = \left(1 - \dfrac{hc}{\lambda \times R_H} \right)^{-1}; \ \ n_i = \left(1 - \dfrac{hc}{\lambda \times R_H} \right)^{-1/2}$$

$$n_i = \left(1 - \dfrac{6.626 \times 10^{-34} \text{ J} \bullet \text{s} \times 2.998 \times 10^8 \text{ m/s}}{9.38 \times 10^{-8} \text{ m} \times 2.18 \times 10^{-18} \text{ J}} \right)^{-1/2} = 6 \ (n \text{ values must be integers})$$

$n_i = 6$, $n_f = 1$

6.33 $\lambda = \dfrac{h}{mv}$; $1 \text{ J} = \dfrac{1 \text{ kg} \bullet \text{m}^2}{\text{s}^2}$;   Change mass to kg and velocity to m/s in each case.

       (a) $\dfrac{60 \text{ km}}{1 \text{ hr}} \times \dfrac{1000 \text{ m}}{1 \text{ km}} \times \dfrac{1 \text{ hr}}{60 \text{ min}} \times \dfrac{1 \text{ min}}{60 \text{ s}} = 16.67 = 17 \text{ m/s}$

$$\lambda = \dfrac{6.626 \times 10^{-34} \text{ kg} \bullet \text{m}^2 \bullet \text{s}}{1 \text{ s}^2} \times \dfrac{1}{85 \text{ kg}} \times \dfrac{1 \text{ s}}{16.67 \text{ m}} = 4.7 \times 10^{-37} \text{ m}$$

       (b) $50 \text{ g} \times \dfrac{1 \text{ kg}}{1000 \text{ g}} = 0.050 \text{ kg}$

$$\lambda = \dfrac{6.626 \times 10^{-34} \text{ kg} \bullet \text{m}^2 \bullet \text{s}}{1 \text{ s}^2} \times \dfrac{1}{0.050 \text{ kg}} \times \dfrac{1 \text{ s}}{400 \text{ m}} = 3.3 \times 10^{-35} \text{ m}$$

(c)   We need to calculate the mass of a single Li atom in kg.

$$\frac{6.94\ g\ Li}{1\ mol\ Li} \times \frac{1\ kg}{1000\ g} \times \frac{1\ mol}{6.022 \times 10^{23}\ Li\ atoms} = 1.152 \times 10^{-26} = 1.15 \times 10^{-26}\ kg$$

$$\lambda = \frac{6.626 \times 10^{-34}\ kg \bullet m^2 \bullet s}{1\ s^2} \times \frac{1}{1.152 \times 10^{-26}\ kg} \times \frac{1\ s}{6.5 \times 10^5\ m} = 8.8 \times 10^{-14}\ m$$

6.35 $v = h/m\lambda$; $\lambda = 1.02\ \text{Å} \times \dfrac{1 \times 10^{-10}\ m}{1\ \text{Å}} = 1.02 \times 10^{-10}\ m$; $m = 1.6749 \times 10^{-27}\ kg$

$$v = \frac{6.626 \times 10^{-34}\ kg \bullet m^2 \bullet s}{1\ s^2} \times \frac{1}{1.6749 \times 10^{-27}\ kg} \times \frac{1}{1.02 \times 10^{-10}\ m} = 3.88 \times 10^3\ m/s$$

6.37   The Bohr model of the hydrogen atom treats the electron strictly as a particle. DeBroglie's hypothesis that electrons (or any particles) have a characteristic wavelength requires revision of Bohr's particle-only model. For example, the idea of a fixed orbit for the electron in hydrogen is hard to reconcile with the wave properties of the electron.

Quantum Mechanics and Atomic Orbitals

6.39   The Bohr model states with 100% certainty that the electron in hydrogen can be found 0.53 Å from the nucleus. The quantum mechanical model, taking the wave nature of the electron and the uncertainty principle into account, is a statistical model that states the probability of finding the electron in certain regions around the nucleus. While 0.53 Å might be the radius with highest probability, that probability would always be less than 100%.

6.41   (a) $n = 4$, $l = 3, 2, 1, 0$ (b) $l = 2$, $m_l = -2, -1, 0, 1, 2$

6.43   (a)   2, 1, 1; 2, 1, 0; 2, 1 -1

        (b)   5, 2, 2; 5, 2, 1; 5, 2, 0; 5, 2, -1; 5, 2, -2

6.45   (a)   permissible, 2p   (b)   forbidden, for $l = 0$, m_l can only equal 0
        (c)   permissible, 4d   (d)   forbidden, for n = 3, the largest l value is 2

6.47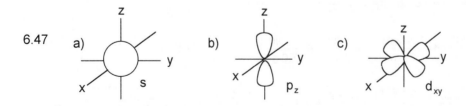

6.49   (a)   The 1s and 2s orbitals of a hydrogen atom have the same overall spherical shape. The 2s orbital has a larger radial extension and one node, while the 1s orbital has continuous electron density. Since the 2s orbital is "larger", there is greater probability of finding an electron further from the nucleus in the 2s orbital.

(b)   A single 2p orbital is directional in that its electron density is concentrated along one of the three cartesian axes of the atom. The $d_{x^2-y^2}$ orbital has electron density along both the x- and y-axes, while the p_x orbital has density only along the x-axis.

(c)   The average distance of an electron from the nucleus in a 3s orbital is greater than for an electron in a 2s orbital. In general, for the same kind of orbital, the larger the *n* value, the greater the average distance of an electron from the nucleus of the atom.

(d)   1s < 2p < 3d < 4f < 6s. In the hydrogen atom, orbitals with the same *n* value are degenerate and energy increases with increasing *n* value. Thus, the order of increasing energy is given above.

Many-Electron Atoms; Electron Spin

6.51   (a)   In the hydrogen atom, orbitals with the same principle quantum number, *n*, are degenerate.

(b)   In a many-electron atom, orbitals with the same principle and azimuthal quantum numbers, *n* and *l*, are degenerate.

6.53   The 2p electron in boron is shielded from the full charge of the nucleus by the 2s electrons. (Both the 2s and 2p electrons are shielded by the 1s electrons). Thus, the 2p electron experiences a smaller nuclear charge than the 2s electrons.

6.55   A 2p electron in Ne experiences a greater effective nuclear charge. The shielding experienced by a 2p electron in the two atoms is similar, so the electron in the atom with the larger Z (Z_{Ne} = 10, Z_O = 8) experiences the larger effective nuclear charge.

6.57   (a)   +1/2, - 1/2

(b)   Electrons with opposite spins are affected differently by a strong inhomogeneous magnetic field. An apparatus similar to that in Figure 6.26 can be used to distinguish electrons with opposite spins.

(c)   The Pauli exclusion principle states that no two electrons can have the same four quantum numbers. Two electrons in a 1s orbital have the same, *n*, *l* and m_l values. They must have different m_s values.

6.59   (a) 10   (b) 2   (c) 6   (d) 14

6.61   2, 1, 1, 1/2;   2, 1, 1, -1/2;   2, 1, 0, 1/2;   2, 1, 0, -1/2;   2, 1, -1, 1/2;   2, 1, -1, -1/2

Electron Configurations

6.63   (a)   Each box represents an orbital.

(b)   Electron spin is represented by the direction of the half-arrows.

(c)   No. The electron configuration of Be is $1s^2 2s^2$. There are no electrons in subshells that have degenerate orbitals, so Hund's rule is not used.

6.65 (a) Rb: [Kr]$5s^1$ (b) Se: [Ar]$4s^2 3d^{10} 4p^4$ (c) Zn: [Ar]$4s^2 3d^{10}$

 (d) V: [Ar]$4s^2 3d^3$ (e) Pb: [Xe]$6s^2 4f^{14} 5d^{10} 6p^2$ (f) Yb: [Xe]$6s^2 4f^{14}$

6.67 (a) As: [Ar] 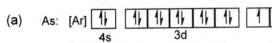 3 unpaired electrons

 (b) Te: [Kr] 2 unpaired electrons

 (c) Sb: [Kr] 3 unpaired electrons

 (d) Ag: [Kr] 1 unpaired electron

 (e) Hf: [Xe] 2 unpaired electrons

6.69 (a) Mg   (b) Al   (c) Cr   (d) Te

Additional Exercises

6.71 (a) $\lambda_A = 1.6 \times 10^{-7}$ m / 4.5 = 3.56×10^{-8} = 3.6×10^{-8} m

 $\lambda_B = 1.6 \times 10^{-7}$ m / 2 = 8.0×10^{-8} m

 (b) $\nu = c/\lambda$; $\nu_A = \dfrac{2.998 \times 10^8 \text{ m}}{1 \text{ s}} \times \dfrac{1}{3.56 \times 10^{-8} \text{ m}} = 8.4 \times 10^{15} \text{ s}^{-1}$

 $\nu_B = \dfrac{2.998 \times 10^8 \text{ m}}{1 \text{ s}} \times \dfrac{1}{8.0 \times 10^{-8} \text{ m}} = 3.7 \times 10^{15} \text{ s}^{-1}$

 (c) A: ultraviolet, B: ultraviolet

6.73 All electromagnetic radiation travels at the same speed, 2.998×10^8 m/s. Change miles to meters and seconds to some appropriate unit of time.

 $522 \times 10^6 \text{ mi} \times \dfrac{1.6093 \text{ km}}{1 \text{ mi}} \times \dfrac{1000 \text{ m}}{1 \text{ km}} \times \dfrac{1 \text{ s}}{2.998 \times 10^8 \text{ m}} \times \dfrac{1 \text{ min}}{60 \text{ s}} = 46.7 \text{ min}$

6.75 $E = hc/\lambda \rightarrow$ J/photon; total energy = power × time; photons = total energy / J / photon

 $E = \dfrac{6.626 \times 10^{-34} \text{ J} \cdot \text{s} \times 2.998 \times 10^8 \text{ m/s}}{780 \times 10^{-9} \text{ m}} = 2.5468 \times 10^{-19} = 2.55 \times 10^{-19}$ J/photon

 $0.12 \text{ mW} = \dfrac{0.12 \times 10^{-3} \text{ J}}{1 \text{ s}} \times 74 \text{ min} \times \dfrac{60 \text{ s}}{1 \text{ min}} = 0.5328 = 0.53$ J

 $0.5328 \text{ J} \times \dfrac{1 \text{ photon}}{2.5468 \times 10^{-19} \text{ J}} = 2.092 \times 10^{18} = 2.1 \times 10^{18}$ photons

6.78 $\dfrac{8.6 \times 10^{-13}\,C}{1\,s} \times \dfrac{1\,e^-}{1.602 \times 10^{-19}\,C} \times \dfrac{1\,photon}{1\,e^-} = 5.368 \times 10^6 = 5.4 \times 10^6$ photons/s

$\dfrac{E}{photon} = hc/\lambda = \dfrac{6.626 \times 10^{-34}\,J \bullet s}{550\,nm} \times \dfrac{2.998 \times 10^8\,m}{1\,s} \times \dfrac{1\,nm}{1 \times 10^{-9}\,m} \times \dfrac{5.368 \times 10^6\,photon}{s}$

$$= 1.9 \times 10^{-12}\,J/s$$

6.80 (a) Gaseous atoms of various elements in the sun's atmosphere typically have ground state electron configurations. When these atoms are exposed to radiation from the sun, the electrons change from the ground state to one of several allowed excited states. Atoms absorb the wavelengths of light which correspond to these allowed energy changes. All other wavelengths of solar radiation pass through the atmosphere unchanged. Thus, the dark lines are the wavelengths that correspond to allowed energy changes in atoms of the solar atmosphere. The continuous background is all other wavelengths of solar radiation.

(b) The scientist should record the absorption spectrum of pure neon or other elements of interest. The black lines should appear at the same wavelengths regardless of the source of neon.

6.82 $\lambda = h/mv$; $v = h/m\lambda$. $\lambda = 0.711\,\text{Å} \times \dfrac{1 \times 10^{-10}\,m}{1\,\text{Å}} = 7.11 \times 10^{-11}\,m$; $m_e = 9.1094 \times 10^{-31}$ kg

$v = \dfrac{6.626 \times 10^{-34}\,J \bullet s}{9.1094 \times 10^{-31}\,kg \times 7.11 \times 10^{-11}\,m} \times \dfrac{1\,kg \bullet m^2/s^2}{1\,J} = 1.02 \times 10^7$ m/s

6.85 (a) l (b) n and l (c) m_s (d) m_l

6.88 (a) The p_z orbital has a nodal plane where z = 0. This is the xy plane.

(b) The d_{xy} orbital has 4 lobes and 2 nodal planes, the two planes where x = 0 and y = 0. These are the yz and xz planes.

(c) The $d_{x^2-y^2}$ has 4 lobes and 2 nodal planes, the planes where $x^2 - y^2 = 0$. These are the planes that bisect the x and y axes and contain the z axis.

6.90 Mt: [Rn] $7s^2 5f^{14}\, 6d^7$

7 Periodic Properties of the Elements

Periodic Table;   Electron Shells; Atomic Radii

7.1   Mendeleev insisted that elements with similar chemical and physical properties be placed within a family or column of the table. Since many elements were as yet undiscovered, Mendeleev left blanks. He predicted properties for the "blanks" based on properties of other elements in the family.

7.3   The quantum mechanical model describes electron structure in terms of the probability of finding electrons in some volume element of space. On a plot of radial electron density (the electron density on the surface of a sphere whose radius is a certain distance from the nucleus) there are certain radii with high electron densities. The number of these maxima corresponds to the number of "electron shells" for a particular atom as proposed by Lewis. This is also the number of principal quantum levels in the atom. In a multielectron atom, the total of the electron densities of all orbitals or subshells in a principal quantum level is roughly spherical, corresponding to the spherical electron shell.

7.5   Krypton has a larger nuclear charge ($Z = 36$) than argon ($Z = 18$).   The shielding of the $n = 3$ shells by the 1s and 2s electrons in the two atoms is approximately equal, so the $n = 3$ electrons in Kr experience a greater effective nuclear charge and are thus situated closer to the nucleus.

7.7   Since the quantum mechanical description of the atom does not specify the exact location of electrons, there is no specific distance from the nucleus where the last electron can be found. Rather, the electron density decreases gradually as the distance from the nucleus increases. There is no quantum mechanical "edge" of an atom.

7.9   The atomic radius of Au is the interatomic Au-Au distance divided by 2, 2.88 Å/2 = 1.44 Å.

7.11   From atomic radii, As-I = 1.19 Å + 1.33 Å = 2.52 Å. This is very close to the experimental value of 2.55 Å.

7.13   (a)   Atomic radii **decrease** moving from left to right across a row and (b) **increase** from top to bottom within a group.

        (c)   F < S < P <As. The order is unambiguous according to the trends of increasing atomic radius moving down a column and to the left in a row of the table.

7.15 (a) The electrons in a He atom experience a nuclear charge of 2 and are drawn closer to the nucleus than the electron in H, which feels a nuclear charge of only 1.

(b) Even though $Z = 10$ for Ne and $Z = 2$ for He, the valence electrons in Ne are in $n = 2$ and those of He are closer to the nucleus in $n = 1$. Also, the 1 s electrons in Ne shield the valence electrons from the full nuclear charge. This shielding, coupled with the larger n value of the valence electrons in the Ne, means that its atomic radius is larger than that of He.

Ionization Energies; Electron Affinities

7.17 $Te(g) \rightarrow Te^+(g) + 1e^-$; $Te^+(g) \rightarrow Te^{2+}(g) + 1e^-$; $Te^{2+}(g) \rightarrow Te^{3+}(g) + 1e^-$

7.19 The electron configuration of Li^+ is $1s^2$ or [He] and that of Be^+ is $[He]2s^1$. Be^+ has one more valence electron to lose while Li^+ has the stable noble gas configuration of He. It requires much more energy to remove a 1s core electron close to the nucleus of Li^+ than a 2s valence electron further from the nucleus of Be^+.

7.21 Moving from He to Rn in group 8A, first ionization energies decrease and atomic radii increase. The greater the atomic radius, the smaller the electrostatic attraction of an outer electron for the nucleus and the smaller the ionization energy of the element.

7.23 (a) Ne (b) Mg (c) Cr (d) Br (e) Ge

7.25 (a) Na. In an isoelectronic series, all electronic effects (shielding and repulsion) are the same, so the particle with the smallest Z will have the smallest effective nuclear charge.

(b) Si^{3+}. Si has the largest Z and effective nuclear charge.

(c) The greater the effective nuclear charge experienced by a valence electron, the larger the ionization energy for that electron. According to Table 7.2, I_1 for Na is 496 kJ/mol. I_4 for Si is 4360 kJ/mol.

7.27 Ionization energy: $Se(g) \rightarrow Se^+(g) + 1e^-$
$[Ar]4s^23e^{10}4p^4$ $[Ar]4s^23d^{10}4p^3$

Electron affinity: $Se(g) + 1e^- \rightarrow Se^-(g)$
$[Ar]4s^23d^{10}4p^4$ $[Ar]4s^23d^{10}4p^5$

7.29 $Li + 1e^- \rightarrow Li^-$; $Be + 1e^- \rightarrow Be^-$
$[He]2s^1$ $[He]2s^2$ $[He]2s^2$ $[He]2s^22p^1$

Adding an electron to Li completes the 2s subshell. The added electron experiences essentially the same effective nuclear charge as the other valence electron, except for the repulsion of pairing electrons in a orbital. There is an overall stabilization; ΔE is negative.

An extra electron in Be would occupy the higher energy 2p subshell. This electron is shielded from the full nuclear charge by the 2s electrons and does not experience a stabilization in energy; ΔE is positive.

Properties of Metals and Nonmetals

7.31 $O_2 < Br_2 < K < Mg$. O_2 and Br_2 are (nonpolar) nonmetals. We expect O_2, with the much lower molar mass, to have the lower melting point. This is confirmed by data in Tables 7.6 and 7.7. K and Mg are metallic solids (all metals are solids), with higher melting points than the two nonmetals. Since alkaline earth metals (Mg) are typically harder, more dense and higher melting than alkali metals (K), we expect Mg to have the highest melting point of the group. This is confirmed by data in Tables 7.4 and 7.5.

7.33   Metallic character increases moving down a family and to the left in a period.

        (a) Li   (b) Na   (c) Sn   (d) Al

7.35   Ionic: MgO, Li_2O, Y_2O_3; molecular: SO_2, P_2O_5, N_2O, XeO_3

        Ionic compounds are formed by combining a metal and a nonmetal; molecular compounds are formed by two or more nonmetals.

7.37   When dissolved in water, an "acidic oxide" produces an acidic (pH < 7) solution. Oxides of nonmetals are acidic. Example: $SO_3(g)$. A "basic oxide" dissolved in water produces a basic (pH > 7) solution. Oxides of metals are basic. Example: CaO (quick lime).

7.39   (a) $CaO(s) + H_2O(l) \rightarrow Ca(OH)_2(aq)$
           (b) $CuO(s) + 2HNO_3(aq) \rightarrow Cu(NO_3)_2(aq) + H_2O(l)$
           (c) $SO_3(g) + H_2O(l) \rightarrow H_2SO_4(aq)$
           (d) $CO_2(g) + 2NaOH(aq) \rightarrow Na_2CO_3(aq) + H_2O(l)$

Group Trends in Metals and Nonmetals

7.41

	Na	**Mg**
(a)	[Ne] $3s^1$	[Ne] $3s^2$
(b)	+1	+2
(c)	+496 kJ/mol	+738 kJ/mol
(d)	very reactive	reacts with steam, but not $H_2O(l)$
(e)	1.54 Å	1.30 Å

        (b)   When forming ions, both adopt the stable configuration of Ne, but Na loses one electron and Mg two electrons to achieve this configuration.

    (c),(e)   The nuclear charge of Mg (Z = 12) is greater than that of Na, so it requires more energy to remove a valence electron with the same *n* value from Mg than Na. It also means that the 2s electrons of Mg are held closer to the nucleus, so the atomic radius (e) is smaller than that of Na.

        (d)   Mg is less reactive because it has a filled subshell and it has a higher ionization energy.

7.43 (a)   Ca and Mg are both metals; they tend to lose electrons and form cations when they react. Ca is more reactive because it has a lower ionization energy than Mg. The Ca valence electrons in the 4s orbital are less tightly held because they are farther from the nucleus and experience more shielding by core electrons than the 3s valence electrons of Mg.

(b)   K and Ca are both metals; they tend to lose electrons and form cations when they react. K is more reactive because it has a lower ionization energy. The 4s valence electron in K is less tightly held because it experiences a smaller nuclear charge (Z = 19 for K versus Z = 20 for Ca) with similar shielding effects than the 4s valence electrons of Ca.

7.45 (a) $2K(s) + 2H_2O(l) \rightarrow 2KOH(aq) + H_2(g)$

(b) $Ba(s) + 2H_2O(l) \rightarrow Ba(OH)_2(aq) + H_2(g)$

(c) $6Li(s) + N_2(g) \rightarrow 2Li_3N(s)$

(d) $2Mg(s) + O_2(g) \rightarrow 2MgO(s)$

7.47 $H - 1s^1$; $Li - [He]\, 2s^1$; $F - [He]\, 2s^2 2p^5$. Like Li, H has only one valence electron, and its most common oxidation number is +1, which both H and Li adopt after losing the single valence electron. Like F, H needs only one electron to adopt the stable electron configuration of the nearest noble gas. Both H and F can exist in the -1 oxidation state, when they have gained an electron to complete their valence shells.

7.49

	F	**Cl**
(a)	$[He]\, 2s^2 2p^5$	$[Ne]\, 3s^2 3p^5$
(b)	-1	-1
(c)	1681 kJ/mol	1251 kJ/mol
(d)	reacts exothermically to form HF	reacts slowly to form HCl
(e)	-328 kJ/mol	-349 kJ/mol
(f)	0.71 Å	0.99 Å

(b)   F and Cl are in the same group, have the same valence electron configuration and common ionic charge.

(c),(f)   The n = 2 valence electrons in F are closer to the nucleus and more tightly held than the n = 3 valence electrons in Cl. Therefore, the ionization energy of F is greater, and the atomic radius is smaller.

(d)   In its reaction with H_2O, F is reduced; it gains an electron. Although the electron affinity, a gas phase single atom property, of F is less negative than that of Cl, the tendency of F to hold its own electrons (high ionization energy) coupled with a relatively large exothermic electron affinity makes it extremely susceptible to reduction and chemical bond formation. Cl is unreactive to water because it is less susceptible to reduction.

(e)   Although F has a larger Z_{eff} than Cl, its small atomic radius gives rise to large repulsions when an extra electron is added, so the overall electron affinity of F is smaller (less exothermic) than that of Cl.

(f)   The n = 2 valence electrons in F are closer to the nucleus so the atomic radius is smaller than that of Cl.

7.51   In the 1960s, scientists discovered that Xe, which has the lowest ionization energy of the nonradioactive Noble gases, would react with substances having a strong tendency to remove electrons, such as PtF_6 or F_2. Thus, the term "inert" no longer described all the Group 8A elements. (Kr also reacts with F_2, but reactions of Ar, Ne and He are as yet unknown.)

7.53   (a) $2O_3(g) \rightarrow 3O_2(g)$

(b) $Xe(g) + F_2(g) \rightarrow XeF_2(g)$

$Xe(g) + 2F_2(g) \rightarrow XeF_4(s)$

$Xe(g) + 3F_2(g) \rightarrow XeF_6(s)$

(c) $2NaCl(aq) + 2H_2O(l) \rightarrow 2NaOH(aq) + Cl_2(g) + H_2(g)$

(d) $S(s) + 2Li(s) \rightarrow Li_2S(s)$

7.55   (a)   Te has more metallic character and is a better electrical conductor.

(b)   At room temperature, oxygen molecules are diatomic and exist in the gas phase. Sulfur molecules are 8-membered rings and exist in the solid state.

(c)   Chlorine is generally more reactive than bromine because Cl atoms have a greater (more exothermic) electron affinity than Br atoms.

Additional Exercises

7.58   Up to Z = 83, there are three instances where atomic weights are reversed relative to atomic numbers: Ar and K; Co and Ni; Te and I.

In each case, the most abundant isotope of the element with the larger atomic number (Z) has one more proton, but fewer neutrons than the element with the smaller atomic number. The smaller number of neutrons causes the element with the larger Z to have a smaller than expected atomic weight.

7.60   (a)   Mo – F distance = $r_{Mo} + r_F$ = 1.45 + 0.71 = 2.16 Å

(b)   S – F distance = $r_S + r_F$ = 1.02 + 0.71 = 1.73 Å

(c)   Cl – F distance = $r_{Cl} + r_F$ = 0.99 + 0.71 = 1.70 Å

7.62   C: $1s^2 2s^2 2p^2$. I_1 through I_4 represent loss of the 2p and 2s electrons in the outer shell of the atom. The values of $I_1 - I_4$ increase as expected. The nuclear charge is constant, but removing each electron reduces repulsive interactions between the remaining electrons, so effective nuclear charge increases and ionization energy increases. I_5 and I_6 represent loss of the 1s core electrons. These 1s electrons are much closer to the nucleus and experience the **full nuclear charge (they are not shielded)**, so the values of I_5 and I_6 are significantly greater than $I_1 - I_4$. I_6 is larger than I_5 because all repulsive interactions have been eliminated.

7.65   Y: $[Kr]5s^2 4d_1$, Z = 39; La: $[Xe]6s^2 5d^1$, Z = 57;   Zr: $[Kr]\ 5s^2 4d^2$, Z = 40; Hf: $[Xe]\ 6s^2 4f^{14} 5d^2$, Z = 72. The completed 4f subshell in Hf leads to a much larger change in Z going from Zr to Hf (72 - 40 = 32) than in going from Y to La (57 - 39 = 18). The 4f electrons in Hf do not completely shield the 5d valence electrons, so there is also a larger increase in Z_{eff}. This larger increase in Z_{eff} going from Zr to Hf leads to a smaller increase in atomic radius than in going from Y to La.

7.68   (a)   The group 2B metals have complete (*n*-1)d subshells. An additional electron would occupy an *n*p subshell and be substantially shielded by both *n*s and (*n*-1) d electrons. Overall this is not a lower energy state than the neutral atom and a free electron.

(b)   Valence electrons in Group 1B elements experience a relatively large effective nuclear charge due to the build-up in Z with the filling of the (*n*-1)d subshell. Thus, the electron affinities are large and negative. Group 1B elements are exceptions to the usual electron filling order and have the generic electron configuration $n s^1 (n-1) d^{10}$. The additional electron would complete the *n*s subshell and experience repulsion with the other *n*s electron. Going down the group, size of the *n*s subshell increases and repulsion effects decrease. That is, effective nuclear charge is greater going down the group because it is less diminished by repulsion, and electron affinities become more negative.

7.71   Moving one place to the right in a horizontal row of the table, for example, from Li to Be, there is an increase in ionization energy. Moving downward in a given family, for example from Be to Mg, there is usually a decrease in ionization energy. Similarly, atomic size decreases in moving one place to the right and increases in moving downward. Thus, two elements such as Li and Mg that are diagonally related tend to have similar ionization energies and atomic sizes. This in turn gives rise to some similarities in chemical behavior. Note, however, that the valences expected for the elements are not the same. That is, lithium still appears as Li^+, magnesium as Mg^{2+}.

7.74   Ionic "inorganic" halogen compounds are formed when a metal with low ionization energy and small negative electron affinity combines with a halogen with large ionization energy and large negative electron affinity. That is, it is relatively easy to remove an electron from a metal, and there is only a small energy payback if a metal gains an electron. The opposite is true of a halogen; it is hard to remove an electron and there is a large energy advantage if a halogen gains an electron. Thus, the metal "gives up" an electron to the halogen and an ionic compound is formed. Carbon, on the other hand, is much closer in ionization energy and electron affinity to the halogens. Carbon has a much greater tendency than a metal to keep its own electrons and at least some attraction for the electrons of other elements. Thus, compounds of carbon and the halogens are molecular, rather than ionic.

Integrative Exercises

7.78 (a) Mg_3N_2

(b) $Mg_3N_2(s) + 3H_2O(l) \rightarrow 3MgO(s) + 2NH_3(g)$
The driving force is the production of $NH_3(g)$.

(c) After the second heating, all the Mg is converted to MgO.
Calculate the initial mass Mg.

$$0.486 \text{ g MgO} \times \frac{24.305 \text{ g Mg}}{40.305 \text{ g MgO}} = 0.293 \text{ g Mg}$$

x = g Mg converted to MgO; y = g Mg converted to Mg_3N_2; $x = 0.293 - y$

$$\text{g MgO} = x \left(\frac{40.305 \text{ g MgO}}{24.305 \text{ g Mg}} \right); \quad \text{g Mg}_3\text{N}_2 = y \left(\frac{100.929 \text{ g Mg}_3\text{N}_2}{72.915 \text{ g Mg}} \right)$$

$\text{g MgO} + \text{g Mg}_3\text{N}_2 = 0.470$

$$(0.293 - y) \left(\frac{40.305}{24.305} \right) + y \left(\frac{100.929}{72.915} \right) = 0.470$$

$(0.293 - y)(1.6583) + y(1.3842) = 0.470$

$-1.6583 \, y + 1.3842 \, y = 0.470 - 0.48588$

$-0.2741 \, y = -0.016$

$y = 0.05794 = 0.058 \text{ g Mg in Mg}_3\text{N}_2$

$$\text{g Mg}_3\text{N}_2 = 0.05794 \text{ g Mg} \times \frac{100.929 \text{ g Mg}_3\text{N}_2}{72.915 \text{ g Mg}} = 0.0802 = 0.080 \text{ g Mg}_3\text{N}_2$$

$$\text{mass \% Mg}_3\text{N}_2 = \frac{0.0802 \text{ g Mg}_3\text{N}_2}{0.470 \text{ g (MgO + Mg}_3\text{N}_2)} \times 100 = 17\%$$

(The final mass % has 2 sig figs because the mass of Mg obtained from solving simultaneous equations has 2 sig figs.)

(d) $3Mg(s) + 2NH_3(g) \rightarrow Mg_3N_2(s) + 3H_2(g)$

$$6.3 \text{ g Mg} \times \frac{1 \text{ mol Mg}}{24.305 \text{ g Mg}} = 0.2592 = 0.26 \text{ mol Mg}$$

$$2.57 \text{ g NH}_3 \times \frac{1 \text{ mol NH}_3}{17.031 \text{ g NH}_3} = 0.1509 = 0.16 \text{ mol NH}_3$$

$$0.2592 \text{ mol Mg} \times \frac{2 \text{ mol NH}_3}{3 \text{ mol Mg}} = 0.1728 = 0.17 \text{ mol NH}_3$$

0.26 mol Mg requires more than the available NH_3 so NH_3 is the limiting reactant.

$$0.1509 \text{ mol NH}_3 \times \frac{3 \text{ mol H}_2}{2 \text{ mol NH}_3} \times \frac{2.016 \text{ g H}_2}{\text{mol H}_2} = 0.4563 = 0.46 \text{ g H}_2$$

(e) $\Delta H^{\circ}_{rxn} = \Delta H^{\circ}_f \, Mg_3N_2(s) + 3\Delta H^{\circ}_f \, H_2(g) - 3\Delta H^{\circ}_f \, Mg(s) - 2\Delta H^{\circ}_f \, NH_3(g)$

$= -461.08 \text{ kJ} + 0 - 3(0) - 2(-46.19) = -368.70 \text{ kJ}$

8 Basic Concepts of Chemical Bonding

Lewis Symbols and Ionic Bonding

8.1   (a)   Valence electrons are those that take part in chemical bonding, those in the outermost electron shell of the atom. This usually means the electrons beyond the core noble-gas configuration of the atom, although it is sometimes only the outer shell electrons.

       (b)   N: [He] $2s^2 2p^3$ A nitrogen atom has 5 valence electrons.

               |___|
              valence electrons

       (c) $1s^2 2s^2 2p^6$ $3s^2 3p^2$ The atom (Si) has 4 valence electrons.

          |_____| |_____|
            [Ne]   valence electrons

8.3   (a)   Ċa·   (b)   ·P̈·   (c)   :N̈e: (d)   ·Ḃ·

8.5   Mg·   +   ·Ö: ⟶ Mg^{2+} + $\left[:\ddot{O}: \right]^{2-}$

8.7   (a) AlF_3 (b) K_2S (c) Y_2O_3 (d) Mg_3N_2

8.9   (a) Sr^{2+}: [Kr], noble-gas configuration   (b) Ti^{2+}: $[Ar]3d^2$
       (c) Se^{2-}: $[Ar]4s^2 3d^{10} 4p^6$ = [Kr], noble-gas configuration   (d) Ni^{2+}: $[Ar]3d^8$
       (e) Br^-: $[Ar]4s^2 3d^{10} 4p^6$ = [Kr], noble-gas configuration   (f) Mn^{3+}: $[Ar]3d^4$

8.11 (a)   *Lattice energy* is the energy required to totally separate one mole of solid ionic compound into its gaseous ions.

       (b)   The magnitude of the lattice energy depends on the magnitudes of the charges of the two ions, their radii and the arrangement of ions in the lattice. The main factor is the charges, because the radii of ions do not vary over a wide range.

8.13   (a)   According to Equation 8.4, electrostatic attraction increases with increasing charges of the ions and decreases with increasing radius of the ions. Thus, lattice energy (i) **increases** as the charges of the ions increase and (ii) **decreases** as the sizes of the ions increase.

      (b)   KBr < KCl < LiCl < CaO. This order is confirmed by the lattice energies given in Table 8.2. CaO has the highest lattice energy because the ions have 2+ and 2- charges. The other compounds have cations with 1+ charges and anions with 1- charges. They are placed in order of decreasing ionic separation. K^+ and Br^- have the largest radii, Cl^- is smaller than Br^-, and Li^+ is smaller than K^+.

8.15   (a) O^{2-} is smaller than S^{2-}; the closer approach of the oppositely charged ions in MgO leads to greater electrostatic attraction.

      (b)   The ions have 1+ and 1- charges in both compounds. However, the fact that the ionic radii are much smaller in LiF means that the ions can approach more closely, with a resultant increase in electrostatic attractive forces.

      (c)   The ions in CaO have 2+ and 2- charges as compared with 1+ and 1- charges in KF.

8.17.   Equation 8.4 predicts that as the oppositely charged ions approach each other, the energy of interaction will be large and negative. This more than compensates for the energy required to form Ca^{2+} and O^{2-} from the neutral atoms (see Figure 8.4 for the formation of NaCl).

8.19 $RbCl(s) \rightarrow Rb^+(g) + Cl^-(g)$ ΔH (lattice energy) = ?

By analogy to NaCl, Figure 8.4, the lattice energy is

$\Delta H_{latt} = -\Delta H_f^\circ \, RbCl(s) + \Delta H_f^\circ \, Rb(g) + \Delta H_f^\circ \, Cl(g) + I_1 \, (Rb) + E \, (Cl)$

      = -(-430.5 kJ) + 85.8 kJ + 121.7 kJ + 403 kJ + (-349 kJ) = +692 kJ

This value is smaller than that for NaCl (+788 kJ) because Rb^+ has a larger ionic radius than Na^+. This means that the value of d in the denominator of Equation 8.4 is larger for RbCl, and the potential energy of the electrostatic attraction is smaller.

Sizes of Ions

8.21   (a)   Electrostatic repulsions are reduced by removing an electron from a neutral atom, Z_{eff} increases, and the cation is smaller.

      (b)   The additional electrostatic repulsion produced by adding an electron to a neutral atom decreases the Z_{eff} of the valence electrons, causing them to be less tightly bound to the nucleus and the size of the anion to be larger.

      (c)   Going down a column, valence electrons are further from the nucleus and they experience greater shielding by core electrons. In spite of an increase in Z, the size of particles with like charge increases.

8.23 (a)   An isoelectronic series is a group of atoms or ions that have the same number of electrons, and thus the same electron configuration.

      (b)   (i) Cl⁻ : **Ar**   (ii) Se²⁻ : **Kr**   (iii) Mg²⁺ : **Ne**

8.25 (a)   Since the number of electrons in an isoelectronic series is the same, repulsion and shielding effects do not vary for the different particles. As Z increases, Z_{eff} increases, the valence electrons are more strongly attracted to the nucleus and the size of the particle decreases.

      (b)   Because F⁻, Ne and Na⁺ have the same electron configuration, the 2p electron in the particle with the largest Z experiences the largest effective nuclear charge. A 2p electron in Na⁺ experiences the greatest effective nuclear charge.

8.27 (a)   Li⁺ < K⁺ < Rb⁺   (b) Mg²⁺ < Na⁺ < Br⁻   (c) K⁺ < Ar < Cl⁻ < S²⁻   (d) Ar < Cl < Cl⁻

Covalent Bonding, Electronegativity and Bond Polarity

8.29 (a)   A *covalent bond* is the bond formed when two atoms share one or more pairs of electrons.

      (b)   The ionic bonding in NaCl is due to strong electrostatic attraction between oppositely charged Na⁺ and Cl⁻ ions. The covalent bonding in Cl_2 is due to sharing of a pair of electrons by two neutral chlorine atoms.

8.31

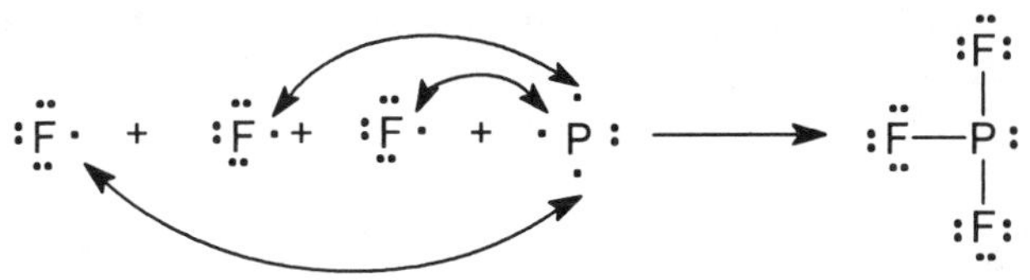

.. ..   :F:
:F· + :F·+ :F· + ·P: ⟶ :F—P:
.. .. ..   :F:
                          ..

8.33 (a) 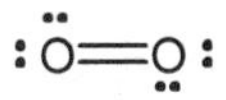   :O̤=O̤:

      (b)   A double bond is required because there are not enough electrons to satisfy the octet rule with single bonds and unshared pairs.

      (c)   The greater the number of shared electron pairs between two atoms, the shorter the distance between the atoms. If O_2 has a double bond, the O-O distance will be shorter than the O-O single bond distance.

8.35 (a)   Electronegativity is the ability of an atom in a molecule (a bonded atom) to attract electrons to itself.

      (b)   The range of electronegativities on the Pauling scale is 0.7-4.0.

      (c)   Fluorine, F, is the most electronegative element.

      (d)   Cesium, Cs, is the least electronegative element that is not radioactive.

8.37   Electronegativity increases going up and to the right in the periodic table.

      (a)   S   (b)   C   (c)   As   (d)   Mg

8.39   The bonds in (a), (b) and (d) are polar because the atoms involved differ in electronegativity. The more electronegative element in each polar bond is: (a) O   (b) F   (d)   O

8.41   (a)   A polar molecule has a measurable dipole moment; its centers of positive and negative charge do not coincide. A nonpolar molecule has a zero net dipole moment; its centers of positive and negative charge do coincide.

        (b)   Yes. If X and Y have different electronegativities, they have different attractions for the electrons in the molecule. The electron density around the more electronegative atom will be greater, producing a charge separation or dipole in the molecule.

        (c) $\mu = Qr$. The dipole moment, μ, is the product of the magnitude of the separated charges, Q, and the distance between them, r.

8.43 Q is the charge at either end of the dipole.

$$Q = \frac{\mu}{r} = \frac{1.82\ D}{0.92\ \text{Å}} \times \frac{1\ \text{Å}}{1 \times 10^{-10}\ m} \times \frac{3.34 \times 10^{-30}\ C \cdot m}{1\ D} \times \frac{1\ e}{1.60 \times 10^{-19}\ C} = 0.41\ e$$

The calculated charge on H and F is 0.41 e. This can be thought of as the amount of charge "transferred" from H to F.

8.45   Generally, compounds formed by a metal and a nonmetal are described as ionic, while compounds formed from two or more nonmetals are covalent.

        (a) MnO_2, ionic

        (b) Ga_2S_3, ionic   (Although their electronegativities are similar, Ga is a metal and S is a nonmetal. Use of a roman numeral usually presumes an ionic compound.)

        (c)   CoO, ionic   (d) copper(I) sulfide, ionic   (e) chlorine trifluoride, covalent

        (f)   vanadium(V) fluoride, ionic

Lewis Structures; Resonance Structures

8.47   Counting the **correct number of valence electrons** is the foundation of every Lewis structure.

        (a)   Count valence electrons: $4 + (4 \times 1) = 8\ e^-$, $4\ e^-$ pairs. Follow the procedure in Sample Exercise 8.8.

$$\begin{array}{c} H \\ | \\ H - Si - H \\ | \\ H \end{array}$$

        (b)   Valence electrons: $4 + 6 = 10\ e^-$, $5\ e^-$ pairs

$$:C \equiv O:$$

(c)   Valence electrons: [6 + (2 × 7)] = 20 e⁻, 10 e⁻ pairs.

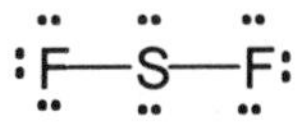

$$:\!\ddot{F}\!-\!\ddot{S}\!-\!\ddot{F}\!:$$

i.   Place the S atom in the middle and connect each F atom with a single bond; this requires 2 e⁻ pairs.

ii.   Complete the octets of the F atoms with nonbonded pairs of electrons; this requires an additional 6 e⁻ pairs.

iii.   The remaining 2 e⁻ pairs complete the octet of the central S atom.

(d)   32 valence e⁻, 16 e⁻ pairs   (e)   20 valence e⁻, 10 e⁻ pairs

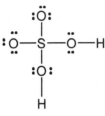

$$\left[\;:\!\ddot{O}\!-\!\ddot{Cl}\!-\!\ddot{O}\!:\;\right]^{-}$$

(Choose the Lewis structure that
obeys the octet rule, Section 8.8.)

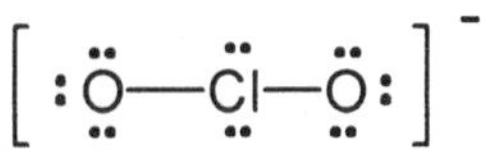

(f)   14 valence e⁻, 7 e⁻ pairs

$$H\!-\!\underset{\underset{H}{|}}{\ddot{N}}\!-\!\ddot{O}\!-\!H$$

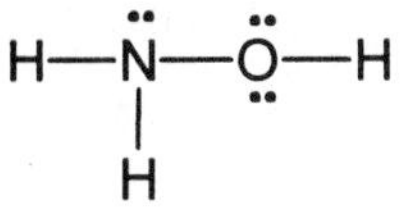

8.49   (a)   10 e⁻, 5 e⁻ pairs 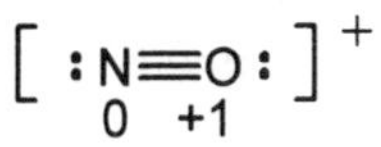   (b)   32 valence e⁻, 16 e⁻ pairs

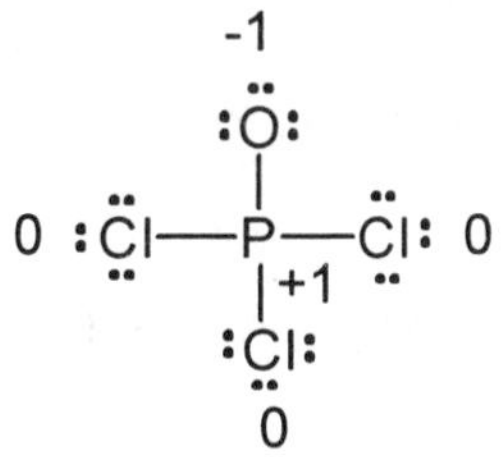

$$\left[\;:\!N\!\equiv\!O\!:\;\right]^{+}$$
$$\quad\;\;0\;\;+1$$

$$\underset{0}{:\!\ddot{Cl}}\!-\!\underset{\underset{\underset{0}{:\!\ddot{Cl}:}}{|+1}}{\overset{\overset{-1}{\overset{:\ddot{O}:}{|}}}{P}}\!-\!\underset{0}{\ddot{Cl}\!:}$$

(c)   32 valence e⁻, 16 e⁻ pairs 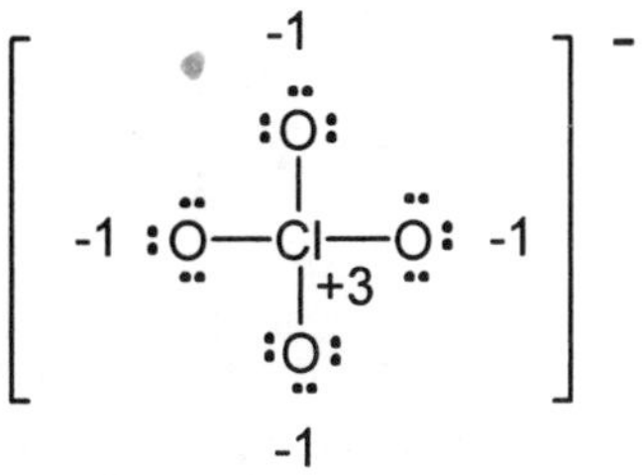   (d)   26 valence e⁻, 13 e⁻ pairs

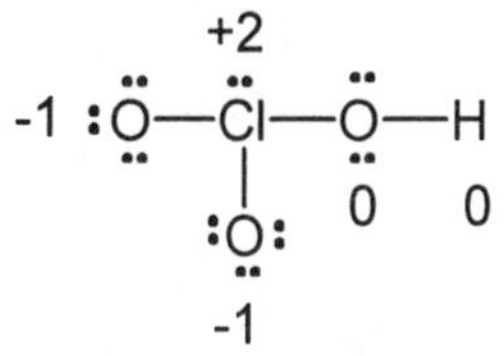

$$\left[\;\underset{-1}{:\!\ddot{O}}\!-\!\underset{\underset{\underset{-1}{:\ddot{O}:}}{|+3}}{\overset{\overset{-1}{\overset{:\ddot{O}:}{|}}}{Cl}}\!-\!\underset{-1}{\ddot{O}:}\;\right]^{-}$$

$$\underset{-1}{:\!\ddot{O}}\!-\!\underset{\underset{\underset{-1}{:\ddot{O}:}}{|}}{\overset{\overset{+2}{\overset{}{}}}{\ddot{Cl}}}\!-\!\underset{0}{\overset{}{\ddot{O}}}\!-\!\underset{0}{H}$$

8.51   (a)   16 e⁻, 8 e⁻ pairs

$$\ddot{N}\!=\!N\!=\!\ddot{O} \longleftrightarrow :\!N\!\equiv\!N\!-\!\ddot{O}\!: \longleftrightarrow :\!\ddot{N}\!-\!N\!\equiv\!O\!:$$

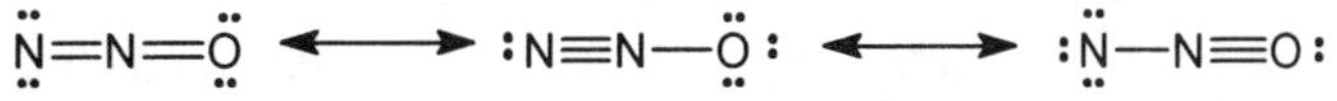

(Based on formal charge arguments, the structure on the right is probably a smaller contributor than the other two.)

(b)   24 e⁻, 12 e⁻ pairs

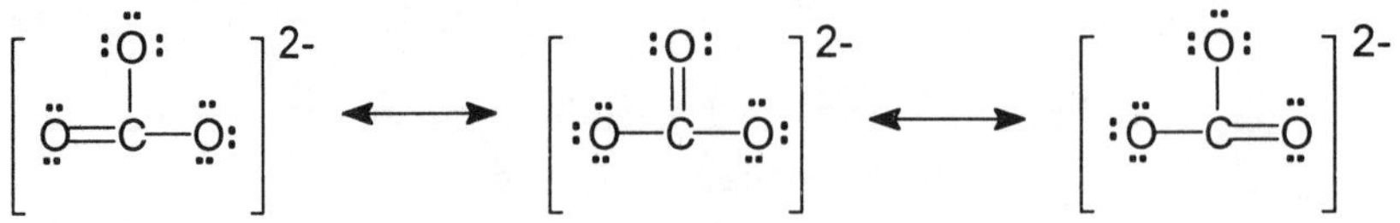

$$\left[\ddot{O}=C-\ddot{O}:\right]^{2-} \longleftrightarrow \left[:\ddot{O}-C-\ddot{O}:\right]^{2-} \longleftrightarrow \left[:\ddot{O}-C=\ddot{O}\right]^{2-}$$

(c)   18 e⁻, 9 e⁻ pairs

$$\left[H-\overset{:O:}{\underset{}{C}}-\ddot{O}:\right]^{-} \longleftrightarrow \left[H-\overset{:\ddot{O}:}{\underset{}{C}}=\ddot{O}\right]^{-}$$

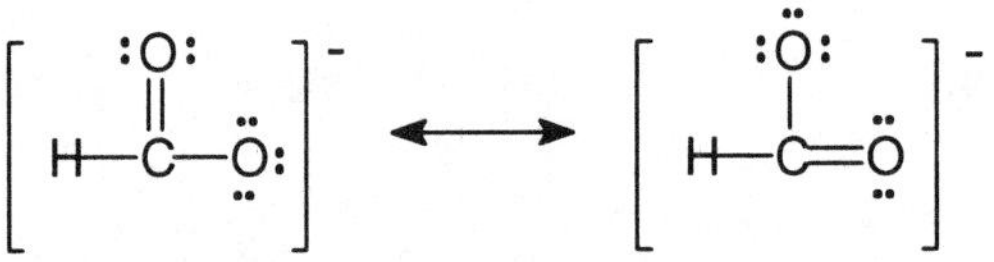

8.53   The Lewis structures are as follows:

    5 e⁻ pairs   8 e⁻ pairs

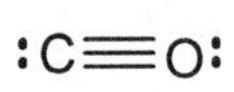

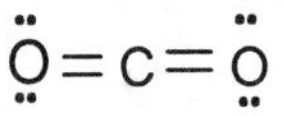

     $:C\equiv O:$ $\ddot{O}=C=\ddot{O}$

    12 e⁻ pairs

$$\left[\overset{:\ddot{O}:}{\underset{:\ddot{O}}{C}}_{\ddot{O}}\right]^{2-} \left[\overset{:\ddot{O}:}{\underset{:\ddot{O}:}{C}}_{\ddot{O}:}\right]^{2-} \left[\overset{:O:}{\underset{:\ddot{O}:}{C}}_{\ddot{O}:}\right]^{2-}$$

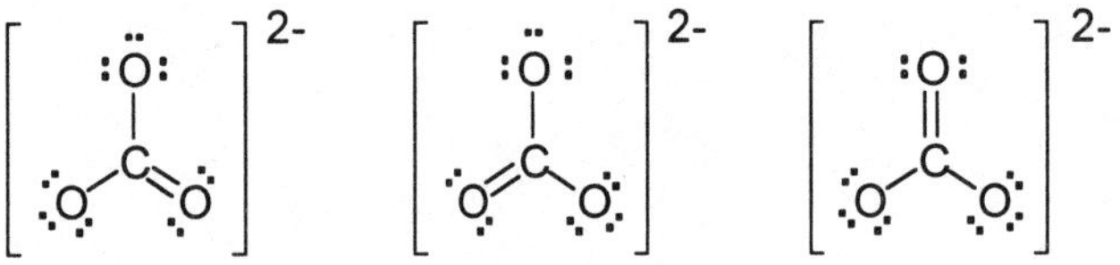

The more pairs of electrons shared by two atoms, the shorter the bond between the atoms. The average number of electron pairs shared by C and O in the three species is 3 for CO, 2 for CO_2 and 1.33 for CO_3^{2-}. This is also the order of increasing bond length: CO < CO_2 < CO_3^{2-}.

8.55   (a)   Two equally valid Lewis structures can be drawn for benzene.

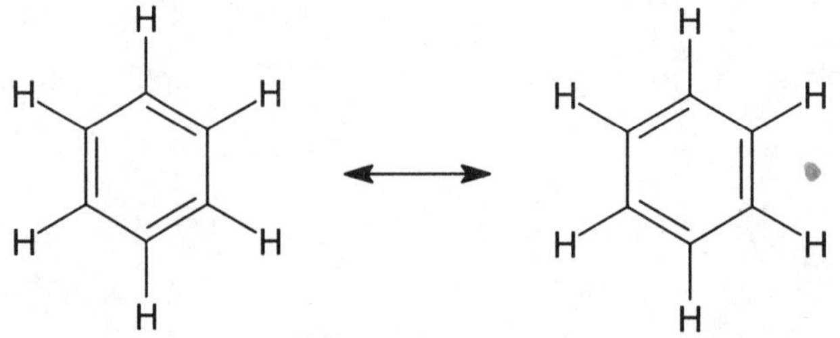

         Since the 6 C-C bond lengths are equal, neither of the individual Lewis structures gives an accurate picture of the bonding. The concept of resonance dictates that the true description of bonding is some hybrid or blend of the two Lewis structures.

    (b)   The resonance model described in (a) has 6 equivalent C-C bonds, each with some double bond character. That is, more than 1 pair but less than 2 pairs of electrons is involved in each C-C bond. We would expect the C-C bond length in benzene to be shorter than a single bond but longer than a double bond.

Exceptions to the Octet Rule

8.57 The most common exceptions to the octet rule are molecules with more than eight electrons around one or more atoms, usually the central atom.

8.59 (a) 24 e⁻, 12 e⁻ pairs

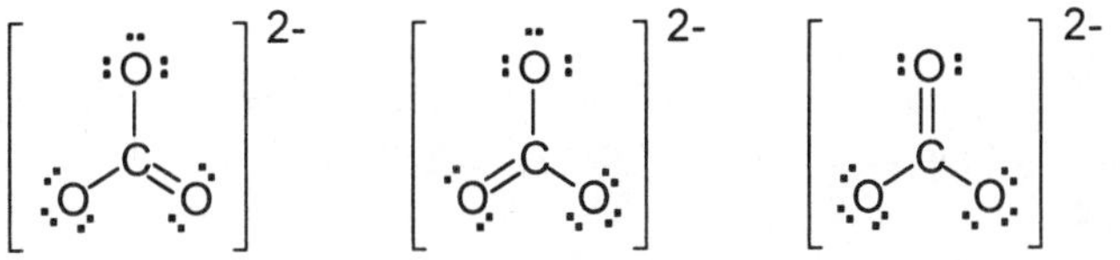

CO₃²⁻ has three resonance structures, but all obey the octet rule.

(b) 6 e⁻, 3 e⁻ pairs, impossible to satisfy octet rule with only 6 valence electrons

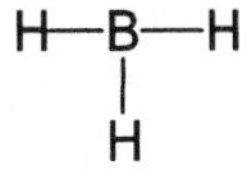

H—B—H
|
H

6 electrons around B

(c) 22 e⁻, 11 e⁻ pairs

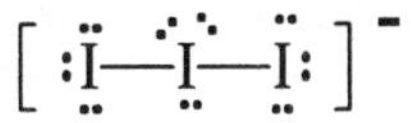

[:Ï—Ï—Ï:]⁻

10 e⁻ around central I

(d) 32 e⁻, 16 e⁻ pairs

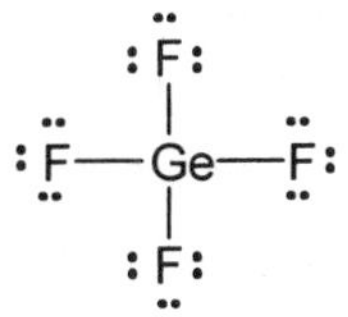

:F:
|
:F—Ge—F:
|
:F:

obeys the octet rule

(e) 48 e⁻, 24 e⁻ pairs

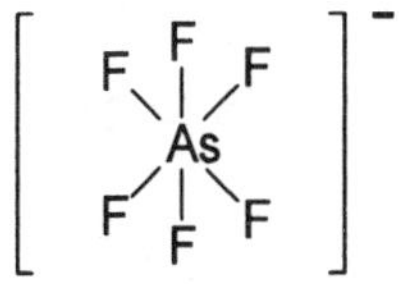

[F\ F /F
      As
   F/ |F]⁻

12 e⁻ around As; three nonbonded pairs on each F have been omitted

8.61 (a) 16 e⁻, 8 e⁻ pairs

This structure violates the octet rule; Be has only 4 e⁻ around it.

(b) Cl=Be=Cl ⟷ :Cl—Be≡Cl: ⟷ :Cl≡Be—Cl:

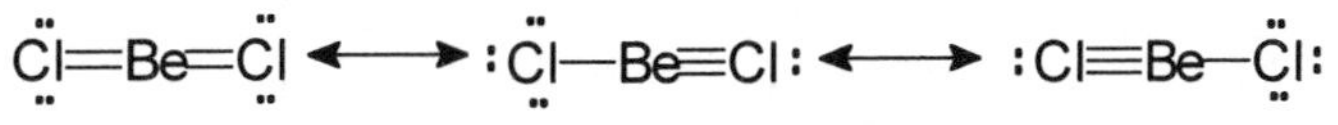

(c) The formal charges on each of the atoms in the four resonance structures are:

:Cl—Be—Cl: Cl=Be=Cl   :Cl—Be≡Cl: :Cl≡Be—Cl:
 0   0   0   +1 -2 +1   0 -2 +2   +2 -2   0

Since formal charges are minimized on the structure that violates the octet rule, this form is probably most important.

Bond Enthalpies

8.63   (a) $\Delta H = 2D(\text{O-H}) + D(\text{O-O}) + 4D(\text{C-H}) + D(\text{C=C})$
                 $- 2D(\text{O-H}) - 2D(\text{O-C}) - 4D(\text{C-H}) - D(\text{C-C})$
      $\Delta H = D(\text{O-O}) + D(\text{C=C}) - 2D(\text{O-C}) - D(\text{C-C})$
         $= 146 + 614 - 2(358) - 348 = -304 \text{ kJ}$

   (b) $\Delta H = 5D(\text{C-H}) + D(\text{C}\equiv\text{N}) + D(\text{C=C}) - 5D(\text{C-H}) - D(\text{C}\equiv\text{N}) - 2D(\text{C-C})$
         $= D(\text{C=C}) - 2D(\text{C-C}) = 614 - 2(348) = -82 \text{ kJ}$

   (c) $\Delta H = 6D(\text{N-Cl}) - 3D(\text{Cl-Cl}) - D(\text{N}\equiv\text{N})$
         $= 6(200) - 3(242) - 941 = -467 \text{ kJ}$

8.65   Draw structural formulas so bonds can be visualized.

   (a)
$$2\ \text{Br}-\underset{\underset{\text{Br}}{|}}{\text{N}}-\text{Br} + 3\ \text{F}-\text{F} \longrightarrow 2\ \text{F}-\underset{\underset{\text{F}}{|}}{\text{N}}-\text{F} + 3\ \text{Br}-\text{Br}$$

      $\Delta H = 6D(\text{N-Br}) + 3D(\text{F-F}) - 6D(\text{N-F}) - 3D(\text{Br-Br})$
         $= 6(243) + 3(155) - 6(272) - 3(193) = -288 \text{ kJ}$

   (b)
$$\text{C}\equiv\text{O} + 2\ \text{H}-\text{H} \longrightarrow \text{H}-\underset{\underset{\text{H}}{|}}{\overset{\overset{\text{H}}{|}}{\text{C}}}-\text{O}-\text{H}$$

      $\Delta H = D(\text{C}\equiv\text{O}) + 2D(\text{H-H}) - 3D(\text{C-H}) - D(\text{C-O}) - D(\text{O-H})$
         $= 1072 + 2(436) - 3(413) - 358 - 463 = -116 \text{ kJ}$

   (c)
$$\text{H}-\text{S}-\text{H} + 3\ \text{F}-\text{F} \longrightarrow \text{F}-\underset{\underset{\text{F}}{|}}{\overset{\overset{\text{F}}{|}}{\text{S}}}-\text{F} + 2\ \text{H}-\text{F}$$

      $\Delta H = 2D(\text{S-H}) + 3D(\text{F-F}) - 4D(\text{S-F}) - 2D(\text{H-F})$
         $= 2(339) + 3(155) - 4(327) - 2(567) = -1299 \text{ kJ}$

8.67   (a)
$$:\text{N}\equiv\text{N}: + 3\ \text{H}-\text{H} \longrightarrow 2\ \text{H}-\underset{\underset{\text{H}}{|}}{\overset{..}{\text{N}}}-\text{H}$$

      $\Delta H = D(\text{N}\equiv\text{N}) + 3D(\text{H-H}) - 6(\text{N-H}) = 941 \text{ kJ} + 3(436 \text{ kJ}) - 6(391 \text{ kJ})$
         $= -97 \text{ kJ} / 2 \text{ mol NH}_3 ;$ **exothermic**

   (b) $\Delta H_f^{\circ} \text{ NH}_3(g) = -46.19 \text{ kJ}; \ \Delta H = 2(-46.19) = -92.38 \text{ kJ}$

      The ΔH calculated from bond enthalpies is slightly more exothermic (more negative) than that obtained using ΔH_f° values.

8.69   The average Ti-Cl bond enthalpy is just the average of the four values listed, 430 kJ/mol.

8.70

$$Cl-P-Cl \,(g) \longrightarrow P\,(g) + 3\,Cl\,(g)$$
(with Cl below the P)

$$\Delta H = \Delta H^\circ_f \, P(g) + 3\Delta H^\circ_f \, Cl(g) - \Delta H^\circ_f \, PCl_3(g)$$
$$= 316.4 \text{ kJ} + 3(121.7 \text{ kJ}) - (-288.07 \text{ kJ})$$
$$= 969.6 \text{ kJ}$$

The reaction above represents the enthalpy of dissociation for 3 P-Cl bonds. The average bond enthalpy of a single P-Cl bond is then $\dfrac{969.6 \text{ kJ}}{3 \text{ P-Cl bonds}}$ = 323.2 kJ/P-Cl bond.

Additional Exercises

8.71   (a)   Group 4A   (b) Group 2A   (c) Group 5A
             (These are the appropriate groups in the s and p blocks, where Lewis symbols are most useful.)

8.73 $E = \dfrac{-8.99 \times 10^9 \text{ J} \cdot \text{m}}{C^2} \times \dfrac{(1.60 \times 10^{-19} \text{ C})^2}{(0.97 + 1.81) \times 10^{-10} \text{ m}} = -8.28 \times 10^{-19}$ J

On a molar basis: $(-8.279 \times 10^{-19} \text{ J})(6.022 \times 10^{23}) = -499$ kJ

Note that its absolute value is less than the lattice energy, 788 kJ/mol. The difference represents the added energy of putting all the Na^+Cl^- ion pairs together in a three-dimensional array, as shown in Figure 8.3.

8.75   (a)

Compound	Lattice Energy (kJ)		Compound	Lattice Energy (kJ)	
NaCl	788	56 kJ	LiCl	834	55 kJ
NaBr	732		**LiBr**	**779**	
Na I	682		Li I	730	

(106 kJ bracket for the Na group; 104 kJ bracket for the Li group)

The difference in lattice energy between LiCl and LiI is 104 kJ. The difference between NaCl and NaI is 106 kJ; the difference between NaCl and NaBr is 56 kJ, or 53% of the difference between NaCl and NaI. Applying this relationship to the Li salts, 0.53(104 kJ) = 55 kJ difference between LiCl and LiBr. The approximate lattice energy of LiBr is (834 - 55) kJ = 779 kJ.

(b)

Compound	Lattice Energy (kJ)		Compound	Lattice Energy (kJ)	
NaCl	788	56 kJ	CsCl	657	30 kJ
NaBr	732		**CsBr**	**627**	
Na I	682		Cs I	600	

(106 kJ bracket for the Na group; 57 kJ bracket for the Cs group)

By analogy to the Na salts, the difference between lattice energies of CsCl and CsBr should be approximately 53% of the difference between CsCl and CsI. The lattice energy of CsBr is approximately 627 kJ.

(c)

	Compound	Lattice Energy (kJ)		Compound	Lattice Energy (kJ)	
578 kJ	MgO CaO SrO	3795 3414 3217	381 kJ	199 kJ	MgCl$_2$ **CaCl$_2$** SrCl$_2$	2326 2195 2127	131 kJ

By analogy to the oxides, the difference between the lattice energies of MgCl$_2$ and CaCl$_2$ should be approximately 66% of the difference between MgCl$_2$ and SrCl$_2$. That is, 0.66(199 kJ) = 131 kJ. The lattice energy of CaCl$_2$ is approximately (2326 - 131) kJ = 2195 kJ.

8.78   Molecule (b) H$_2$S and ion (c) NO$_2^-$ contain polar bonds. The atoms that form the bonds (H-S) and N-O) have different electronegativity values.

8.81   Formal charge (FC) = # valence e$^-$ - (# nonbonding e$^-$ + 1/2 # bonding e$^-$)

      (a)   18 e$^-$, 9 e$^-$ pairs

FC for the central O = 6 - [2 + 1/2 (6)] = +1

      (b)   48 e$^-$, 24 e$^-$ pairs

FC for P = 5 - [0 + 1/2 (12)] = -1

The three nonbonded pairs on each F have been omitted.

      (c)   17 e$^-$; 8 e$^-$ pairs, 1 odd e$^-$

The odd electron is probably on N because it is less electronegative than O.
Assuming the odd electron is on N, FC for N = 5 - [1+ 1/2 (6)] = +1.
If the odd electron is on O, FC for N = 5 - [2 + 1/2 (6)] = 0.

      (d)   28 e$^-$, 14 e$^-$ pairs   (e)   32 e$^-$, 16 e$^-$ pairs

FC for I = 7 - [4 + 1/2 (6)] = 0   FC for Cl = 7 - [0 + 1/2 (8)] = +3

8.83   (a) $:N\equiv N-\ddot{O}: \longleftrightarrow :\ddot{N}-N\equiv O: \longleftrightarrow :\ddot{N}=N=\ddot{O}:$

                0 +1 -1   -2 +1 +1   -1 +1   0

In the leftmost structure, the more electronegative O atom has the negative formal charge, so this structure is likely to be most important.

(b)   In general, the more shared pairs of electrons between two atoms, the shorter the bond, and vice versa. That the N-N bond length in N_2O is slightly longer than the typical $N\equiv N$ indicates that the middle and right resonance structures where the N atoms share less than 3 electron pairs are contributors to the true structure. That the N-O bond length is slightly shorter than a typical N=O indicates that the middle structure, where N and O share more than 2 electron pairs, does contribute to the true structure. This physical data indicates that while formal charge can be used to predict which resonance form will be more important to the observed structure, the influence of minor contributors on the true structure cannot be ignored.

8.86 $\Delta H = 8D(C\text{-}H) - D(C\text{-}C) - 6D(C\text{-}H) - D(H\text{-}H)$

       $= 2D(C\text{-}H) - D(C\text{-}C) - D(H\text{-}H)$

       $= 2(413) - 348 - 436 = +42 \text{ kJ}$

$\Delta H = 8D(C\text{-}H) + 1/2\ D(O\text{=}O) - D(C\text{-}C) - 6D(C\text{-}H) - 2D(O\text{-}H)$

       $= 2D(C\text{-}H) + 1/2\ D(O\text{=}O) - D(C\text{-}C) - 2D(O\text{-}H)$

       $= 2(413) + 1/2\ (495) - 348 - 2(463) = -200 \text{ kJ}$

The fundamental difference in the two reactions is the formation of 1 mol of H-H bonds versus the formation of 2 mol of O-H bonds. The latter is much more exothermic, so the reaction involving oxygen is more exothermic.

8.88   (a)

nitroglycerine

$\Delta H = 20D(C\text{-}H) + 8D(C\text{-}C) + 12D(C\text{-}O) + 24D(O\text{-}N) + 12D(N\text{=}O)$

         $- [6D(N\equiv N) + 24D(C\text{=}O) + 20D(H\text{-}O) + D(O\text{=}O)]$

$\Delta H = 20(413) + 8(348) + 12(358) + 24(201) + 12(607)$

         $- [6(941) + 24(799) + 20(463) + 495]$

   $= -7129 \text{ kJ}$

$$1.00 \text{ g } C_3H_5N_3O_9 \times \frac{1 \text{ mol } C_3H_5N_3O_9}{227.1 \text{ g } C_3H_5N_3O_9} \times \frac{-7129 \text{ kJ}}{4 \text{ mol } C_3H_5N_3O_9} = 7.85 \text{ kJ/g } C_3H_5N_3O_9$$

(b) $4C_7H_5N_3O_6(s) \rightarrow 6N_2(g) + 7CO_2(g) + 10H_2O(g) + 21C(s)$

Integrative Exercises

8.90   (a) Ti^{2+}: $[Ar]3d^2$; Ca: $[Ar]4s^2$. Yes. The 2 valence electrons in Ti^{2+} and Ca are in different principle quantum levels and different subshells.

     (b)   According to the Aufbau Principle, valence electrons will occupy the lowest energy empty orbital. Thus, in Ca the 4s is lower in energy than the 3d, while in Ti^{2+}, the 3d is lower in energy than the 4s.

     (c)   Since there is only one 4s orbital, the 2 valence electrons in Ca are paired. There are 5 degenerate 3d orbitals, so the 2 valence electrons in Ti^{2+} are unpaired. Ca has no unpaired electrons, Ti^{2+} has 2.

8.92   The pathway to the formation of K_2O can be written:

$2K(s) \rightarrow 2K(g)$	$2\Delta H_f^{\circ} K(g)$
$2K(g) \rightarrow 2K^+(g) + 2\,e^-$	$2\,I_1(K)$
$1/2\,O_2(g) \rightarrow O(g)$	$\Delta H_f^{\circ} O(g)$
$O(g) + 1\,e^- \rightarrow O^-(g)$	$E_1(O)$
$O^-(g) + 1\,e^- \rightarrow O^{2-}(g)$	$E_2(O)$
$2K^+(g) + O^{2-}(g) \rightarrow K_2O(s)$	$-\Delta H_{latt} K_2O(s)$

$2K(s) + 1/2\,O_2(g) \rightarrow K_2O(s)$	$\Delta H_f^{\circ} K_2O(s)$

$\Delta H_f^{\circ} K_2O(s) = 2\Delta H_f^{\circ} K(g) + 2\,I_1(K) + \Delta H_f^{\circ} O(g) + E_1(O) + E_2(O) - \Delta H_{latt} K_2O(s)$

$E_2(O) = \Delta H_f^{\circ} K_2O(s) + \Delta H_{latt} K_2O(s) - 2\Delta H_f^{\circ} K(g) - 2\,I_1(K) - \Delta H_f^{\circ} O(g) - E_1(O)$

$E_2(O) = -363.2\ kJ + 2238\ kJ - 2(89.99)\ kJ - 2(419)\ kJ - 247.5\ kJ - (-141)\ kJ$

$\qquad = +750\ kJ$

8.95   (a)

$HF(g) \rightarrow H(g) + F(g)$	$D\ (H\text{-}F)$	$567\ kJ$
$H(g) \rightarrow H^+(g) + 1\,e^-$	$I\ (H)$	$1312\ kJ$
$F(g) + 1\,e^- \rightarrow F^-(g)$	$E\ (F)$	$-328\ kJ$

$HF(g) \rightarrow H^+(g) + F^-(g)$	ΔH	$1551\ kJ$

     (b) $\Delta H = D(H\text{-}Cl) + I(H) + E(Cl)$
            $\Delta H = 431\ kJ + 1312\ kJ + (-349)\ kJ = 1394\ kJ$

     (c) $\Delta H = D(H\text{-}Br) + I(H) + E(Br)$
            $\Delta H = 366\ kJ + 1312\ kJ + (-325)\ kJ = 1353\ kJ$

8.97 (a) $Br_2(l) \rightarrow 2Br(g)$ $\Delta H° = 2\Delta H°_f\ Br(g) = 2(111.8)\ kJ = 223.6\ kJ$

(b) $CCl_4(l) \rightarrow C(g) + 4Cl(g)$

$\Delta H° = \Delta H°_f\ C(g) + 4\Delta H°_f\ Cl(g) - \Delta H°_f\ CCl_4(l)$
$\quad = 718.4\ kJ + 4(121.7)\ kJ - (-139.3)\ kJ = 1344.5$

$$\frac{1344.5\ kJ}{4\ C\text{--}Cl\ bonds} = 336.1\ kJ$$

(c) $\qquad H_2O_2(l) \rightarrow 2H(g) + 2O(g)$

$2H(g) + 2O(g) \rightarrow 2OH(g)$

$\overline{\qquad\qquad\qquad\qquad\qquad}$

$\qquad H_2O_2(l) \rightarrow 2OH(g)$

$D(O\text{-}O)(l) = 2\Delta H°_f\ H(g) + 2\Delta H°_f\ O(g) - \Delta H°_f\ H_2O_2(l) - 2D(O\text{-}H)(g)$
$\qquad\qquad = 2(217.94)\ kJ + 2(247.5)\ kJ - (-187.8)\ kJ - 2(463)\ kJ$
$\qquad\qquad = 193\ kJ$

(d) The data are listed below.

bond	D gas kJ/mol	D liquid kJ/mol
Br-Br	193	223.6
C-Cl	328	336.1
O-O	146	192.7

Breaking bonds in the liquid requires more energy than breaking bonds in the gas phase. For simple molecules, bond dissociation from the liquid phase can be thought of in two steps:

$\qquad$ molecule (l) $\rightarrow$ molecule (g)
$\qquad$ molecule (g) $\rightarrow$ atoms (g)

The first step is evaporation or vaporization of the liquid and the second is bond dissociation in the gas phase. Average bond enthalpy in the liquid phase is then the sum of the enthalpy of vaporization for the molecule and the gas phase bond dissociation enthalpies, divided by the number of bonds dissociated. This is greater than the gas phase bond dissociation enthalpy owing to the contribution from the enthalpy of vaporization.

9 Molecular Geometry and Bonding Theories

Molecular Shapes; the VSEPR Model

9.1 (a) No. A set of bonds with particular lengths can be placed in many different relative orientations. Bond lengths alone do not define the size and shape of a molecule.

    (b) Yes. This description means that the three terminal atoms point toward the corners of an equilateral triangle and the central atom is in the plane of this triangle. Only 120° bond angles are possible in this arrangement.

9.3 (a)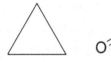

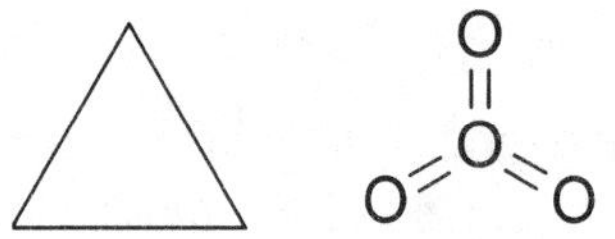

    (b) 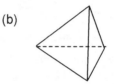

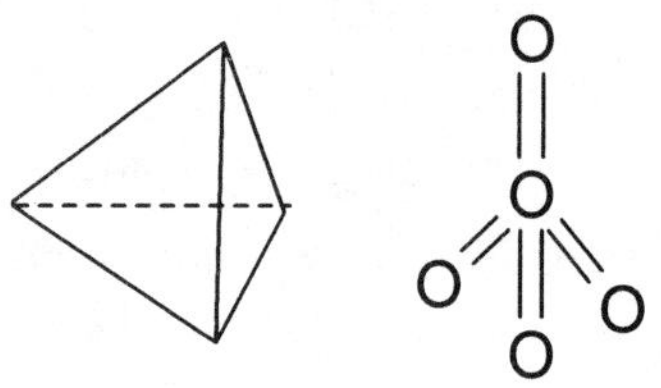

    (c)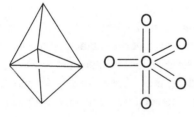

9.5 (a) An *electron domain* is a region in a molecule where electrons are most likely to be found.

    (b) Each balloon in Figure 9.3 occupies a volume of space. The best arrangement is one where each balloon has its "own" space, where they are as far apart as possible and repulsions are minimized. Electron domains are negatively charged regions, so they also adopt an arrangement where repulsions are minimized.

9.7 (a) trigonal planar   (b) tetrahedral   (c) trigonal bipyramidal   (d) octahedral

9.9   The electron-domain geometry indicated by VSEPR describes the arrangement of all bonding and nonbonding electron domains. The molecular geometry describes just the atomic positions. NH_3 has the Lewis structure given below; there are four electron domains around nitrogen so the electron-domain geometry is tetrahedral, but the molecular geometry of the four atoms is trigonal pyramidal.

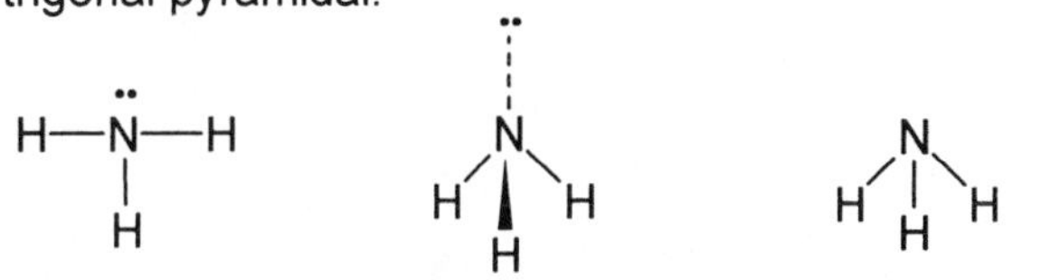

Lewis structure	electron-domain geometry	molecular geometry

9.11   (a)

Lewis structure	electron-domain geometry	molecular geometry
	tetrahedral	tetrahedral

(b)

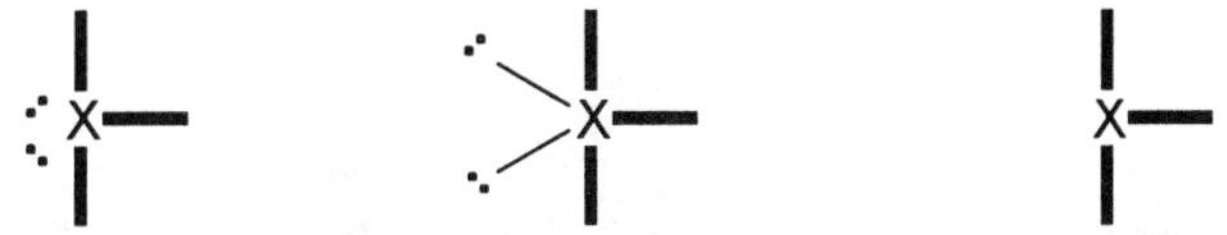

	trigonal bipyramidal	T-shaped

(c)

	octahedral	square pyramidal

9.13   bent (b), linear (l), octahedral (oh), seesaw (ss) square pyramidal (sp), tetrahedral (td), trigonal bipyramidal (tbp), trigonal planar (tr), trigonal pyramidal (tp), T-shaped (T)

	Molecule or ion	Valence electrons	Lewis structure		Electron-domain geometry	Molecular geometry
(a)	PBr_3	26	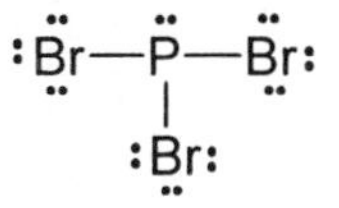	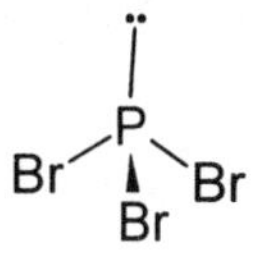	td	tp
(b)	CH_3^+	6	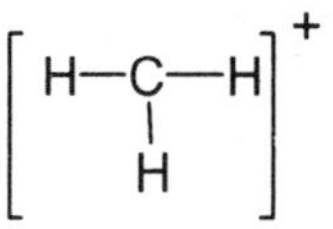	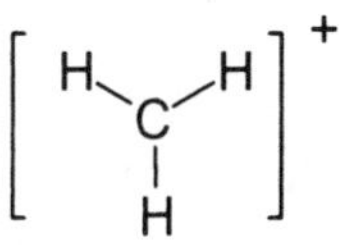	tr	tr

9.13   (continued)

	Molecule or ion	Valence electrons	Lewis structure		Electron-domain geometry	Molecular geometry
(c)	BH_4^-	8			td	td
(d)	SO_3	24			tr	tr
(e)	$AsCl_5$	40			tbp	tbp
(f)	BrF_5	42			oh	sp

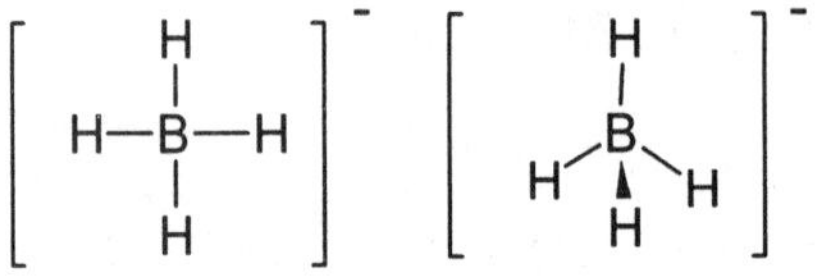

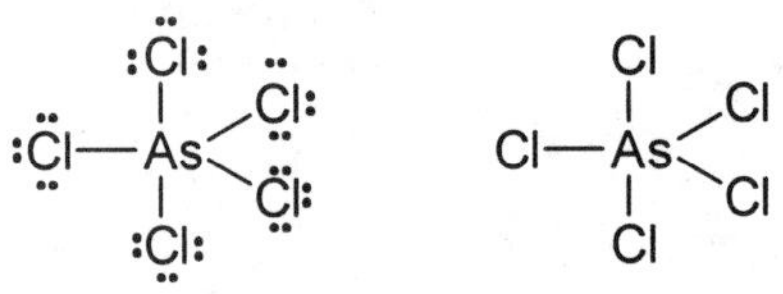

9.15   (a)   electron-domain geometries: i, trigonal planar; ii, tetrahedral; iii, trigonal bipyramidal

         (b)   nonbonding electron domains: i, 0;   ii, 1;   iii, 2

         (c)   N and P. Shape ii has 3 bonding and 1 nonbonding electron domains. Li and Al would form ionic compounds with F, so there would be no nonbonding electron domains. Assuming that F always has 3 nonbonding domains, BF_3 and ClF_3 would have the wrong number of nonbonding domains to produce shape ii.

         (d)   Cl (also Br and I, since they have 7 valence electrons). This T-shaped molecular geometry arises from a trigonal bipyramidal electron-domain geometry with 2 nonbonding domains (Table 9.3). Assuming each F atom has 3 nonbonding domains and forms only single bonds with A, A must have 7 valence electrons to produce these electron-domain and molecular geometries. It must be in or below the third row of the periodic table, so that it can accommodate more than 4 electron domains.

9.17

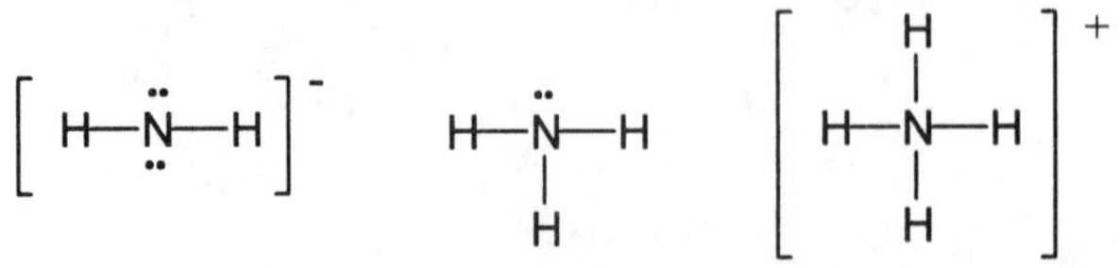

Each species has 4 electron domains around the N atom, but the number of nonbonding domains decreases from 2 to 0, going from NH_2^- to NH_4^+. Since nonbonding domains occupy more space than bonding domains, the bond angles expand as the number of nonbonding domains decreases.

9.19   (a) $1 - 109°$, $2 - 109°$ (b) $3 - 109°$, $4 - 109°$

       (c) $5 - 180°$ (d) $6 - 120°$, $7 - 109°$, $8 - 109°$

Polarity of Polyatomic Molecules

9.21   Molecules ii and iii will have nonzero dipole moments. Molecule i has no nonbonding electron pairs on A, and the 3 A-F dipoles are oriented so that the sum of their vectors is zero (the bond dipoles cancel). Molecules ii and iii have nonbonding electron pairs on A and their bond dipoles do not cancel. A nonbonding electron pair (or pairs) on a central atom guarantees at least a small molecular dipole moment, because no bond dipole exactly cancels a nonbonding pair.

9.23   (a)   **Nonpolar,** in a symmetrical tetrahedral structure (Figure 9.1), the bond dipoles cancel.

               (b)   **Nonpolar,** the molecule is linear and the bond dipoles cancel.

$$S=C=S$$

       (c)   **Nonpolar,** in a symmetrical trigonal planar structure Exercise (9.13 (d)), the bond dipoles cancel.

               (d)   **Polar,** in the see-saw molecular geometry, the dipoles don't cancel and there is an unequal charge distribution due to the nonbonded electron pair on S.

       (e)   **Polar,** there is an unequal charge distribution due to the nonbonded electron pair on N.

               (f)   **Nonpolar,** in a symmetrical trigonal bipyramid, the bond dipoles cancel.

9.25

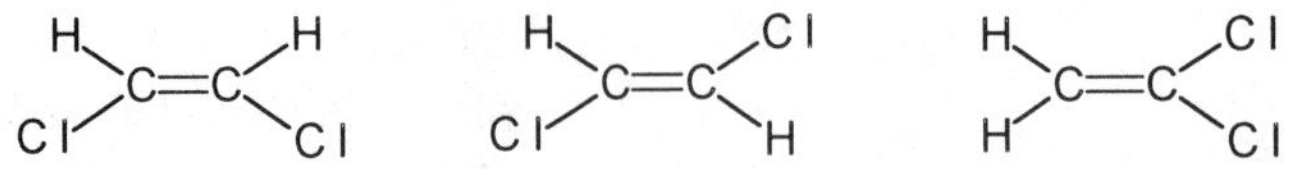

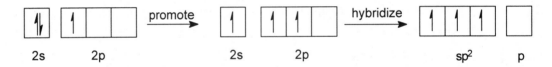

polar	nonpolar	polar

All three isomers are planar. The molecules on the left and right are polar because the C-Cl bond dipoles do not point in opposite directions. In the middle isomer, the C-Cl bonds and dipoles are pointing in opposite directions (as are the C-H bonds), the molecule is nonpolar and has a measured dipole moment of zero.

Orbital Overlap; Hybrid Orbitals

9.27 (a) *Orbital overlap* occurs when a valence atomic orbital on one atom shares the same region of space with a valence atomic orbital on an adjacent atom.

(b) In valence bond theory, overlap of orbitals allows the two electrons in a chemical bond to mutually occupy the space between the bonded nuclei.

(c) Valence bond theory is a combination of the atomic orbital concept with the Lewis model of electron pair bonding.

9.29 (a) sp -- 180°   (b) sp^3 -- 109°   (c) sp^2 -- 120°
(d) sp^3d^2 -- 90° and 180°   (e) sp^3d -- 90°, 120° and 180°

9.31 (a) B: $[He]2s^2 2p^1$

(b) The hybrid orbitals are called sp^2.   (c)

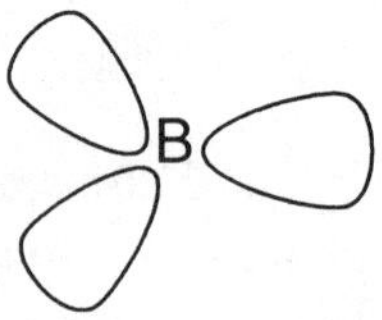

(d) A single 2p orbital is unhybridized. It lies perpendicular to the trigonal plane of the sp^2 hybrid orbitals.

9.33 (a) 8 e⁻, 4 e⁻ pairs   (b) 6 e⁻, 3 e⁻ pairs

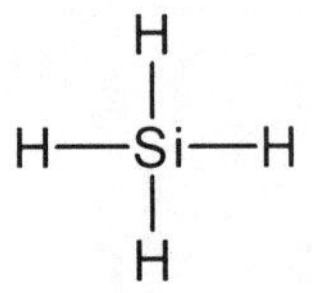

4 e⁻ pairs around Si
tetrahedral e⁻ domain geometry
sp^3 hybrid orbitals

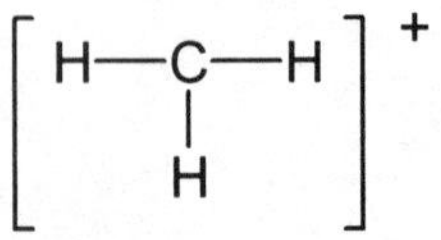

3 e⁻ pairs around C
trigonal planar e⁻ domain geometry
sp^2 hybrid orbitals

(c)   22 e⁻, 11 e⁻ pairs

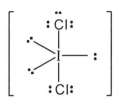

5 e⁻ domains around I, trigonal
bipyramidal e⁻ domain geometry
sp^3d hybrid orbitals (In a trigonal
bipyramid, placing nonbonding e⁻ pairs
in the equatorial position minimizes
repulsion.)

(d) $MgCl_2$ is an ionic molecule.
Valence bond theory is not an
appropriate model to describe
the bonding in $MgCl_2$.

(e)   48 e⁻, 24 e⁻ pairs

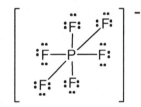

6 e⁻ pairs around P
octahedral e⁻ domain geometry,
sp^3d^2 hybrid orbitals

Multiple Bonds

9.35   (a)

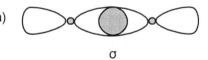

σ

(b)

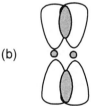

π

(c)   A σ bond is generally stronger than a π bond, because there is more extensive
orbital overlap.

9.37   (a)

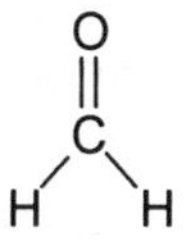

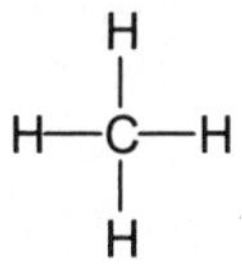

(b) sp^3 sp^2

(c)   The C atom in CH_4 is sp^3 hybridized; there are no unhybridized p orbitals available
for the π overlap required by multiple bonds. In CH_2O, the C atom is sp^2 hybridized,
with 1 p atomic orbital available to form the π overlap in the C=O double bond.

9.39   (a) C_3H_6O has $3(4) + 6(1) + 6 = 24$ valence electrons

       (b)   9 pairs or 18 total valence electrons form σ bonds

       (c)   1 pair or 2 total valence electrons form π bonds

       (d)   2 pairs or 4 total valence electrons are nonbonding

       (e)   The central C atom is sp^2 hybridized

9.41   (a)   ~109° about the left most C, sp^3; ~120° about the right-hand C, sp^2

       (b)   The doubly bonded O can be viewed as sp^2, the other as sp^3; the nitrogen is sp^3 with approximately 109° bond angles.

       (c)   nine σ bonds, one π bond

9.43   (a)   In a localized π bond, the electron density is concentrated strictly between the two atoms forming the bond. In a delocalized π bond, parallel p orbitals on more than two adjacent atoms overlap and the electron density is spread over all the atoms that contribute p orbitals to the network. There are still two regions of overlap, above and below the σ framework of the molecule.

       (b)   The existence of more than one resonance form is a good indication that a molecule will have delocalized π bonding.

       (c)

             The existence of more than one resonance form for NO_2^- indicates that the π bond is delocalized. From an orbital perspective, the electron-domain geometry around N is trigonal planar, so the hybridization at N is sp^2. This leaves a p orbital on N and one on each O atom perpendicular to the trigonal plane of the molecule, in the correct orientation for delocalized π overlap. Physically, the two N-O bond lengths are equal, indicating that the two N-O bonds are equivalent, rather than one longer single bond and one shorter double bond.

Molecular Orbitals

9.45   (a)   Both atomic and molecular orbitals have a characteristic energy and shape (region where there is a high probability of finding an electron). Each atomic or molecular orbital can hold a maximum of two electrons. Atomic orbitals are localized on single atoms and their energies are the result of interactions between the subatomic particles in a single atom. MOs can be delocalized over several or even all the atoms in a molecule and their energies are influenced by interactions between electrons on several atoms.

       (b)   There is a net stabilization (lowering in energy) that accompanies bond formation because the bonding electrons in H_2 are strongly attracted to both H nuclei.

       (c)   2

9.47   (a)

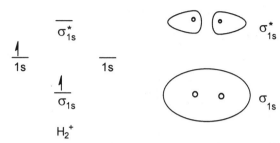

(b)   There is 1 electron in H_2^+. The Lewis model of bonding indicates that a bond is a pair of electrons. Since there is only 1 electron in H_2^+, there is no bond by the Lewis definition, so it is not possible to write a Lewis structure.

(c)   □ σ_{1s}^* (d)   Bond order = 1/2 (1-0) = 1/2

         [↑] σ_{1s}

(e)   Yes. The stability of H_2^+ is due to the lower energy state of the σ bonding molecular orbital relative to the energy of a H 1s atomic orbital. If the single electron in H_2^+ is excited to the σ_{1s}^* orbital, its energy is higher than the energy of a H 1s atomic orbital and H_2^+ will decompose into a hydrogen atom and a hydrogen ion.

$$H_2^+ \xrightarrow{h\nu} H + H^+.$$

9.49   In a σ molecular orbital, the electron density is spherically symmetric about the internuclear axis and is concentrated along this axis. In a π MO, the electron density is concentrated above and below the internuclear axis and zero along it.

(a)

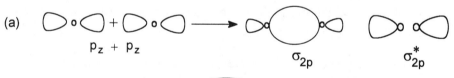

       $p_z + p_z$ σ_{2p} σ_{2p}^*

(b)

       $p_x + p_x$ π_{2p} π_{2p}^*

(c) σ_{2p} is lower in energy than π_{2p} due to greater extent of orbital overlap in the σ MO. $\sigma_{2p} < \pi_{2p} < \pi_{2p}^* < \sigma_{2p}^*$

9.51   Be$_2$, 4 e$^-$ Be$_2^+$, 3 e$^-$

| $\boxed{\uparrow\downarrow}$ | σ_{2s}^* | | $\boxed{\uparrow}$ | σ_{2s}^* |
| $\boxed{\uparrow\downarrow}$ | σ_{2s} | | $\boxed{\uparrow\downarrow}$ | σ_{2s} |

BO = 1/2(2-2) = 0   BO = 1/2(2-1) = 0.5

Be$_2$ has a bond order of zero and is not energetically favored over isolated Be atoms; it is not expected to exist. Be$_2^+$ has a bond order of 0.5 and is slightly lower in energy than isolated Be atoms. It will probably exist under special experimental conditions, but be unstable.

9.53   (a)   Substances with unpaired electrons are attracted into a magnetic field. This property is called *paramagnetism*.

       (b)   Weigh the substance normally and in a magnetic field. Paramagnetic substances appear to have a larger mass when weighed in a magnetic field.

       (c)   O$_2^+$, N$_2^{2-}$, Li$_2^+$ (see Figure 9.39)

9.55   (a)   The separation between related bonding and antibonding molecular orbitals is directly related to the extent of overlap of the atomic orbitals. The Li 2s orbitals are larger than the 1s, the overlap is greater and the energy separation of the resulting σ_{2s} and σ_{2s}^* MOs is larger than that between σ_{1s} and σ_{1s}^*.

       (b)   O$_2^{2-}$ has a bond order of 1.0, while O$_2^-$ has a bond order of 1.5. For the same bonded atoms, the greater the bond order the shorter the bond, so O$_2^-$ has the shorter bond.

       (c)   Interactions between electrons in 2s atomic orbitals on one atom and 2p orbitals on the other has an effect on the energies of the σ_{2s}, σ_{2s}^*, σ_{2p} and σ_{2p}^* molecular orbitals. The energy of the σ_{2s} is lowered and the energy of the σ_{2p} is raised. If the 2s-2p interaction is substantial, as it is in B$_2$, the energy of the σ_{2p} is actually raised above the energy of the π_{2p}.

9.57

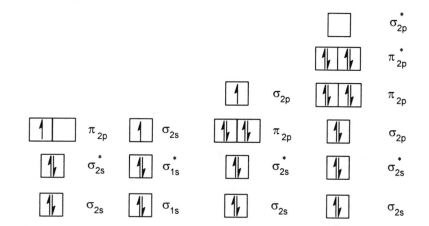

(a)	B_2^+ increase	(b)	Li_2^+ increase

(c) N_2^+
increase

(d) Ne_2^{2+}
decrease

Addition of an electron increases bond order if it occupies a bonding MO and decreases stability if it occupies an antibonding MO.

9.59   (a)   3s, $3p_x$, $3p_y$, $3p_z$ (b) π_{3p} (c) 2

       (d)   If the MO diagram for P_2 is similar to that of N_2, P_2 will have no unpaired electrons and be diamagnetic.

Additional Exercises

9.62   (a)   32 e⁻, 16 e⁻ pairs   (b)   18 e⁻, 9 e⁻ pairs

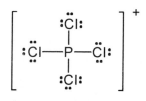

4 e⁻ domains
tetrahedral domain and
molecular geometry

$$\ddot{\text{O}}=\ddot{\text{S}}-\ddot{\text{O}}\colon \longleftrightarrow \colon\ddot{\text{O}}-\ddot{\text{S}}=\ddot{\text{O}}$$

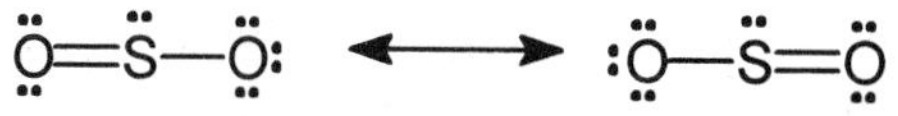

3 e⁻ domains
trigonal planar domain geometry
bent molecular geometry

     (c)   10 e⁻, 5 e⁻ pairs   (d)   8 e⁻, 4 e⁻ pairs

$$\text{H}-\text{C}\equiv\text{N}$$

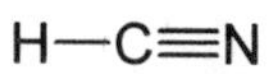

2 e⁻ domains
linear domain and
molecular geometry

$$\text{H}-\ddot{\text{Te}}-\text{H}$$

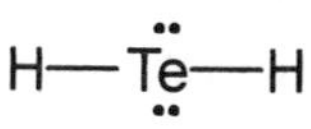

4 e⁻ domains
tetrahedral domain geometry
bent molecular geometry

(e) Br_3^- ;   22 e⁻ 11 e⁻ pairs

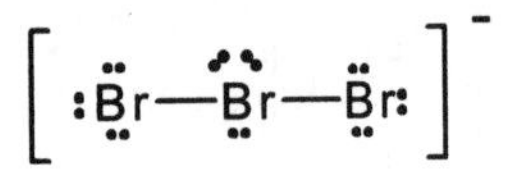

$$\left[\ddot{:}\ddot{B}r - \overset{\overset{\displaystyle \cdot\cdot}{}}{\underset{\cdot\cdot}{B}r} - \ddot{B}r\ddot{:} \right]^-$$

5 e⁻ domains
trigonal bipyramidal e⁻ domain geometry
linear molecular geometry
(In a trigonal bipyramid, nonbonded
pairs lie in the trigonal plane.)

9.66   (a) CO_2, 16 valence e⁻   (b) NCS^-, 16 valence e⁻

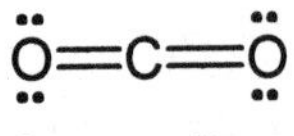

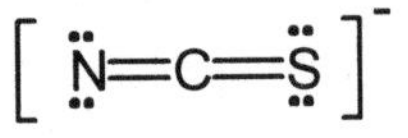

$$\ddot{O} = C = \ddot{O}$$
$$2\,\sigma \quad 2\,\pi$$

$$\left[\ddot{N} = C = \ddot{S} \right]^- \; + \quad$$ two other resonance structures

$$2\,\sigma \quad 2\,\pi$$ (for any of the resonance structures)

(c) H_2CO, 12 valence e⁻   (d) $HCO(OH)$, 18 valence e⁻

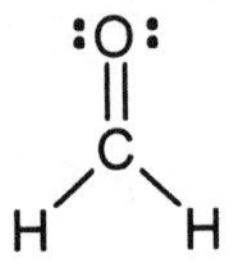

$$\overset{\displaystyle :\!O\!:}{\underset{\displaystyle H \qquad H}{\overset{\|}{C}}}$$

3 σ, 1 π

$$H - C \overset{\displaystyle \ddot{O}}{\underset{\displaystyle \ddot{O} - H}{<}}$$

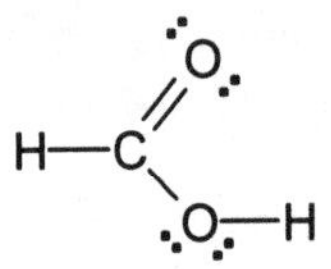

4 σ, 1 π

9.68   The compound on the right has a dipole moment. In the square planar *trans* structure on the left, all equivalent bond dipoles can be oriented opposite each other, for a net dipole moment of zero.

9.72

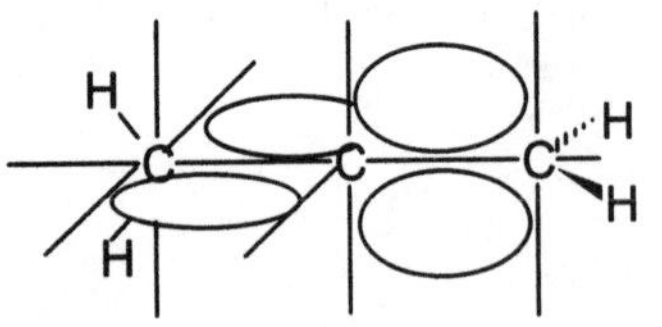

(a)   The molecule is nonplanar. The CH_2 planes at each end are twisted 90° from one another.

(b)   Allene has no dipole moment.

(c)   The bonding in allene would not be described as delocalized. The π electron clouds of the two adjacent C=C are mutually perpendicular. The mechanism for delocalization of π electrons is mutual overlap of parallel p atomic orbitals on adjacent atoms. If adjacent π electron clouds are mutually perpendicular, there is no overlap and no delocalization of π electrons.

9.75   (a)  $\ddot{O}{=}\ddot{O}{-}\ddot{O}{:} \longleftrightarrow {:}\ddot{O}{-}\ddot{O}{=}\ddot{O}$

To accommodate the π bonding by all 3 O atoms indicated in the resonance structures above, all O atoms are sp^2 hybridized.

(b)   For the first resonance structure, both sigma bonds are formed by overlap of sp^2 hybrid orbitals, the π bond is formed by overlap of atomic p orbitals, one of the nonbonded pairs on the right terminal O atom is in a p atomic orbital, and the remaining 5 nonbonded pairs are in sp^2 hybrid orbitals.

(c)   Only unhybridized p atomic orbitals can be used to form a delocalized π system.

(d)   The unhybridized p orbital on each O atom is used to form the delocalized π system, and in both resonance structures one nonbonded electron pair resides in a p atomic orbital. The delocalized π system then contains 4 electrons, 2 from the π bond and 2 from the nonbonded pair in the p orbital.

9.78   (a)   11 valence electrons, $\sigma_{2s}^2 \; \sigma_{2s}^{*\,2} \; \pi_{2p}^4 \; \sigma_{2p}^2 \; \pi_{2p}^{*\,1}$ (b)   paramagnetic

(c)   The bond order of NO is $[1/2\,(8 - 3)] = 2.5$. The electron that is lost is in an antibonding molecular orbital, so the bond order in NO^+ is 3.0. The increase in bond order is the driving force for the formation of NO^+.

(d)   To form NO^-, an electron is added to an antibonding orbital, and the new bond order is $[1/2\,(8 - 4)] = 2$. The order of increasing bond order and bond strength is: $NO^- < NO < NO^+$.

(e) NO^+ is isoelectronic with N_2, and NO^- is isoelectronic with O_2.

Integrative Exercises

9.82   (a)   Assume 100 g of compound

$$2.1 \text{ g H} \times \frac{1 \text{ mol H}}{1.008 \text{ g H}} = 2.1 \text{ mol H}; \; 2.1\,/\,2.1 = 1$$

$$29.8 \text{ g N} \times \frac{1 \text{ mol N}}{14.01 \text{ g N}} = 2.13 \text{ mol N}; \; 2.13\,/\,2.1 \approx 1$$

$$68.1 \text{ g O} \times \frac{1 \text{ mol O}}{16.00 \text{ g O}} = 4.26 \text{ mol O}; \; 4.26\,/\,2.1 \approx 2$$

The empirical formula is HNO_2; formula weight = 47. Since the approximate molecular weight is 50, the **molecular formula is HNO_2.**

(b)   Assume N is central, since it is unusual for O to be central, and part (d) indicates as much. HNO_2: 18 valence e^-

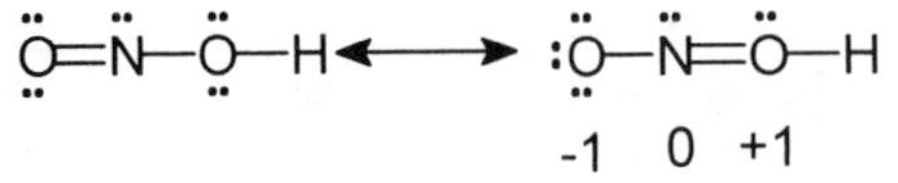

$$\ddot{\text{O}}{=}\text{N}{-}\ddot{\text{O}}{-}\text{H} \longleftrightarrow :\ddot{\text{O}}{-}\text{N}{=}\ddot{\text{O}}{-}\text{H}$$

$$ \text{-1} \quad \text{0} \quad \text{+1}$$

The second resonance form is a minor contributor due to unfavorable formal charges.

(c)   The electron pair geometry around N is trigonal planar; if the resonance structure on the right makes a significant contribution to the molecular structure, all 4 atoms would lie in a plane. If only the left structure contributes, the H could rotate in and out of the molecular plane. The relative contributions of the two resonance structures could be determined by measuring the O-N-O and N-O-H bond angles.

(d)   3 VSEPR e^- domains around N, sp^2 hybridization

(e)   3 σ, 1 π for both structures (or for H bound to N).

9.85   (g) $\longrightarrow$ 6C(g) + 6H(g)

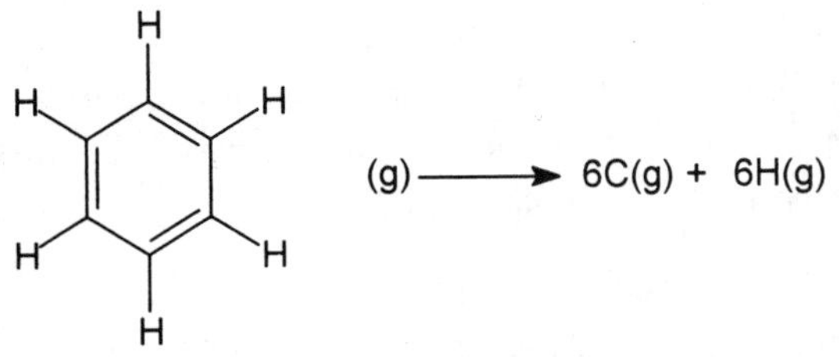

ΔH = 6D(C-H) + 3D(C-C) + 3D(C=C) - 0   (The products are isolated atoms;
      = 6(413 kJ) + 3(348 kJ) + 3(614 kJ)   there is no bond making.)
      = 5364 kJ

According to Hess's Law:

$\Delta H°$ = $6\Delta H_f°$ C(g) + $6\Delta H_f°$ H(g) - $\Delta H_f°$ C_6H_6(g)
      = 6(718.4 kJ) + 6(217.94 kJ) - (+82.9 kJ)
      = 5535 kJ

The difference in the two results, 171 kJ/mol C_6H_6 is due to the resonance stabilization in benzene. That is, because the π electrons are delocalized, the molecule has a lower overall energy than that predicted for the presence of 3 localized C-C and C=C bonds. Thus, the amount of energy actually required to decompose 1 mole of C_6H_6(g), represented by the Hess's Law calculation, is greater than the sum of the localized bond enthalpies (not taking resonance into account) from the first calculation above.

$\boldsymbol{10}$ Gases

Gas Characteristics; Pressure

10.1   In the gas phase molecules are far apart, while in the liquid they are touching.

    (a)   A gas is much less dense than a liquid because most of the volume of a gas is empty space.

    (b)   A gas is much more compressible because of the distance between molecules.

    (c)   Gaseous molecules are so far apart that there is no barrier to mixing, regardless of the identity of the molecule. All mixtures of gases are homogeneous. Liquid molecules are touching. In order to mix, they must displace one another. Similar molecules displace each other and form homogeneous mixtures. Very dissimilar molecules form heterogeneous mixtures.

10.3   (a)   F = m × a. Since both people have the same mass and both experience the acceleration of gravity, the forces they exert on the floor are exactly equal.

    (b)   P = F / A. The two forces are equal, but the person standing on one foot exerts this force over a smaller area. Thus, the person standing on one foot exerts a greater pressure on the floor.

10.5   (a) $P_{Hg} = P_{H_2O}$; Using the relationship derived in 10.4: $(d \times h \times a)_{H_2O} = (d \times h \times a)_{Hg}$

Since a, the acceleration due to gravity, is equal in both liquids,

$(d \times h)_{H_2O} = (d \times h)_{Hg}$

1.00 g/mL × h_{H_2O} = 13.6 g/mL × 760 mm

$$h_{H_2O} = \frac{13.6 \text{ g/mL} \times 760 \text{ mm}}{1.00 \text{ g/mL}} = 1.034 \times 10^4 = 1.03 \times 10^4 \text{ mm} = 10.3 \text{ m}$$

    (b)   Pressure due to H_2O:

1 atm = 1.034×10^4 mm H_2O (from part (a))

$$25 \text{ ft } H_2O \times \frac{12 \text{ in}}{1 \text{ ft}} \times \frac{2.54 \text{ cm}}{1 \text{ in}} \times \frac{10 \text{ mm}}{1 \text{ cm}} \times \frac{1 \text{ atm}}{1.034 \times 10^4 \text{ mm}} = 0.737 = 0.74 \text{ atm}$$

$P_{total} = P_{atm} + P_{H_2O}$ = 0.97 atm + 0.737 atm = 1.71 atm

10.7   (a) $265 \text{ torr} \times \dfrac{1 \text{ atm}}{760 \text{ torr}} = 0.349 \text{ atm}$

      (b) $265 \text{ torr} \times \dfrac{1 \text{ mm Hg}}{1 \text{ torr}} = 265 \text{ mm Hg}$

      (c) $265 \text{ torr} \times \dfrac{1.01325 \times 10^5 \text{ Pa}}{760 \text{ torr}} = 3.53 \times 10^4 \text{ Pa}$

      (d) $265 \text{ torr} \times \dfrac{1.01325 \times 10^5 \text{ Pa}}{760 \text{ torr}} \times \dfrac{1 \text{ bar}}{1 \times 10^5 \text{ Pa}} = 0.353 \text{ bar}$

10.9   (a) $30.45 \text{ in Hg} \times \dfrac{25.4 \text{ mm}}{1 \text{ in}} \times \dfrac{1 \text{ torr}}{1 \text{ mm Hg}} = 773.4 \text{ torr}$

           [The result has 4 sig figs because 25.4 mm/in is considered to be an exact number. (section 1.5)]

      (b)   The pressure in Chicago is greater than **standard atmospheric pressure**, 760 torr, so it makes sense to classify this weather system as a "high pressure system."

10.11 $P = \dfrac{m \times a}{A} = \dfrac{125 \text{ lb}}{0.50 \text{ in}^2} \times \dfrac{9.81 \text{ m}}{1 \text{ s}^2} \times \dfrac{0.454 \text{ kg}}{1 \text{ lb}} \times \dfrac{39.4^2 \text{ in}^2}{1 \text{ m}^2} = 1.7 \times 10^3 \text{ kPa}$

10.13 (i)   The Hg level is lower in the open end than the closed end, so the gas pressure is less than atmospheric pressure.

           $P_{gas} = 0.975 \text{ atm} - \left(52 \text{ cm} \times \dfrac{1 \text{ atm}}{76 \text{ cm}} \right) = 0.29 \text{ atm}$

      (ii)   The Hg level is higher in the open end, so the gas pressure is greater than atmospheric pressure.

           $P_{gas} = 0.975 \text{ atm} + \left(67 \text{ mm Hg} \times \dfrac{1 \text{ atm}}{760 \text{ mm Hg}} \right) = 1.063 \text{ atm}$

      (iii)   This is a closed-end manometer so $P_{gas} = h$.

           $P_{gas} = 10.3 \text{ cm} \times \dfrac{1 \text{ atm}}{76 \text{ cm}} = 0.136 \text{ atm}$

The Gas Laws

10.15 (a) $V_1/T_1 = V_2/T_2$ (b) $P_1V_1 = P_2V_2$

            $V_1/300 \text{ K} = V_2/400 \text{ K}$ $1 \text{ atm} \times V_1 = 2 \text{ atm} \times V_2$

            $V_2 = 4/3 \, V_1$ $V_2 = 1/2 \, V_1$

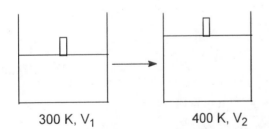

300 K, V_1 400 K, V_2

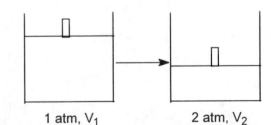

1 atm, V_1 2 atm, V_2

10.17   (a) $P_1V_1 = P_2V_2$; the proportionality holds true for any pressure or volume units.

$P_1 = 748$ torr, $V_1 = 10.3$ L, $P_2 = 1.55$ atm

$$V_2 = \frac{P_1V_1}{P_2} \quad \frac{748 \text{ torr} \times 10.3 \text{ L}}{1.55 \text{ atm}} \times \frac{1 \text{ atm}}{760 \text{ torr}} = 6.54 \text{ L}$$

       (b) $V_1/T_1 = V_2/T_2$;   T must be in Kelvins for the relationship to be true.

$V_1 = 10.3$ L, $T_1 = 23°C = 296$ K, $T_2 = 145°C = 418$ K

$$V_2 = \frac{V_1 T_2}{T_1} = \frac{10.3 \text{ L} \times 418 \text{ K}}{296 \text{ K}} = 14.5 \text{ L}$$

10.19   (a)   Avogadro's hypothesis states that equal volumes of gases at the same temperature and pressure contain equal numbers of molecules. Since molecules react in the ratios of small whole numbers, it follows that the volumes of reacting gases (at the same temperature and pressure) are in the ratios of small whole numbers.

       (b)   Since the two gases are at the same temperature and pressure, the ratio of the numbers of atoms is the same as the ratio of volumes. There are 1.5 times as many Xe atoms as Ne atoms.

The Ideal-Gas Equation

(In *Solutions to Exercises*, the symbol for molar mass is $\mathcal{M}$.)

10.21   (a)   An ideal gas exhibits pressure, volume and temperature relationships which are described by the equation $PV = nRT$. (An ideal gas obeys the ideal-gas equation.)

       (b) $PV = nRT$;   P in atmospheres, V in liters, n in moles, T in kelvins

10.23   (a) $n = 1.57$ mol, $P = 0.86$ atm, $T = -12°C = 261$ K

$$V = \frac{nRT}{P} = 1.57 \text{ mol} \times \frac{0.08206 \text{ L} \cdot \text{atm}}{\text{K} \cdot \text{mol}} \times \frac{261 \text{ K}}{0.86 \text{ atm}} = 39 \text{ L}$$

       (b) $n = 6.79 \times 10^{-2}$ mol, $V = 164$ mL $= 0.164$ L

$$P = 693 \text{ torr} \times \frac{1 \text{ atm}}{760 \text{ torr}} = 0.9118 = 0.912 \text{ atm}$$

$$T = \frac{PV}{nR} = 0.9118 \text{ atm} \times \frac{0.164 \text{ L}}{0.0679 \text{ mol}} \times \frac{1 \text{ K} \cdot \text{mol}}{0.08206 \text{ L} \cdot \text{atm}} = 26.8 \text{ K}$$

       (c) $n = 8.25 \times 10^{-2}$ mol, $V = 255$ mL, $T = 115°C = 388$ K

$$P = \frac{nRT}{V}; = 0.0825 \text{ mol} \times \frac{0.08206 \text{ L} \cdot \text{atm}}{\text{K} \cdot \text{mol}} \times \frac{388 \text{ K}}{0.255 \text{ L}} = 10.3 \text{ atm}$$

(d)   V = 5.49 L, T = 35°C = 308 K,

$$P = 11.25 \text{ kPa} \times \frac{1 \text{ atm}}{101.325 \text{ kPa}} = 0.11103 = 0.1110 \text{ atm}$$

$$n = \frac{PV}{RT} = 0.11103 \text{ atm} \times \frac{K \cdot mol}{0.08206 \text{ L} \cdot \text{atm}} \times \frac{5.49 \text{ L}}{308 \text{ K}} = 0.0241 \text{ mol}$$

10.25 $n = g/\mathcal{M}$; PV = nRT; $PV = gRT/\mathcal{M}$; $g = \mathcal{M}\,PV/RT$

P = 1.0 atm, T = 23°C = 296 K, V = 2.0 × 10^5 m^3. Change m^3 to L, then calculate grams (or kg).

$$2.0 \times 10^5 \text{ m}^3 \times \frac{10^3 \text{ dm}^3}{1 \text{ m}^3} \times \frac{1 \text{ L}}{1 \text{ dm}^3} = 2.0 \times 10^8 \text{ L } H_2$$

$$g = \frac{2.02 \text{ g } H_2}{1 \text{ mol } H_2} \times \frac{K \cdot mol}{0.08206 \text{ L} \cdot \text{atm}} \times \frac{1.0 \text{ atm} \times 2.0 \times 10^8 \text{ L}}{296 \text{ K}} = 1.7 \times 10^7 \text{ g} = 1.7 \times 10^4 \text{ kg } H_2$$

10.27   Air is a mixture of N_2 and O_2, but for the purpose of calculating pressure, only the total number of gas molecules is important, not the identity of these molecules.

$$V = 2.55 \text{ L}, \ T = 37°C = 310 \text{ K}, \ P = 740 \text{ mm Hg} \times \frac{1 \text{ atm}}{760 \text{ mm}} = 0.9737 = 0.974 \text{ atm}$$

$$n = \frac{PV}{RT} = 0.9737 \text{ atm} \times \frac{K \cdot mol}{0.08206 \text{ L} \cdot \text{atm}} \times \frac{2.55 \text{ L}}{310 \text{ K}} = 0.097605 = 0.0976 \text{ mol of gas}$$

$$0.097605 \text{ mol} \times \frac{6.022 \times 10^{23} \text{ molecules}}{1 \text{ mol}} = 5.88 \times 10^{22} \text{ gas molecules}$$

10.29   (a) $P = \dfrac{nRT}{V}$; $n = 0.29 \text{ kg } O_2 \times \dfrac{1000 \text{ g}}{1 \text{ kg}} \times \dfrac{1 \text{ mol } O_2}{32.00 \text{ g } O_2} = 9.0625 = 9.1 \text{ mol}$; V = 2.3 L;

T = 273 + 9°C = 282 K

$$P = \frac{9.0625 \text{ mol}}{2.3 \text{ L}} \times \frac{0.08206 \text{ L} \cdot \text{atm}}{K \cdot mol} \times 282 \text{ K} = 91 \text{ atm}$$

(b) $V = \dfrac{nRT}{P}$; $= \dfrac{9.0625 \text{ mol}}{0.95 \text{ atm}} \times \dfrac{0.08206 \text{ L} \cdot \text{atm}}{K \cdot mol} \times 299 \text{ K} = 2.3 \times 10^2 \text{ L}$

10.31   (a) $g = \dfrac{\mathcal{M}\,PV}{RT}$; V = 8.73 L, T = 24°C = 297 K, $P = 755 \text{ torr} \times \dfrac{1 \text{ atm}}{760 \text{ torr}} = 0.9934$

$$= 0.993 \text{ atm}$$

$$g = \frac{70.91 \text{ g } Cl_2}{1 \text{ mol } Cl_2} \times \frac{K \cdot mol}{0.08206 \text{ L} \cdot \text{atm}} \times \frac{0.9934 \text{ atm}}{297 \text{ K}} \times 8.73 \text{ L} = 25.2 \text{ g } Cl_2$$

(b) $V_2 = \dfrac{P_1 V_1 T_2}{T_1 P_2} = \dfrac{755 \text{ torr} \times 8.73 \text{ L} \times 273 \text{ K}}{297 \text{ K} \times 760 \text{ torr}} = 7.97 \text{ L}$

(c) $\quad T_2 = \dfrac{P_2 V_2 T_1}{P_1 V_1} = \dfrac{8.00 \times 10^2 \text{ torr} \times 3.00 \text{ L} \times 297 \text{ K}}{755 \text{ torr} \times 8.73 \text{ L}} = 108 \text{ K}$

(d) $\quad P_2 = \dfrac{P_1 V_1 T_2}{V_2 T_1} = \dfrac{755 \text{ torr} \times 8.73 \text{ L} \times 340 \text{ K}}{5.00 \text{ L} \times 297 \text{ K}} = 1.51 \times 10^3 \text{ torr} = 1.99 \text{ atm}$

10.33 (a) $\quad 5.2 \text{ g} \times 1 \text{ hr} \times \dfrac{0.8 \text{ mL O}_2}{1 \text{ g} \bullet \text{hr}} = 4.16 = 4 \text{ mL O}_2$ consumed

$n = \dfrac{PV}{RT} = 1 \text{ atm} \times \dfrac{\text{K} \bullet \text{mol}}{0.08206 \text{ L} \bullet \text{atm}} \times \dfrac{0.00416 \text{ L}}{297 \text{ K}} = 1.71 \times 10^{-4} = 2 \times 10^{-4} \text{ mol O}_2$

(b) $\quad 1 \text{ qt air} \times \dfrac{0.946 \text{ L}}{1 \text{ qt}} \times 0.21\% \text{ O}_2 \text{ in air} = 0.199 \text{ L O}_2$ available

$n = 1 \text{ atm} \times \dfrac{\text{K} \bullet \text{mol}}{0.08206 \text{ L} \bullet \text{atm}} \times \dfrac{0.199 \text{ L}}{297 \text{ K}} = 8.16 \times 10^{-3} = 8 \times 10^{-3} \text{ mol O}_2$ available

roach uses $\dfrac{1.71 \times 10^{-4} \text{ mol}}{1 \text{ hr}} \times 48 \text{ hr} = 8.19 \times 10^{-3} = 8 \times 10^{-3} \text{ mol O}_2$ consumed

Not only does the roach use 20% of the available O_2, it needs all the O_2 in the jar.

Further Applications of the Ideal-Gas Equation

10.35 (c) $Cl_2(g)$ is the most dense at 1.00 at and 298 K. Gas density is directly proportional to molar mass and pressure, and inversely proportional to temperature. For gas samples at the same conditions, molar mass determines density. Of the three gases listed, Cl_2 has the largest molar mass.

10.37 (a) $\quad d = \dfrac{\mathscr{M} P}{RT}$; $\mathscr{M} = 46.0 \text{ g/mol}$; $P = 0.970 \text{ atm}$, $T = 35°C = 308 \text{ K}$

$d = \dfrac{46.0 \text{ g NO}_2}{1 \text{ mol}} \times \dfrac{\text{K} \bullet \text{mol}}{0.08206 \text{ L} \bullet \text{atm}} \times \dfrac{0.970 \text{ atm}}{308 \text{ K}} = 1.77 \text{ g/L}$

(b) $\quad \mathscr{M} = \dfrac{gRT}{PV} = \dfrac{2.50 \text{ g}}{0.875 \text{ L}} \times \dfrac{0.08206 \text{ L} \bullet \text{atm}}{\text{K} \bullet \text{mol}} \times \dfrac{308 \text{ K}}{685 \text{ torr}} \times \dfrac{760 \text{ torr}}{1 \text{ atm}} = 80.1 \text{ g/mol}$

10.39 $\mathscr{M} = \dfrac{gRT}{PV} = \dfrac{1.012 \text{ g}}{0.354 \text{ L}} \times \dfrac{0.08206 \text{ L} \bullet \text{atm}}{\text{K} \bullet \text{atm}} \times \dfrac{372 \text{ K}}{742 \text{ torr}} \times \dfrac{760 \text{ torr}}{1 \text{ atm}} = 89.4 \text{ g/mol}$

10.41 $\text{mol O}_2 = \dfrac{PV}{RT} = 3.5 \times 10^{-6} \text{ torr} \times \dfrac{1 \text{ atm}}{760 \text{ torr}} \times \dfrac{\text{K} \bullet \text{mol}}{0.08206 \text{ L} \bullet \text{atm}} \times \dfrac{0.382 \text{ L}}{300 \text{ K}} = 7.146 \times 10^{-11}$

$= 7.1 \times 10^{-11} \text{ mol O}_2$

$7.146 \times 10^{-11} \text{ mol O}_2 \times \dfrac{2 \text{ mol Mg}}{1 \text{ mol O}_2} \times \dfrac{24.3 \text{ g Mg}}{1 \text{ mol Mg}} = 3.5 \times 10^{-9} \text{ g Mg}$

10.43   kg H_2SO_4 → g H_2SO_4 → mol H_2SO_4 → mol NH_3 → V NH_3

150 kg × $\dfrac{1000 \text{ g}}{1 \text{ kg}}$ = 1.50 × 10^5 g H_2SO_4 × $\dfrac{1 \text{ mol}}{98.08 \text{ g}}$ = 1.529 × 10^3 = 1.53 × 10^3 mol H_2SO_4

1.529 × 10^3 mol H_2SO_4 × $\dfrac{2 \text{ mol } NH_3}{1 \text{ mol } H_2SO_4}$ = 3.059 × 10^3 = 3.06 × 10^3 mol NH_3

$V_{NH_3} = \dfrac{nRT}{P}$ = 3.059 × 10^3 mol × $\dfrac{0.08206 \text{ L}\cdot\text{atm}}{\text{K}\cdot\text{mol}}$ × $\dfrac{293 \text{ K}}{25.0 \text{ atm}}$ = 2.94 × 10^3 L NH_3

10.45   The gas sample is a mixture of $H_2(g)$ and $H_2O(g)$. Find the partial pressure of $H_2(g)$ and then the moles of $H_2(g)$ and $Zn(s)$.

P_t = 738 torr = P_{H_2} + P_{H_2O}

From Appendix B, the vapor pressure of H_2O at 24°C = 22.38 torr

P_{H_2} = (738 torr - 22.38 torr) × $\dfrac{1 \text{ atm}}{760 \text{ torr}}$ = 0.9416 = 0.942 atm

$n_{H_2} = \dfrac{P_{H_2}V}{RT}$ = 0.9416 atm × $\dfrac{\text{K}\cdot\text{mol}}{0.08206 \text{ L}\cdot\text{atm}}$ × $\dfrac{0.159 \text{ L}}{297 \text{ K}}$ = 0.006143 = 0.00614 mol H_2

0.006143 mol H_2 × $\dfrac{1 \text{ mol Zn}}{1 \text{ mol } H_2}$ × $\dfrac{65.39 \text{ g Zn}}{1 \text{ mol Zn}}$ = 0.402 g Zn

Partial Pressures

10.47   (a)   When the stopcock is opened, the volume occupied by $N_2(g)$ increases from 2.0 L to 5.0 L. At constant T, $P_1V_1 = P_2V_2$. 1.0 atm × 2.0 L = P_2 × 5.0 L; P_2 = 0.40 atm

        (b)   When the gases mix, the volume of $O_2(g)$ increases from 3.0 L to 5.0 L. At constant T, $P_1V_1 = P_2V_2$. 2.0 atm × 3.0 L = P_2 × 5.0 L; P_2 = 1.2 atm

        (c) $P_T = P_{N_2} + P_{O_2}$ = 0.40 atm + 1.2 atm = 1.6 atm

10.49   (a) $P_{He} = \dfrac{nRT}{V}$ = 0.538 mol × $\dfrac{0.08206 \text{ L}\cdot\text{atm}}{\text{K}\cdot\text{atm}}$ × $\dfrac{298 \text{ K}}{7.00 \text{ L}}$ = 1.88 atm

              $P_{Ne} = \dfrac{nRT}{V}$ = 0.315 mol × $\dfrac{0.08206 \text{ L}\cdot\text{atm}}{\text{K}\cdot\text{atm}}$ × $\dfrac{298 \text{ K}}{7.00 \text{ L}}$ = 1.10 atm

              $P_{Ar} = \dfrac{nRT}{V}$ = 0.103 mol × $\dfrac{0.08206 \text{ L}\cdot\text{atm}}{\text{K}\cdot\text{atm}}$ × $\dfrac{298 \text{ K}}{7.00 \text{ L}}$ = 0.360 atm

        (b) P_t = 1.88 atm + 1.10 atm + 0.360 atm = 3.34 atm

10.51   The partial pressure of each component is equal to the mole fraction of that gas times the total pressure of the mixture. Find the mole fraction of each component and then its partial pressure.

n_t = 0.75 mol N_2 + 0.30 mol O_2 + 0.15 mol CO_2 = 1.20 mol

$$\chi_{N_2} = \frac{0.75}{1.20} = 0.625 = 0.63; \quad P_{N_2} = 0.625 \times 1.56 \text{ atm} = 0.98 \text{ atm}$$

$$\chi_{O_2} = \frac{0.30}{1.20} = 0.250 = 0.25; \quad P_{O_2} = 0.250 \times 1.56 \text{ atm} = 0.39 \text{ atm}$$

$$\chi_{CO_2} = \frac{0.15}{1.20} = 0.125 = 0.13; \quad P_{CO_2} = 0.125 \times 1.56 \text{ atm} = 0.20 \text{ atm}$$

10.53 $\chi_{O_2} = \dfrac{P_{O_2}}{P_t} = \dfrac{0.21 \text{ atm}}{8.38 \text{ atm}} = 0.025$; mole % = 0.025 × 100 = 2.5%

10.55 $P_{N_2} = \dfrac{P_1 V_1 T_2}{V_2 T_1} = \dfrac{3.80 \text{ atm} \times 1.00 \text{ L} \times 293 \text{ K}}{10.0 \text{ L} \times 299 \text{ K}} = 0.372 \text{ atm}$

$P_{O_2} = \dfrac{P_1 V_1 T_2}{V_2 T_1} = \dfrac{4.75 \text{ atm} \times 5.00 \text{ L} \times 293 \text{ K}}{10.0 \text{ L} \times 299 \text{ K}} = 2.33 \text{ atm}$

P_T = 0.372 atm + 2.33 atm = 2.70 atm

Kinetic - Molecular Theory; Graham's Law

10.57   (a) Increase in temperature at constant volume, decrease in volume, increase in pressure (b) decrease in temperature   (c) increase in volume   (d) increase in temperature

10.59   (a) $n \propto P/T$ (V/R is the same for A and B.) Since P is greater and T is smaller for vessel A, it has more molecules.

(b)   Vessel A has more molecules but the molar mass of CO is smaller than the molar mass of SO_2, so we need to calculate the masses. Since volume is not specified, calculate g/L.

$$\frac{g_A}{V} = \frac{\mathcal{M} P}{RT} = \frac{28.01 \text{ g CO}}{1 \text{ mol CO}} \times \frac{K \cdot mol}{0.08206 \text{ L} \cdot atm} \times \frac{1 \text{ atm}}{273 \text{ K}} = 1.25 \text{ g CO/L}$$

$$\frac{g_B}{V} = \frac{\mathcal{M} P}{RT} = \frac{64.07 \text{ g SO}_2}{1 \text{ mol SO}_2} \times \frac{K \cdot mol}{0.08206 \text{ L} \cdot atm} \times \frac{0.5 \text{ atm}}{293 \text{ K}} = 1.33 \text{ g SO}_2/L$$

Vessel B has more mass.

(c)   Vessel B is at a higher temperature so the average kinetic energy of its molecules is higher.

(d)   The two factors that affect rms speed are temperature and molar mass. The molecules in vessel A have smaller molar mass but are at the lower temperature, so we must calculate the rms speeds.

Mathematically, according to Equation 10.24,

$$\frac{u_A}{u_B} = \sqrt{\frac{T_A / \mathcal{M}_A}{T_B / \mathcal{M}_B}} = \sqrt{\frac{273/28.01}{293/64.07}} = 1.46$$

The ratio is greater than 1; vessel A has the greater rms speed.

10.61 (a)   In order of increasing speed (and decreasing molar mass):

$$CO_2 \approx N_2O < F_2 < HF < H_2$$

(b) $$u_{H_2} = \sqrt{\frac{3RT}{\mathcal{M}}} = \left(\frac{3 \times 8.314 \text{ kg} \cdot \text{m}^2/\text{s}^2 \cdot \text{K} \cdot \text{mol} \times 300 \text{ K}}{2.02 \times 10^{-3} \text{ kg/mol}}\right)^{1/2} = 1.92 \times 10^3 \text{ m/s}$$

$$u_{CO_2} = \left(\frac{3 \times 8.314 \text{ kg} \cdot \text{m}^2/\text{s}^2 \cdot \text{K} \cdot \text{mol} \times 300 \text{ K}}{44.0 \times 10^{-3} \text{ kg/mol}}\right)^{1/2} = 4.12 \times 10^2 \text{ m/s}$$

As expected, the lighter molecule moves at the greater speed.

10.63   The heavier the molecule, the slower the rate of effusion. Thus, the order for increasing rate of effusion is in the order of decreasing mass.

rate $^2H^{37}Cl$ < rate $^1H^{37}Cl$ < rate $^2H^{35}Cl$ < rate $^1H^{35}Cl$

10.65 $$\frac{\text{rate (sulfide)}}{\text{rate (Ar)}} = \left[\frac{39.9}{\mathcal{M}\text{(sulfide)}}\right]^{1/2} = 0.28$$

$\mathcal{M}$ (sulfide) = $(39.9 / 0.28)^2$ = 510 g/mol (two significant figures)

The empirical formula of arsenic(III) sulfide is As_2S_3, which has a formula mass of 246.1. Twice this is 490 g/mol, close to the value estimated from the effusion experiment. Thus, the formula of the vapor phase molecule is As_4S_6.

Nonideal-Gas Behavior

10.67 (a)   Nonideal gas behavior is observed at very high pressures and/or low temperatures.

(b)   The real volumes of gas molecules and attractive intermolecular forces between molecules cause gases to behave nonideally.

10.69   The ratio PV/RT is equal to the number of moles of molecules in an ideal-gas sample; this number should be a constant for all pressure, volume and temperature conditions. If the value of this ratio changes with increasing pressure, the gas sample is not behaving ideally (according to the ideal-gas equation).

10.71 The constants a and b are part of the correction terms in the van der Waals equation. The smaller the values of a and b, the smaller the corrections and the more ideal the gas. Ar ($a = 1.34$, $b = 0.0322$) will behave more like an ideal gas than CO_2 ($a = 3.59$, $b = 0.0427$) at high pressures.

10.73 (a) $P = 1.00 \text{ mol} \times \dfrac{0.08206 \text{ L} \cdot \text{atm}}{\text{K} \cdot \text{mol}} \times \dfrac{313 \text{ K}}{28.0 \text{ L}} = 0.917 \text{ atm}$

       (b) $P = \dfrac{nRT}{V - nb} - \dfrac{an^2}{V^2} = \dfrac{1.00 \times 0.08206 \times 313}{28.0 - (1.00 \times 0.1383)} - \dfrac{20.4(1.00)^2}{(28.0)^2} = 0.896 \text{ atm}$

Additional Exercises

10.75 Over time, the gases will mix perfectly. Each bulb will contain 4 blue and 3 red atoms.

10.77 $P_1V_1 = P_2V_2$; $V_2 = P_1V_1/P_2$

       $V_2 = \dfrac{3.0 \text{ atm} \times 1.0 \text{ mm}^3}{695 \text{ torr}} \times \dfrac{760 \text{ torr}}{1 \text{ atm}} = 3.3 \text{ mm}^3$

10.80 If the air in the room is at STP, the partial pressure of O_2 is $0.2095 \times 1 \text{ atm} = 0.2095 \text{ atm}$. Since the gases in air are perfectly mixed, the volume of O_2 is the volume of the room.

       $V = 10.0 \text{ ft} \times 8.0 \text{ ft} \times 8.0 \text{ ft} \times \dfrac{(12)^3 \text{ in}^3}{\text{ft}^3} \times \dfrac{(2.54)^3 \text{cm}^3}{\text{in}^3} \times \dfrac{1 \text{ L}}{1000 \text{ cm}^3} = 1.812 \times 10^4$
       $= 1.8 \times 10^4 \text{ L}$

       $g = \dfrac{\mathscr{m}PV}{RT} = \dfrac{32.00 \text{ g } O_2}{\text{mol } O_2} \times \dfrac{\text{K} \cdot \text{mol}}{0.08026 \text{ L} \cdot \text{atm}} \times \dfrac{0.2095 \text{ atm} \times 1.812 \times 10^4 \text{ L}}{273 \text{ K}} = 5.4 \times 10^3 \text{ g } O_2$

10.83 (a) $5.00 \text{ g HCl} \times \dfrac{1 \text{ mol HCl}}{36.46 \text{ g HCl}} = 0.1371 = 0.137 \text{ mol HCl}$

             $5.00 \text{ g NH}_3 \times \dfrac{1 \text{ mol NH}_3}{17.03 \text{ g NH}_3} = 0.2936 = 0.294 \text{ mol NH}_3$

       The gases react in a 1:1 mole ratio, HCl is the limiting reactant and is completely consumed. $(0.2936 \text{ mol} - 0.1371 \text{ mol}) = 0.1565 = 0.157 \text{ mol NH}_3$ remain in the system. $NH_3(g)$ is the only gas remaining after reaction. $V_t = 4.00 \text{ L}$

       (b) $P = \dfrac{nRT}{V} = 0.1565 \text{ mol} \times \dfrac{0.08206 \text{ L} \cdot \text{atm}}{\text{K} \cdot \text{mol}} \times \dfrac{298 \text{ K}}{4.00 \text{ L}} = 0.957 \text{ atm}$

10.86 $\mathscr{m}_{avg} = \dfrac{dRT}{P} = \dfrac{1.104 \text{ g}}{1 \text{ L}} \times \dfrac{0.08206 \text{ L} \cdot \text{atm}}{\text{K} \cdot \text{mol}} \times \dfrac{300 \text{ K}}{435 \text{ torr}} \times \dfrac{760 \text{ torr}}{1 \text{ atm}}$

                                                                 $= 47.48 = 47.5 \text{ g/mol}$

χ = mole fraction O_2; 1 - χ = mole fraction Kr

47.48 g = χ(32.00) + (1-χ)(83.80)

36.3 = 51.8 χ; χ = 0.701; 70.1% O_2

10.89   The balloon will expand; H_2 ($\mathcal{M}$ = 2 g/mol) will effuse in through the walls of the balloon faster than He ($\mathcal{M}$ = 4 g/mol) will effuse out, because the gas with the smaller molar mass effuses more rapidly.

10.92   (a)   The effect of intermolecular attraction becomes more significant as a gas is compressed to a smaller volume at constant temperature. This compression causes the pressure, and thus the number of intermolecular collisions, to increase. Intermolecular attraction causes some of these collisions to be inelastic, which amplifies the deviation from ideal behavior.

        (b)   The effect of intermolecular attraction becomes less significant as the temperature of a gas is increased at constant pressure. An increase in temperature increases the average kinetic energy of the gas molecules. A larger fraction of the molecules has sufficient kinetic energy to overcome intermolecular attractions. This increases the fraction of elastic collisions, and the gas more closely obeys the ideal-gas equation.

Integrative Exercises

10.94 $\mathcal{M} = \dfrac{gRT}{VP} = \dfrac{1.56\,g}{1.00\,L} \times \dfrac{0.08206\,L\bullet atm}{K\bullet mol} \times \dfrac{323\,K}{0.984\,atm} = 42.0\,g/mol$

Assume 100 g cyclopropane

$100\,g \times 0.857\%\,C = 85.7\,g\,C \times \dfrac{1\,mol\,C}{12.01\,g} = \dfrac{7.136\,mol\,C}{7.136} = 1\,mol\,C$

$100\,g \times 0.143\%\,H = 14.3\,g\,H \times \dfrac{1\,mol\,H}{1.008\,g} = \dfrac{14.19\,mol\,H}{7.136} = 2\,mol\,H$

The empirical formula of cyclopropane is CH_2 and the empirical formula weight is 12 + 2 = 14 g. The ratio of molar mass to empirical formula weight, 42.0 g/14 g, is 3; therefore, there are three empirical formula units in one cyclopropane molecule. The molecular formula is 3 × (CH_2) = C_3H_6.

10.96   Strategy: Calculate ΔH°_{rxn} using Hess's Law and data from Appendix C. Using the ideal-gas equation, calculate moles CO_2 produced. Use stoichiometry to calculate the overall enthalpy change, ΔH.

$\Delta H^{\circ}_{rxn} = \Delta H^{\circ}_f\,Na^+(aq) + \Delta H^{\circ}_f\,CO_2(g) + \Delta H^{\circ}_f\,H_2O(l) - \Delta H^{\circ}_f\,NaHCO_3(s) - \Delta H^{\circ}_f\,H^+(aq)$

$= (-240.1\,kJ - 393.5\,kJ - 285.83\,kJ) - (-947.7\,kJ + 0) = 28.27 = 28.3\,kJ$

$n = \dfrac{PV}{RT} = 715\,torr \times \dfrac{1\,atm}{760\,torr} \times \dfrac{K\bullet mol}{0.08206\,L\bullet atm} \times \dfrac{10.0\,L}{292\,K} = 0.3926 = 0.393\,mol\,CO_2$

$\Delta H = \dfrac{28.27\,kJ}{1\,mol\,CO_2} \times 0.3926\,mol\,CO_2 = 11.1\,kJ$

10.99   After reaction, the flask contains $IF_5(g)$ and whichever reactant is in excess. Determine the
limiting reactant, which regulates the moles of IF_5 produced and moles of excess reactant.

$$I_2(s) + 5F_2(g) \rightarrow 2\ IF_5(g)$$

$$10.0\ g\ I_2 \times \frac{1\ mol\ I_2}{253.8\ g\ I_2} \times \frac{5\ mol\ F_2}{1\ mol\ I_2} = 0.1970 = 0.197\ mol\ F_2$$

$$10.0\ g\ F_2 \times \frac{1\ mol\ F_2}{38.00\ g\ F_2} = 0.2632 = 0.263\ mol\ F_2\ available$$

I_2 is the limiting reactant; F_2 is in excess.

0.263 mol F_2 available - 0.197 mol F_2 reacted = 0.066 mol F_2 remain.

$$10.0\ g\ I_2 \times \frac{1\ mol\ I_2}{253.8\ g\ I_2} \times \frac{2\ mol\ IF_5}{1\ mol\ I_2} = 0.0788\ mol\ IF_5\ produced$$

(a) $$P_{IF_5} = \frac{nRT}{V} = 0.0788\ mol \times \frac{0.08206\ L\cdot atm}{K\cdot mol} \times \frac{398\ K}{5.00\ L} = 0.515\ atm$$

(b) $$\chi_{IF_5} = \frac{mol\ IF_5}{mol\ IF_5\ +\ mol\ F_2} = \frac{0.0788}{0.0788\ +\ 0.066} = 0.544$$

11 Intermolecular Forces, Liquids and Solids

Kinetic-Molecular Theory

11.1 (a) solid < liquid < gas   (b) gas < liquid < solid

11.3 (a) liquid   (b) gas

11.5 As the temperature of a substance is increased, the average kinetic energy of the particles increases. In a collection of particles (molecules), the state is determined by the strength of interparticle forces relative to the average kinetic energy of the particles. As the average kinetic energy increases, more particles are able to overcome intermolecular attractive forces and move to a less ordered state, from solid to liquid to gas.

Intermolecular Forces

11.7 (a) London-dispersion forces   (b) dipole-dipole and London-dispersion forces

       (c) dipole-dipole or in certain cases hydrogen bonding

11.9 (a) Br_2 is a nonpolar covalent molecule, so only London-dispersion forces must be overcome to convert the liquid to a gas.

       (b) CH_3OH is a polar covalent molecule that experiences London-dispersion, dipole-dipole and hydrogen-bonding (O-H bonds) forces. All of these forces must be overcome to convert the liquid to a gas.

       (c) H_2S is a polar covalent molecule that experiences London-dispersion and dipole-dipole forces, so these must be overcome to change the liquid into a gas. (H-S bonds do not lead to hydrogen-bonding interactions.)

11.11 (a) *Polarizability* is the ease with which the charge distribution (electron cloud) in a molecule can be distorted to produce a transient dipole.

       (b) Te is most polarizable because its valence electrons are farthest from the nucleus and least tightly held.

       (c) Polarizability increases as molecular size (and thus molecular weight) increases. In order of increasing polarizability: $CH_4 < SiH_4 < SiCl_4 < GeCl_4 < GeBr_4$

(d)   The magnitude of London-dispersion forces and thus the boiling points of molecules increase as polarizability increases. The order of increasing boiling points is the order of increasing polarizability: $CH_4 < SiH_4 < SiCl_4 < GeCl_4 < GeBr_4$

11.13   For molecules with similar structures, the strength of dispersion forces increases with molecular size (molecular weight and number of electrons in the molecule).

       (a) H_2S (b) O_2 (c) CCl_4

11.15   Both hydrocarbons experience dispersion forces. Rod-like butane molecules can contact each other over the length of the molecule, while spherical 2-methylpropane molecules can only touch tangentially. The larger contact surface of butane produces greater polarizability and a higher boiling point.

11.17   Molecules with N-H, O-H and F-H bonds form hydrogen bonds with like molecules. **CH_3NH_2** and **CH_3OH** have N-H and O-H bonds, respectively. (CH_3F has C-F and C-H bonds, but no H-F bonds.)

11.19   (a) C_6H_{14} -- dispersion; C_8H_{18} -- dispersion. C_8H_{18} has the higher boiling point due to greater molar mass and similar strength of forces.

       (b) C_3H_8 -- dispersion; CH_3OCH_3 -- dipole-dipole and dispersion. CH_3OCH_3 has the higher boiling point due to stronger intermolecular forces and similar molar mass.

       (c) CH_3OH -- hydrogen bonding, dipole-dipole and dispersion; CH_3SH -- dipole-dipole and dispersion. CH_3OH has the higher boiling point due to the influence of hydrogen bonding (Figure 11.7).

       (d) NH_2NH_2 -- hydrogen bonding, dipole-dipole and dispersion; CH_3CH_3 -- dispersion. NH_2NH_2 has the higher boiling point due to much stronger intermolecular forces.

11.21   Surface tension (Section 11.3), high boiling point (relative to H_2S, H_2Se, H_2Te, Figure 11.7), high heat capacity per gram, high enthalpy of vaporization; the solid is less dense than the liquid; it is a liquid at room temperature despite its low molar mass.

Viscosity and Surface Tension

11.23   (a)   Viscosities and surface tensions of liquids both increase as intermolecular forces become stronger.

       (b)   As temperature increases, the average kinetic energy of the molecules increases and intermolecular attractions are more easily overcome. Surface tensions and viscosities decrease.

11.25   (a) $CHBr_3$ has a higher molar mass, is more polarizable and has stronger dispersion forces, so the surface tension is greater (see Exercise 11.20(b)).

       (b)   As temperature increases, the viscosity of the oil decreases because the average kinetic energies of the molecules increase (Exercise 11.23(b)).

    (c)   Adhesive forces between polar water and nonpolar car wax are weak, so the large surface tension of water draws the liquid into the shape with the smallest surface area, a sphere.

Changes of State

11.27   Endothermic: melting (s → l), vaporization (l → g), sublimation (s → g)
          Exothermic: condensation (g → l), freezing (l → s), deposition (g → s)

11.29   (a)   Ice, $H_2O(s)$, sublimes to water vapor, $H_2O(g)$.

        (b)   The heat energy required to increase the kinetic energy of molecules enough to melt the solid does not produce a large separation of molecules. The specific order is disrupted, but the molecules remain close together. On the other hand, when a liquid is vaporized, the intermolecular forces which maintain close molecular contacts must be overcome. Because molecules are being separated, the energy requirement is higher than for melting.

11.31   Evaporation of 10 g of water requires:

$$50 \text{ g } H_2O \times \frac{2.4 \text{ kJ}}{1 \text{ g } H_2O} = 1.2 \times 10^2 \text{ kJ or } 1.2 \times 10^5 \text{ J}$$

Cooling a certain amount of water by 13°C:

$$1.2 \times 10^5 \text{ J} \times \frac{1 \text{ g} \cdot \text{K}}{4.184 \text{ J}} \times \frac{1}{13°C} = 2206 = 2.2 \times 10^3 \text{ g } H_2O$$

11.33   Heat the solid from -120°C to -114°C (153 K to 159 K), using the specific heat of the solid.

$$75.0 \text{ g } C_2H_5OH \times \frac{0.97 \text{ J}}{\text{g} \cdot \text{K}} \times 6 \text{ K} \times \frac{1 \text{ kJ}}{1000 \text{ J}} = 0.4365 = 0.4 \text{ kJ}$$

At -114°C (159 K), melt the solid, using its enthalpy of fusion.

$$75.0 \text{ g } C_2H_5OH \times \frac{1 \text{ mol } C_2H_5OH}{46.07 \text{ g } C_2H_5OH} \times \frac{5.02 \text{ kJ}}{1 \text{ mol}} = 8.172 = 8.17 \text{ kJ}$$

Heat the liquid from -114°C to 78°C (159 K to 351 K), using the specific heat of the liquid.

$$75.0 \text{ g } C_2H_5OH \times \frac{2.3 \text{ J}}{\text{g} \cdot \text{K}} \times 192 \text{ K} \times \frac{1 \text{ kJ}}{1000 \text{ J}} = 33.12 = 33 \text{ kJ}$$

At 78°C (351 K), vaporize the liquid, using its enthalpy of vaporization.

$$75.0 \text{ g } C_2H_5OH \times \frac{1 \text{ mol } C_2H_5OH}{46.07 \text{ g } C_2H_5OH} \times \frac{38.56 \text{ kJ}}{1 \text{ mol}} = 62.77 = 62.8 \text{ kJ}$$

The total energy required is 0.4365 kJ + 8.172 kJ + 33.12 kJ + 62.77 kJ = 104.50 = 105 kJ. (The result has zero decimal places, from 33 kJ required to heat the liquid.)

11.35 (a)   The critical temperature is the highest temperature at which a gas can be liquefied, regardless of pressure.

(b)   Those gases whose critical temperatures are greater than 298 K can be liquefied at room temperature. The gases in Table 11.4 that meet this criterion are: NH_3, CO_2, Freon-12™ and H_2O.

Vapor Pressure and Boiling Point

11.37 (a)   No effect.   (b)   No effect.

(c)   Vapor pressure decreases with increasing intermolecular attractive forces because fewer molecules have sufficient kinetic energy to overcome the attractive forces and escape to the vapor phase.

(d)   Vapor pressure increases with increasing temperature because average kinetic energies of molecules increase.

11.39 (a)   The less volatile compound, $AsCl_3$, has the stronger intermolecular forces. In the more volatile one, PCl_3, more molecules have sufficient kinetic energy to overcome intermolecular attractive forces and escape to the gas phase. Since both compounds have the same distribution of kinetic energies at 25°C, the attractive forces must be stronger and harder to overcome in $AsCl_3$. This makes sense, because $AsCl_3$ is heavier and has stronger dispersion forces than PCl_3. $AsCl_3$ is also slightly more polar, but dispersion forces account for most of the volatility difference between these two compounds.

(b) PCl_3; the more volatile compound has the higher vapor pressure.

(c) $AsCl_3$; the less volatile compound requires a greater increase in temperature (kinetic energy) to promote enough molecules to the gas phase so that vapor pressure is equal to atmospheric pressure.

11.41 (a)   The water in the two pans is at the same temperature, the boiling point of water at the atmospheric pressure of the room. During a phase change, the temperature of a system is constant. All energy gained from the surroundings is used to accomplish the transition, in this case to vaporize the liquid water. The pan of water that is boiling vigorously is gaining more energy and the liquid is being vaporized more quickly than in the other pan, but the temperature of the phase change is the same.

(b)   Vapor pressure does not depend on either volume or surface area of the liquid. As long as the containers are at the same temperature, the vapor pressures of water in the two containers are the same.

11.43 The boiling point is the temperature at which the vapor pressure of a liquid equals atmospheric pressure.

(a)   The boiling point of diethyl ether at 400 torr is ~17°C, or, at 17°C, the vapor pressure of diethyl ether is 400 torr.

(b)   At a pressure of 25 torr, water would boil at ~28°C, or, the vapor pressure of water at 28°C is 25 torr.

11.45   From Appendix B, a vapor pressure of 340 torr is in the 70-80°C range. By linear interpolation,

$$\text{b.p.} = 70°C + \left[\frac{340 - 234}{355 - 234} \times 10°C \right] \approx 79°C$$

Phase Diagrams

11.47   The liquid/gas line of a phase diagram ends at the critical point, the temperature and pressure beyond which the gas and liquid phases are indistinguishable. At temperatures higher than the critical temperature, a gas cannot be liquefied, regardless of pressure.

11.49   (a)   The water vapor would condense to form a solid at a pressure of around 4 torr. At higher pressure, perhaps 5 atm or so, the solid would melt to form liquid water. This occurs because the melting point of ice, which is 0°C at 1 atm, decreases with increasing pressure.

       (b)   In thinking about this exercise, keep in mind that the **total** pressure is being maintained at a constant 0.50 atm. That pressure is composed of water vapor pressure and some other pressure, which could come from an inert gas. At 100°C and 0.50 atm, water is in the vapor phase. As it cools, the water vapor will condense to the liquid at the temperature where the vapor pressure of liquid water is 0.50 atm. From Appendix B, we see that condensation occurs at approximately 82°C. Further cooling of the liquid water results in freezing to the solid at approximately 0°C. The freezing point of water increases with decreasing pressure, so at 0.50 atm, the freezing temperature is very slightly above 0°C.

11.51   (a)

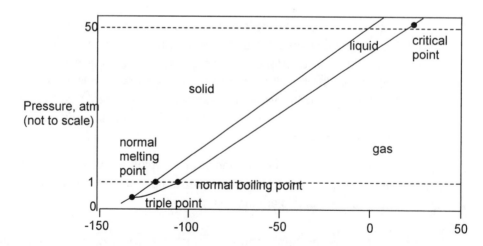

       (b)   The solid-liquid line on the phase diagram is normal and the melting point of Xe(s) increases with increasing pressure. This means that Xe(s) is denser than Xe(l).

(c)　　Cooling Xe(g) at 100 torr will cause deposition of the solid. A pressure of 100 torr is below the pressure of the triple point, so the gas will change directly to the solid upon cooling.

Structures of Solids

11.53　In a crystalline solid, the component particles (atoms, ions or molecules) are arranged in an ordered repeating pattern. In an amorphous solid, there is no orderly structure.

11.55　The unit cell is the building block of the crystal lattice. When repeated in three dimensions, it produces the crystalline solid. It is a parallelepiped with characteristic distances and angles. Unit cells can be primitive (lattice points only at the corners of the parallelepiped) or centered (lattice points at the corners and at the middle of faces or the middle of the parallelepiped).

11.57　Ca: Ca atoms occupy the 8 corners of the cube. 8 corners × 1/8 sphere/corner = 1 Ca atom
　　　　O: O atoms occupy the centers of the 6 faces of the cube.
　　　　　　6 faces × 1/2 atom/face = 3 O atoms

　　　　Ti: There is 1 Ti atom at the body center of the cube.

　　　　Formula: $CaTiO_3$

11.59　(a)　　4 [See Exercise 11.56(c).]

　　　　(b)　　Each aluminum atom is in contact with 12 nearest neighbors, 6 in one plane, 3 above that plane, and 3 below. Its coordination number is thus 12.

　　　　(c)　　The length of the face diagonal of a face-centered cubic unit cell is four times the radius of the metal and $\sqrt{2}$ times the unit cell dimension (usually designated a for cubic cells).

　　　　　　$4 \times 1.43 \text{ Å} = \sqrt{2} \times a; \quad a = \dfrac{4 \times 1.43 \text{ Å}}{\sqrt{2}} = 4.0447 = 4.04 \text{ Å} = 4.04 \times 10^{-8} \text{ cm}$

　　　　(d)　　The density of the metal is the mass of the unit cell contents divided by the volume of the unit cell.

　　　　　　$\text{density} = \dfrac{4 \text{ Al atoms}}{(4.0447 \times 10^{-8} \text{ cm})^3} \times \dfrac{26.98 \text{ g Al}}{6.022 \times 10^{23} \text{ Al atoms}} = 2.71 \text{ g/cm}^3$

11.61　The volume of the unit cell is $(2.86 \times 10^{-8} \text{ cm})^3$. The mass of the unit cell is:

$$\dfrac{7.92 \text{ g}}{\text{cm}^3} \times \dfrac{(2.86 \times 10^{-8})^3 \text{ cm}^3}{\text{unit cell}} = 1.853 \times 10^{-22} \text{ g/unit cell}$$

There are two atoms of the element present in the body-centered cubic unit cell. Thus the atomic weight is:

$$\dfrac{1.853 \times 10^{-22} \text{ g}}{\text{unit cell}} \times \dfrac{1 \text{ unit cell}}{2 \text{ atoms}} \times \dfrac{6.022 \times 10^{23} \text{ atoms}}{1 \text{ mol}} = 55.8 \text{ g/mol}$$

11.63 (a) Each sphere is in contact with 12 nearest neighbors; its coordination number is thus 12.

(b) Each sphere has a coordination number of six.

(c) Each sphere has a coordination number of eight.

11.65 In the face-centered cubic structure, there are four NiO units in the unit cell. Density is the mass of the unit cell contents divided by the unit cell volume (a^3).

$$\text{density} = \frac{4 \text{ NiO units}}{(4.18 \text{ Å})^3} \times \frac{74.7 \text{ g NiO}}{6.022 \times 10^{23} \text{ NiO units}} \times \left(\frac{1 \text{ Å}}{1 \times 10^{-8} \text{ cm}}\right)^3 = 6.79 \text{ g/cm}^3$$

11.67 (a) According to Figure 11.42(b), there are 4 AgI units in the "zinc blende" unit cell [4 complete Ag^+ spheres, 6(1/2) + 8(1/8) I^- sphere's.]

$$5.69 \frac{\text{g}}{\text{cm}^3} = \frac{4 \text{ AgI units}}{a^3} \times \frac{234.8 \text{ g}}{6.022 \times 10^{23} \text{ AgI units}} \times \left(\frac{1 \text{ Å}}{1 \times 10^{-8} \text{ cm}}\right)^3$$

$a^3 = 274.10 \text{ Å}^3$, $a = 6.50$ Å

(b) In an orthonormal coordinate system, the distance between two points (x_1, y_1, z_1) and (x_2, y_2, z_2) is $\sqrt{(x_1 - x_2)^2 + (y_1 - y_2)^2 + (z_1 - z_2)^2}$.

On Figure 11.42(b), select a right-handed coordinate system and select a bonded pair of ions. One possibility is shown at the right.

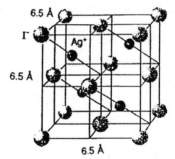

In a cubic unit cell, the lengths of all three cell edges are the same, in this case 6.50 Å.

For Ag^+: x = 0.75(6.50 Å), y = 0.25(6.50 Å), z = 0.25(6.50 Å)

x = 4.875, y = 1.625, z = 1.625

I^-: x = 6.50, y = 0, z = 0

The Ag-I distance is then $\sqrt{(4.875 - 6.50)^2 + (1.625 - 0)^2 + (1.625 - 0)^2}$.

Ag-I = $\sqrt{(1.625)^2 + (1.625)^2 + (1.625)^2}$ = 2.81 Å

Bonding in Solids

11.69 (a) Hydrogen bonding, dipole-dipole forces, London dispersion forces

(b) covalent chemical bonds (mainly)

(c) ionic bonds (mainly)

(d) metallic bonds

11.71   In molecular solids, relatively weak intermolecular forces (hydrogen bonding, dipole-dipole, dispersion) bind the molecules in the lattice, so relatively little energy is required to disrupt these forces. In covalent-network solids, covalent bonds join atoms into an extended network. Melting or deforming a covalent-network solid means breaking these covalent bonds, which requires a large amount of energy.

11.73   Because of its relatively high melting point and properties as a conducting solution, the solid must be ionic.

11.75   (a)   Xe – greater atomic weight, stronger dispersion forces

       (b) SiO_2 – covalent-network lattice versus weak dispersion forces

       (c)   KBr – strong ionic versus weak dispersion forces

       (d) C_6Cl_6 – both are influenced by dispersion forces, C_6Cl_6 has the higher molar mass.

Additional Exercises

11.77   (a)   Dipole-dipole attractions (polar covalent molecules): SO_2, IF, HBr

       (b)   Hydrogen bonding (O-H, N-H or F-H bonds): CH_3NH_2, HCOOH

11.79   (a)   The *cis* isomer has stronger dipole-dipole forces; the *trans* isomer is nonpolar. The higher boiling point of the *cis* isomer supports this conclusion.

       (b)   While boiling points are primarily a measure of strength of intermolecular forces, melting points are influenced by crystal packing efficiency as well as intermolecular forces. Since the nonpolar *trans* isomer with weaker intermolecular forces has the higher melting point, it must pack more efficiently.

11.82   (a) Decrease   (b) increase   (c) increase   (d) increase

       (e) increase   (f) increase   (g) increase

11.85   The two O-H groups in ethylene glycol are involved in many hydrogen bonding interactions, leading to its high boiling point and viscosity, relative to pentane, which experiences only dispersion forces.

11.87   The vacuum pump reduces the pressure of the atmosphere (air + water vapor) above the water. Eventually, atmospheric pressure equals the vapor pressure of water and the water boils. Boiling is an endothermic process, and the temperature drops if the system is not able to absorb heat from the surroundings fast enough. As the temperature of the water decreases, the water freezes. (On a molecular level, the evaporation of water removes the molecules with the highest kinetic energies from the liquid. This decrease in average kinetic energy is what we experience as a temperature decrease.)

11.90 Physical data for the two compounds from the *Handbook of Chemistry and Physics*:

	$\mathscr{m}$	dipole moment	boiling point
CH_2Cl_2	85 g/mol	1.60 D	40.0°C
CH_3I	142 g/mol	1.62 D	42.4°C

(a) The two substances have very similar molecular structures; each is an unsymmetrical tetrahedron with a single central carbon atom and no hydrogen bonding. Since the structures are very similar, the magnitudes of the dipole-dipole forces should be similar. This is verified by their very similar dipole moments. The heavier compound, CH_3I, will have slightly stronger London dispersion forces. Since the nature and magnitude of the intermolecular forces in the two compounds are nearly the same, it is very difficult to predict which will be more volatile (or which will have the higher boiling point as in part (b)).

(b) Given the structural similarities discussed in part (a), one would expect the boiling points to be very similar, and they are. Based on its larger molar mass (and dipole-dipole forces being essentially equal) one might predict that CH_3I would have a slightly higher boiling point; this is verified by the known boiling points.

(c) According to Equation 11.1, $\ln P = \dfrac{-\Delta H_{vap}}{RT} + C$

A plot of $\ln P$ vs. $1/T$ for each compound is linear. Since the order of volatility changes with temperature for the two compounds, the two lines must cross at some temperature; the slopes of the two lines, ΔH_{vap} for the two compounds, and the y-intercepts, C, must be different.

(d)

CH_2Cl_2

ln P	T(K)	1/T
2.303	229.9	4.351×10^{-3}
3.689	250.9	3.986×10^{-3}
4.605	266.9	3.747×10^{-3}
5.991	297.3	3.364×10^{-3}

CH_3I

ln P	T(K)	1/T
2.303	227.4	4.398×10^{-3}
3.689	249.0	4.016×10^{-3}
4.605	266.2	3.757×10^{-3}
5.991	298.5	3.350×10^{-3}

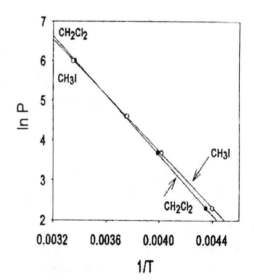

For CH_2Cl_2, $-\Delta H_{vap}/R$ = slope =

$$\frac{(5.991 - 2.303)}{(3.364 \times 10^{-3} - 4.350 \times 10^{-3})} = \frac{-3.688}{0.987 \times 10^{-3}} = -3.74 \times 10^3 = -\Delta H_{vap}/R$$

$\Delta H_{vap} = 8.314 (3.74 \times 10^3) = 3.107 \times 10^4$ J/mol = 31.1 kJ/mol

For CH_3I, $-\Delta H_{vap}/R$ = slope =

$$\frac{(5.991 - 2.303)}{(3.350 \times 10^{-3} - 4.398 \times 10^{-3})} = \frac{-3.688}{1.048 \times 10^{-3}} = -3.519 \times 10^3 = -\Delta H_{vap}/R$$

$\Delta H_{vap} = 8.314 (3.519 \times 10^3) = 2.926 \times 10^4$ J/mol = 29.3 kJ/mol

11.92   The most effective diffraction of light by a grating occurs when the wavelength of light and the separation of the slits in the grating are similar. When X-rays are diffracted by a crystal, layers of atoms serve as the "slits." The most effective diffraction occurs when the distances between layers of atoms are similar to the wavelength of the X-rays. Typical interlayer distances in crystals range from 2 Å to 20 Å. Visible light, 400-700 nm or 4,000 to 7,000 Å, is too long to be diffracted effectively by crystals. Molybdenum x-rays of 0.71 Å are on the same order of magnitude as interlayer distances in crystals and are diffracted.

Integrative Exercises

11.94   (a)   The greater dipole moment of HCl (1.08 D vs 0.82 D for HBr) indicates that it will experience greater dipole-dipole forces.

   (b)   The longer bond length in HBr (1.41 Å vs 1.27 Å for HCl) indicates a more diffuse and therefore more polarizable electron cloud in HBr. It experiences stronger London-dispersion forces.

   (c)   For molecules with similar structures, the compound with the higher boiling point experiences stronger intermolecular forces. Since HBr has the higher boiling point, weaker dipole-dipole forces but stronger dispersion forces, dispersion forces must determine the boiling point.

   (d)   HF experiences hydrogen bonding, a much stronger force than the dipole-dipole and dispersion forces operating in the other hydrogen halides, which results in the high boiling point.

   HI, with the longest bond length and greatest polarizability in the series, has the strongest dispersion forces and highest boiling point of the compounds that do not experience hydrogen bonding.

11.97 $n = \dfrac{PV}{RT} = 735$ torr $\times \dfrac{1 \text{ atm}}{760 \text{ torr}} \times \dfrac{K \cdot mol}{0.08206 \text{ L} \cdot atm} \times \dfrac{3.00 \text{ L}}{290 \text{ K}} = 0.1219 = 0.122$ mol C_4H_{10}

0.1219 mol $C_4H_{10} \times \dfrac{21.3 \text{ kJ}}{1 \text{ mol } C_4H_{10}} = 2.60$ kJ

11.99 $P = \dfrac{nRT}{V} = \dfrac{g\,RT}{\mathcal{m}\,V}$;   T = 273 + 26°C = 299 K;   V = 5.00 L

g C_6H_6(g) = 7.2146 - 5.1493 = 2.0653 g C_6H_6(g)

P (vapor) = $\dfrac{2.0653\,g}{78.11\,g/mol}$ × $\dfrac{299\,K}{5.00\,L}$ × $\dfrac{0.08206\,L \cdot atm}{K \cdot mol}$ × $\dfrac{760\,torr}{1\,atm}$ = 98.6 torr

11.101 (a)   There are 90 bonds in the C_{60} molecule. [Hint: Use a soccer ball to count.]

   (b)   If 60 C atoms each share four pairs of electrons with atoms other than C, a total of 240 bonds are required. If C is bound only to C, as is the case in C_{60}, two C atoms participate in each single bond, so 120 single bonds are required to satisfy each C atom. Since there are only 90 bonds in C_{60}, some of these must be double bonds. In a double bond, two C atoms each share two pairs of electrons; each double bond takes care of four of the required bonds. Thus,

       60 single bonds × 2 C atoms
       + 30 double bonds × 2 C atoms × 2 pairs of electrons
       240 total "bonds"

   Of the 90 bonds in C_{60}, 30 are formally double bonds.

12 Modern Materials

Liquid Crystals

12.1   Both an ordinary liquid and a nematic liquid crystal phase are fluids; they are converted directly to the solid phase upon cooling. The nematic phase is cloudy and more viscous than an ordinary liquid. Upon heating, the nematic phase is converted to an ordinary liquid.

12.3   Reinitzer observed that cholesteryl benzoate has a phase that exhibits properties intermediate between those of the solid and liquid phases. This "liquid-crystalline" phase, formed by melting at 145°C, is opaque, changes color as the temperature increases, and becomes clear at 179°C.

12.5   Because order is maintained in at least one dimension, the molecules in a liquid-crystalline phase are not totally free to change orientation. This makes the liquid-crystalline phase more resistant to flow, more viscous, than the isotropic liquid.

12.7   In the nematic phase, molecules are aligned in one dimension, the long dimension of the molecule. In a smectic phase (A or C), molecules are aligned in two dimensions. Not only are the long directions of the molecules aligned, but the ends are also aligned. The molecules are organized into layers; the height of the layer is related to the length of the molecule.

12.9   As the temperature of a substance increases, the average kinetic energy of the molecules increases. More molecules have sufficient kinetic energy to overcome intermolecular attractive forces, so overall ordering of the molecules decreases as temperature increases. Melting provides kinetic energy sufficient to disrupt alignment in one dimension in the solid, producing a smectic phase with ordering in two dimensions. Additional heating of the smectic phase provides kinetic energy sufficient to disrupt alignment in another dimension, producing a nematic phase with one-dimensional order.

Polymers

12.11   *n*-decane does not have a sufficiently high chain length or molecular mass to be considered a polymer.

12.13

12.15   (a)

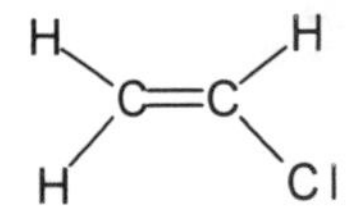

vinyl chloride (chloroethylene or chloroethene)

(b)

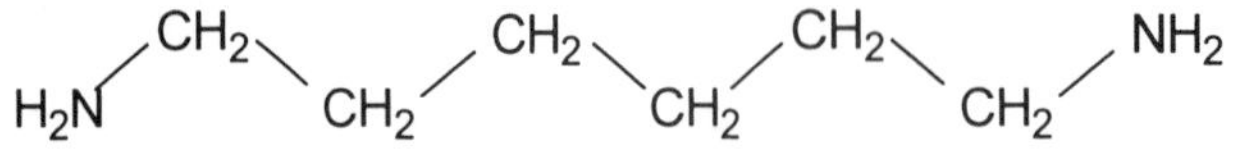

hexanediamine

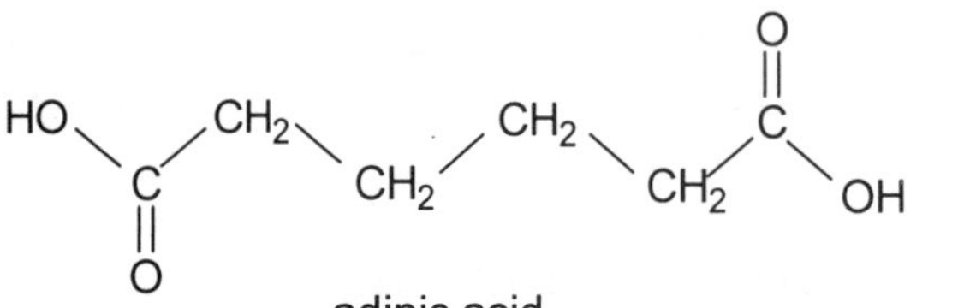

adipic acid

(Formulas given in Equation 12.3.)

(c)

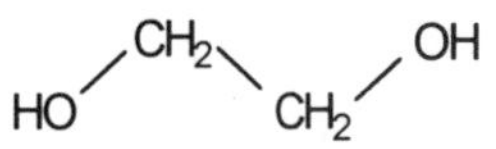

ethylene glycol 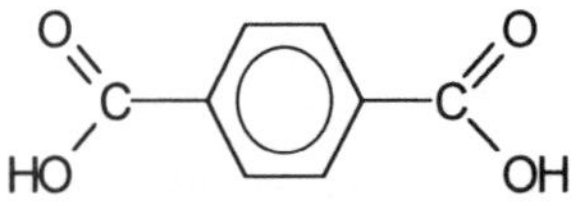   terephthalic acid

12.17

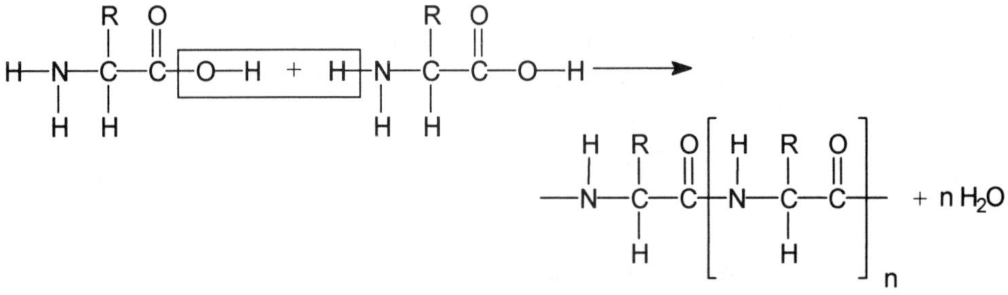

12.19   At the molecular level, the longer, unbranched chains of HDPE fit closer together and have more crystalline (ordered, aligned) regions than the shorter, branched chains of LDPE. Closer packing leads to higher density.

12.21   The function of the material (polymer) determines whether high molecular mass and high degree of crystallinity are desirable properties. If the material will be formed into containers or pipes, rigidity and structural strength are required. If the polymer will be used as a flexible wrapping or as a garment material, rigidity is an undesirable property.

Biomaterials

12.23   Is the neoprene biocompatible: is the surface smooth enough and is the chemical composition appropriate so that there are no inflammatory reactions in the body? Does neoprene meet the physical requirements of a flexible lead: will it remain resistant to degradation by body fluids over a long time period; will it maintain elasticity over the same time period? Can neoprene be prepared in sufficiently pure form (free of trace amounts of monomer, catalyst, etc.) so that it can be classified as *medical grade*?

12.25 Surface roughness in synthetic heart valves causes *hemolysis*, the breakdown of red blood cells. The surface of the valve implant was probably not smooth enough.

12.27 In order for skin cells in a culture medium to develop into synthetic skin, a mechanical matrix must be present that holds the cells in contact with one another and allows them to differentiate. The matrix must be mechanically strong, biocompatible and biodegradable. It probably has polar functional groups that are capable of hydrogen bonding with biomolecules in the tissue cells.

Ceramics

12.29 Structurally, polymers are formed from organic monomers held together by covalent bonds, whereas ceramics are formed from inorganic materials linked by ionic or highly polar covalent bonds. Ceramics are often stabilized by a three-dimensional bonding network, whereas in polymers, covalent bonds link atoms into a long, chain-like molecule with only weak interactions between molecules. Polymers are nearly always amorphous, and though ceramics can be amorphous, they are often crystalline.

In terms of physical properties, ceramics are generally much harder, more heat-stable and higher melting than polymers. (These properties are true in general for network solids relative to molecular solids, as described in Table 11.6.)

12.31 Since Zr and Ti are in the same family, assume that the stoichiometry of the compounds in a sol-gel process will be the same for the two metals.

i.   Alkoxide formation: oxidation-reduction reaction

$Zr(s) + 4CH_3CH_2OH(l) \rightarrow Zr(OCH_2CH_3)_4(s) + 2H_2(g)$
         alkoxide

ii.   Sol formation: metathesis reaction

$Zr(OCH_2CH_3)_4(soln) + 4H_2O(l) \rightarrow Zr(OH)_4(s) + 4CH_3CH_2OH(l)$
    "precipitate"   nonelectrolyte
    sol

$Zr(OCH_2CH_3)_4(s)$ is dissolved in an alcohol solvent and then reacted with water. In general, reaction with water is called *hydrolysis*. The alkoxide anions $(CH_3CH_2O^-)$ combine with H^+ from H_2O to form the nonelectrolyte $CH_3CH_2OH(l)$, and Zr^{2+} cations combine with OH^- to form the $Zr(OH)_4$ solid. The product $Zr(OH)_4(s)$ is not a traditional coagulated precipitate, but a finely divided evenly dispersed collection of particles called a sol.

iii.   Gel formation: condensation reaction

$(OH)_3Zr\text{-}O\text{-}H(s) + H\text{-}O\text{-}Zr(OH)_3(s) \rightarrow (HO)_3Zr\text{-}O\text{-}Zr(OH)_3(s) + H_2O(l)$
    gel

Adjusting the acidity of the $Zr(OH)_4$ sol initiates condensation, the splitting-out of $H_2O(l)$ and formation of a zirconium-oxide network solid. The solid remains suspended in the solvent mixture and is called a gel.

iv.   Processing: physical changes
The gel is heated to drive off solvent and the resulting solid consists of dry, uniform and finely divided ZrO_2 particles.

12.33   Concrete is a typically brittle ceramic that is susceptible to catastrophic fracture. Steel reinforcing rods are added to resist stress applied along the long direction of the rod. By analogy, the shape of the reinforcing material in the ceramic composite should be rod-like, with a length much greater than its diameter. This is the optimal shape because rods have great strength when the load or stress is applied parallel to the long direction of the rod. Rods can be oriented in many directions, so that the material (concrete or ceramic composite) is strengthened in all directions.

12.35   By analogy to the ZnS structure, the C atoms form a face-centered cubic array with Si atoms occupying **alternate** tetrahedral holes in the lattice. This means that the coordination numbers of both Si and C are 4; each Si is bound to 4 C atoms in a tetrahedral arrangement, and each C is bound to 4 Si atoms in a tetrahedral arrangement, producing an extended three-dimensional network. ZnS, an ionic solid, sublimes at 1185° and 1 atm pressure and melts at 1850° and 150 atm pressure. The considerably higher melting point of SiC, 2800° at 1 atm, indicates that SiC is probably not a purely ionic solid and that the Si-C bonding network has significant covalent character. This is reasonable, since the electronegativities of Si and C are similar (Figure 8.7). SiC is high-melting because a great deal of chemical energy is stored in the covalent Si-C bonds, and it is hard because the three-dimensional lattice resists any change that would weaken the Si-C bonding network.

12.37   A superconducting material offers no resistance to the flow of electrical current; *superconductivity* is the frictionless flow of electrons. Superconductive materials could transmit electricity with no heat loss and therefore much greater efficiency than current carriers. Because of the Meisner effect, they are also potential materials for magnetically levitated trains.

Thin Films

12.39   In general, a useful thin film should:

   (a)   be chemically stable in its working environment
   (b)   adhere to its substrate
   (c)   have a uniform thickness
   (d)   have an easily controllable composition
   (e)   be nearly free of imperfections

12.41   There are three major methods of producing thin films.

   (i)   In *vacuum deposition*, a substance is vaporized or evaporated by heating under vacuum and then deposited on the desired substrate. No chemical change occurs.

   (ii)   In *sputtering*, ions accelerated to high energies by applying a high voltage are allowed to strike the target material, knocking atoms from its surface. These target material atoms are further accelerated toward the substrate, forming a thin film. No net chemical change occurs, because the material in the film is the target material.

   (iii)   In *chemical vapor deposition*, two gas phase substances react at the substrate surface to form a stable product which is deposited as a thin film. This involves a net chemical change.

Additional Exercises

12.43   A dipole moment (permanent, partial charge separation) roughly parallel to the long dimension of the molecule would cause the molecules to reorient when an electric field is applied perpendicular to the usual direction of molecular orientation.

12.46   At the temperature where a substance changes from the solid to the liquid-crystalline phase, kinetic energy sufficient to overcome most of the long range order in the solid has been supplied. A few van der Waals forces have sufficient attractive energy to impose the one-dimensional order characteristic of the liquid-crystalline state. Very little additional kinetic energy (and thus a relatively small increase in temperature) is required to overcome these aligning forces and produce an isotropic liquid.

12.48   Ceramics are usually three-dimensional network solids, whereas plastics most often consist of large, chain-like molecules (the chain may be branched) held loosely together by relatively weak van der Waals forces. Ceramics are rigid precisely because of the many strong bonding interactions intrinsic to the network. Once a crack forms, atoms near the defect are subject to great stress, and the crack is propagated. They are stable to high temperatures because tremendous kinetic energy (temperature) is required for an atom to break free from the bonding network. On the other hand, plastics are flexible because the molecules themselves are flexible (free rotation around the sigma bonds in the polymer chain), and it is easy for the molecules to move relative to one another (weak intermolecular forces). (However, recall that rigidity of the plastic increases as crosslinking of the polymer chain increases. The melamine-formaldehyde polymer in Figure 12.18 is a very rigid, brittle polymer.) Plastics are not thermally stable because their largely organic molecules are subject to oxidation and/or bond breaking at high temperatures.

12.51   The degree of crystallinity of polyethylene increases with increasing molecular weight. Following the trends in Table 12.3, ultra high molecular weight polyethylene will be dense, mechanically strong and high melting. The important properties in this application are density and mechanical strength, so that the coating does not deform or wear down under load. Movement of the metal ball around the polymer surface should be essentially frictionless; adhesive forces between metal and polymer should be minimal. The high density polymer has no pockets of empty space, so it forms a smooth surface. Attractive interactions between the nonpolar hydrocarbon polymer and the metallic ball are essentially absent, facilitating frictionless movement of the ball.

12.52   (a)

(b) $2NbBr_5(g) + 5H_2(g) \rightarrow 2Nb(s) + 10HBr(g)$

(c) $SiCl_4(l) + 4C_2H_5OH(l) \rightarrow Si(OC_2H_5)_4(s) + 4HCl(g)$

(d)

12.56 The formula of the compound deposited as a thin film is indicated by boldface type.

  (a) $SiH_4(g) + 2H_2(g) + 2CO_2(g) \rightarrow \textbf{SiO}_2\textbf{(s)} + 4H_2(g) + 2CO(g)$

  (b) $TiCl_4(g) + 2H_2O(g) \rightarrow \textbf{TiO}_2\textbf{(s)} + 4HCl(g)$

  (c) $GeCl_4(g) \rightarrow \textbf{Ge(s)} + 2Cl_2(g)$ The H_2 carrier gas dilutes the $GeCl_4(g)$ so the reaction occurs more evenly and at a controlled rate; it does not participate in the reaction.

12.58 These compounds cannot be vaporized without destroying their chemical identities. Anions with names ending in "ite" or "ate" are oxyanions with nonmetallic elements as central atoms. Under the conditions of vacuum deposition, high temperatures and low pressures, these anions tend to chemically decompose to form gaseous nonmetal oxides. For example:

$$MnSO_4(s) \rightarrow MnO(s) + SO_3(g)$$

Integrative Exercises

12.62 (a) The data (14.99%) has 4 sig figs, so use molar masses to 5 sig figs.

$$\text{mass \% O} = 14.99 = \frac{(8+x)\,15.999}{746.04 + (8+x)\,15.999} \times 100$$

rounded (to show sig figs)

(8+x)15.999
 = 0.1499 [746.04 + (8+x) 15.999]
127.99 + 15.999x
 = 0.1499(874.04 + 15.999x)
15.999x - 2.398x
 = 131.0 - 127.99
13.601x = 3.0; x = 0.22

unrounded

(8+x)15.999
 = 0.1499 [746.04 + (8+x) 15.999]
127.992 + 15.999x
 = 0.1499 (874.036 + 15.999x)
15.999x - 2.3983x
 = 131.018 - 127.992
13.6007x = 3.026; x = 0.2225

  (b) **Hg** and **Cu** both have more than one stable oxidation state. If different Cu ions (or Hg ions) in the solid lattice have different charges, then the average charge is a noninteger value. Ca and Ba are stable only in the +2 oxidation state; they are unlikely to have noninteger average charge.

  (c) Ba^{2+} is largest; Cu^{2+} is smallest. For ions with the same charge, size decreases going up or across the periodic table. In the +2 state, Hg is smaller than Ba. If Hg has an average charge greater than 2+, it will be smaller yet. The same argument is true for Cu and Ca.

13 Properties of Solutions

The Solution Process

13.1   If the enthalpy released due to solute-solvent attractive forces (ΔH_3) is at least as large as the enthalpy required to separate the solute particles (ΔH_1), the overall enthalpy of solution (ΔH_{soln}) will be either slightly endothermic (owing to $+\Delta H_2$) or exothermic. Even if ΔH_{soln} is slightly endothermic, the increase in disorder due to mixing will cause a significant amount of solute to dissolve. If the magnitude of ΔH_3 is small relative to the magnitude of ΔH_1, ΔH_{soln} will be large and endothermic (energetically unfavorable) and not much solute will dissolve.

13.3   (a) dispersion   (b) ion-dipole   (c) hydrogen bonding   (d) dipole-dipole

13.5   The overall energy change associated with dissolution depends on the relative magnitudes of the solute-solute, solvent-solvent, and solute-solvent interactions. If disrupting the "old" solute-solute and solvent-solvent interactions requires more energy than is released by the "new" solute-solvent interactions, the process is endothermic. When $NH_4NO_3(s)$ dissolves in water, disrupting the ion-ion interactions among NH_4^+ and NO_3^- ions of the solute (ΔH_1) and the hydrogen bonding among H_2O molecules of the solvent (ΔH_2) requires more energy than is released by subsequent ion-dipole and hydrogen bonding interactions among NH_4^+ and H_2O and NO_3^- and H_2O (ΔH_3).

13.7   (a) ΔH_{soln} is determined by the relative magnitudes of the "old" solute-solute (ΔH_1) and solvent-solvent (ΔH_2) interactions and the new solute-solvent interactions (ΔH_3); $\Delta H_{soln} = \Delta H_1 + \Delta H_2 + \Delta H_3$. Since the solute and solvent in this case experience very similar London dispersion forces, the energy required to separate them individually and the energy released when they are mixed are approximately equal. $\Delta H_1 + \Delta H_2 \approx -\Delta H_3$. Thus, ΔH_{soln} is nearly zero.

        (b)   Mixing hexane and heptane produces a homogeneous solution from two pure substances, and the randomness of the system increases. Since no strong intermolecular forces prevent the molecules from mixing, they do so spontaneously due to the increase in disorder.

Saturated Solutions; Factors Affecting Solubility

13.9   (a)   Supersaturated

        (b)   Add a seed crystal. Supersaturated solutions exist because not enough solute molecules are properly aligned for crystallization to occur. A seed crystal provides a nucleus of already aligned molecules, so that ordering of the dissolved particles is more facile.

13.11 (a) unsaturated (b) saturated (c) saturated (d) unsaturated

13.13 Glycerol has an -OH group on each C atom in the molecule. This structure facilitates strong hydrogen bonding similar to that in water.

13.15 Water, H_2O, is a polar solvent that forms hydrogen bonds with other H_2O molecules. The more soluble solute in each case will have intermolecular interactions that are most similar to the hydrogen bonding in H_2O.

(a) CH_3CH_2OH is more soluble because it has a shorter nonpolar hydrocarbon chain. The longer nonpolar hydrocarbon chain of $CH_3CH_2CH_2CH_2OH$ is capable only of dispersion forces and interferes with hydrogen bonding interactions between the -OH group and water.

(b) Ionic $CaCl_2$ is more soluble because ion-dipole solute-solvent interactions are more similar to ionic solute-solute and hydrogen bonding solvent-solvent interactions than the weak dispersion forces between CCl_4 and H_2O.

(c) C_6H_5OH is more soluble because it is capable of hydrogen bonding. Nonpolar C_6H_6 is capable only of dispersion force interactions and does not have strong intermolecular interactions with polar (hydrogen bonding) H_2O.

13.17 (a) Carbonated beverages are stored with a partial pressure of $CO_2(g)$ greater than 1 atm above the liquid. A sealed container is required to maintain this CO_2 pressure.

(b) Since the solubility of gases increases with decreasing temperature, some $CO_2(g)$ will remain dissolved in the beverage if it is kept cool.

13.19 $C_{He} = 3.7 \times 10^{-4}$ *M*/atm $\times 2.5$ atm $= 9.2 \times 10^{-4}$ *M*

$C_{N_2} = 6.0 \times 10^{-4}$ *M*/atm $\times 2.5$ atm $= 1.5 \times 10^{-3}$ *M*

Concentrations of Solutions

13.21 (a) $\text{mass \%} = \dfrac{\text{mass solute}}{\text{total mass solution}} \times 100 = \dfrac{14.7 \text{ g Na}_2\text{SO}_4}{14.7 \text{ g Na}_2\text{SO}_4 + 345 \text{ g H}_2\text{O}} \times 100 = 4.09\%$

(b) $\text{ppm} = \dfrac{\text{mass solute}}{\text{total mass solution}} \times 10^6;\ \dfrac{7.35 \text{ g Ag}}{1 \text{ ton ore}} \times \dfrac{1 \text{ ton}}{2000 \text{ lb}} \times \dfrac{1 \text{ lb}}{453.6 \text{ g}} \times 10^6$

$= 8.10$ ppm

13.23 (a) $7.5 \text{ g CH}_3\text{OH} \times \dfrac{1 \text{ mol CH}_3\text{OH}}{32.04 \text{ g CH}_3\text{OH}} = 0.234 = 0.23 \text{ mol CH}_3\text{OH}$

$245 \text{ g H}_2\text{O} \times \dfrac{1 \text{ mol H}_2\text{O}}{18.02 \text{ g H}_2\text{O}} = 13.60 = 13.6 \text{ mol H}_2\text{O}$

$\chi_{CH_3OH} = \dfrac{0.234}{0.234 + 13.60} = 0.0169 = 0.017$

(b) $\dfrac{55.7 \text{ g } CH_3OH}{32.04 \text{ g/mol}} = 1.738 = 1.74 \text{ mol } CH_3OH;$ $\dfrac{164 \text{ g } CCl_4}{153.8 \text{ g/mol}} = 1.066 = 1.07 \text{ mol } CCl_4$

$\chi_{CH_3OH} = \dfrac{1.738}{1.738 + 1.066} = 0.6198 = 0.620$

13.25 (a) $M = \dfrac{\text{mol solute}}{\text{L soln}}; \dfrac{10.5 \text{ g } KCl}{0.250 \text{ L soln}} \times \dfrac{1 \text{ mol } KCl}{74.55 \text{ } KCl} = 0.563 \text{ } M \text{ } KCl$

(b) $\dfrac{30.7 \text{ g } LiClO_4 \cdot 3H_2O}{0.125 \text{ L soln}} \times \dfrac{1 \text{ mol } LiClO_4 \cdot 3H_2O}{160.4 \text{ g } LiClO_4 \cdot 3H_2O} = 1.53 \text{ } M \text{ } LiClO_4 \cdot 3H_2O$

(c) $M_c \times L_c = M_d \times L_d;$ $1.50 \text{ } M \text{ } HNO_3 \times 0.0250 \text{ L} = ?M \text{ } HNO_3 \times 0.500 \text{ L}$

500 mL of 0.0750 M HNO_3

13.27 (a) $m = \dfrac{\text{mol solute}}{\text{kg solvent}}; \dfrac{13.0 \text{ g } C_6H_6}{17.0 \text{ g } CCl_4} \times \dfrac{1 \text{ mol } C_6H_6}{78.11 \text{ g } C_6H_6} \times \dfrac{1000 \text{ g } CCl_4}{1 \text{ kg } CCl_4} = 9.79 \text{ } m \text{ } C_6H_6$

(b) The density of H_2O = 0.997 g/mL = 0.997 kg/L.

$\dfrac{4.75 \text{ g } NaCl}{0.250 \text{ L } H_2O} \times \dfrac{1 \text{ mol } NaCl}{58.44 \text{ g } NaCl} \times \dfrac{1 \text{ L } H_2O}{0.997 \text{ kg } H_2O} = 0.326 \text{ } m \text{ } NaCl$

13.29 (a) $\dfrac{571.6 \text{ g } H_2SO_4}{1 \text{ L soln}} \times \dfrac{1 \text{ L soln}}{1329 \text{ g soln}} = 0.430098 \text{ g } H_2SO_4/\text{g soln}$

mass percent is thus 0.4301 × 100 = 43.01% H_2SO_4

(b) In a liter of solution there are 1329 - 571.6 = 757.4 = 757 g H_2O.

$\dfrac{571.6 \text{ g } H_2SO_4}{98.09 \text{ g/mol}} = 5.827 \text{ mol } H_2SO_4;$ $\dfrac{757.4 \text{ g } H_2O}{18.02 \text{ g/mol}} = 42.03 = 42.0 \text{ mol } H_2O$

$\chi_{H_2SO_4} = \dfrac{5.827}{42.03 + 5.827} = 0.122$

(The result has 3 sig figs because 42.0 mol H_2O limits the denominator to 3 sig figs.)

(c) $\text{molality} = \dfrac{5.827 \text{ mol } H_2SO_4}{0.7574 \text{ kg } H_2O} = 7.693 = 7.69 \text{ } m \text{ } H_2SO_4$

(d) $\text{molarity} = \dfrac{5.827 \text{ mol } H_2SO_4}{1 \text{ L soln}} = 5.827 \text{ } M \text{ } H_2SO_4$

13.31 Given: 100.0 mL of $CH_3CN(l)$, 0.786 g/mL; 20.0 mL CH_3OH, 0.791 g/mL

(a) $\text{mol } CH_3CN = \dfrac{0.786 \text{ g}}{1 \text{ mL}} \times 100.0 \text{ mL} \times \dfrac{1 \text{ mol } CH_3CN}{41.05 \text{ g } CH_3CN} = 1.9147 = 1.91 \text{ mol}$

$\text{mol } CH_3OH = \dfrac{0.791 \text{ g}}{1 \text{ mL}} \times 20.0 \text{ mL} \times \dfrac{1 \text{ mol } CH_3OH}{32.04 \text{ g } CH_3OH} = 0.4938 = 0.494 \text{ mol}$

$\chi_{CH_3OH} = \dfrac{0.4938 \text{ mol } CH_3OH}{1.9147 \text{ mol } CH_3CN + 0.4938 \text{ mol } CH_3OH} = 0.205$

(b)   Assuming CH_3OH is the solute and CH_3CN is the solvent,

$$100.0 \text{ mL } CH_3CN \times \frac{0.786 \text{ g}}{1 \text{ mL}} \times \frac{1 \text{ kg}}{1000 \text{ g}} = 0.0786 \text{ kg } CH_3CN$$

$$m_{CH_3OH} = \frac{0.4938 \text{ mol } CH_3OH}{0.0786 \text{ kg } CH_3CN} = 6.28 \text{ } m \text{ } CH_3OH$$

(c)   The total volume of the solution is 120.0 mL, assuming volumes are additive.

$$M = \frac{0.4938 \text{ mol } CH_3OH}{0.1200 \text{ L solution}} = 4.12 \text{ } M \text{ } CH_3OH$$

13.33 (a) $\dfrac{0.215 \text{ mol } CaBr_2}{1 \text{ L soln}} \times 0.355 \text{ L} = 7.63 \times 10^{-2} \text{ mol } CaBr_2$

(b)   Assume that for dilute aqueous solutions, the mass of the solvent is the mass of solution.

$$\frac{0.150 \text{ mol KCl}}{1 \text{ kg } H_2O} = \frac{x \text{ mol KCl}}{0.0350 \text{ kg } H_2O}; \quad x = 5.25 \times 10^{-3} \text{ mol KCl}$$

(c) $\dfrac{5.3 \text{ g } C_6H_{12}O_6}{100 \text{ g soln}} = \dfrac{x \text{ g } C_6H_{12}O_6}{50.0 \text{ g soln}}; \quad x = 2.65 = 2.7 \text{ g } C_6H_{12}O_6$

$$2.65 \text{ g } C_6H_{12}O_6 \times \frac{1 \text{ mol } C_6H_{12}O_6}{180.2 \text{ g } C_6H_{12}O_6} = 0.0147 = 0.015 \text{ mol } C_6H_{12}O_6$$

13.35 (a) $\dfrac{1.50 \times 10^{-2} \text{ mol KBr}}{1 \text{ L soln}} \times 0.85 \text{ L} \times \dfrac{119.0 \text{ g KBr}}{1 \text{ mol KBr}} = 1.5 \text{ g KBr}$

Weigh out 1.5 g KBr, dissolve in water, dilute with stirring to 0.85 L (850 mL).

(b)   Determine the mass % of KBr:

$$\frac{0.180 \text{ mol KBr}}{1000 \text{ g } H_2O} \times \frac{119.0 \text{ g KBr}}{1 \text{ mol KBr}} = 21.42 = 21.4 \text{ g KBr/kg } H_2O$$

Thus, mass fraction $= \dfrac{21.42 \text{ g KBr}}{1000 + 21.42} = 0.02097 = 0.0210$

In 165 g of the 0.180 m solution, there are

$$(165 \text{ g soln}) \times \frac{0.02097 \text{ g KBr}}{1 \text{ g soln}} = 3.460 = 3.46 \text{ g KBr}$$

Weigh out 3.46 g KBr, dissolve it in 165 - 3.46 = 162 g H_2O to make exactly 165 g of 0.180 m solution.

(c)   Calculate the total mass of 1.85 L of solution, and from the mass % of KBr, the mass of KBr required.

$$1.85 \text{ L soln} \times \frac{1000 \text{ mL}}{1 \text{ L}} \times \frac{1.10 \text{ g soln}}{1 \text{ mL}} = 2035 = 2.04 \times 10^3 \text{ g soln}$$

0.120 (2035 g soln) = 244.2 = 244 g KBr

Dissolve 244 g KBr in water, dilute with stirring to 1.85 L.

(d)   Calculate moles KBr needed to precipitate 16.0 g AgBr.

$$16.0 \text{ g AgBr} \times \frac{1 \text{ mol AgBr}}{187.8 \text{ g AgBr}} \times \frac{1 \text{ mol KBr}}{1 \text{ mol AgBr}} = 0.08520 = 0.0852 \text{ mol KBr}$$

$$0.0852 \text{ mol KBr} \times \frac{1 \text{ L soln}}{0.150 \text{ mol KBr}} = 0.568 \text{ L soln}$$

Weigh out 0.0852 mol KBr (10.1 g KBr), dissolve it in a small amount of water and dilute to 0.568 L.

13.37   Assume 1.00 L of solution. Calculate mol NH_3 in 1.00 L.

$$1.00 \text{ L soln} \times \frac{1000 \text{ mL}}{1 \text{ L}} \times \frac{0.90 \text{ g soln}}{1 \text{ mL soln}} = 9.0 \times 10^2 \text{ g soln/L}$$

$$\frac{900 \text{ g soln}}{1.00 \text{ L soln}} \times \frac{28 \text{ g NH}_3}{100 \text{ g soln}} \times \frac{1 \text{ mol NH}_3}{17.03 \text{ g NH}_3} = 14.80 = 15 \text{ mol NH}_3/\text{L soln} = 15 \text{ } M \text{ NH}_3$$

13.39 $\chi_{C_3H_6(OH)_2} = 0.100 = \dfrac{\text{mol C}_3\text{H}_6(\text{OH})_2}{\text{mol C}_3\text{H}_6(\text{OH})_2 + \text{mol H}_2\text{O}}$

0.100 [mol $C_3H_6(OH)_2$ + mol H_2O] = mol $C_3H_6(OH)_2$

0.100 mol H_2O = 0.900 mol $C_3H_6(OH)_2$; mol H_2O = 9[mol $C_3H_6(OH)_2$]

The solution has nine times as many moles of H_2O as moles of $C_3H_6(OH)_2$. Assume 1.00 mol $C_3H_6(OH)_2$ and 9.00 mol H_2O.

(a)   76.09 = 76.1 g $C_3H_6(OH)_2$; 9.00 mol H_2O × 18.02 g H_2O/mol = 162.18 = 162 g H_2O

$$\text{mass \%} = \frac{76.09 \text{ g C}_3\text{H}_6(\text{OH})_2}{76.09 \text{ g C}_3\text{H}_6(\text{OH})_2 + 162.18 \text{ g H}_2\text{O}} \times 100 = 31.9\% \text{ C}_3\text{H}_6(\text{OH})_2 \text{ by mass}$$

(b) $m = \dfrac{\text{mol C}_3\text{H}_6(\text{OH})_2}{\text{kg H}_2\text{O}}$; $\dfrac{1.00 \text{ mol C}_3\text{H}_6(\text{OH})_2}{0.16218 \text{ kg H}_2\text{O}} = 6.166 = 6.17 \text{ } m \text{ C}_3\text{H}_6(\text{OH})_2$

Colligative Properties

13.41   freezing point depression, $\Delta T_f = K_f(m)$; boiling point elevation, $\Delta T_b = K_b(m)$; osmotic pressure, $\pi = MRT$;   vapor pressure lowering, $P_A = \chi_A P_A°$

13.43   (a)   An *ideal solution* is a solution that obeys Raoult's Law.

(b)   Calculate the vapor pressure predicted by Raoult's law and compare it to the experimental vapor pressure. Assume ethylene glycol (eg) is the solute.

$\chi_{H_2O} = \chi_{eg} = 0.500$; $P_A = \chi_A P_A° = 0.500(149)$ mm Hg = 74.5 mm Hg

The experimental vapor pressure (P_A), 67 mm Hg, is less than the value predicted by Raoult's law for an ideal solution. The solution is not ideal.

13.45 (a) H_2O vapor pressure will be determined by the mole fraction of H_2O in the solution. The vapor pressure of pure H_2O at 338 K (65°C) = 187.5 torr.

$$\frac{16.2\ g\ C_{12}H_{22}O_{11}}{342.3\ g/mol} = 0.04733 = 0.0473\ mol; \quad \frac{105.7\ g\ H_2O}{18.02\ g/mol} = 5.8657 = 5.866\ mol$$

$$P_{H_2O} = \chi_{H_2O}\ P^{\circ}_{H_2O} = \frac{5.8657\ mol\ H_2O}{5.8657 + 0.04733} \times 187.5\ torr = 186.0\ torr$$

   (b)   For this problem, it will be convenient to express Raoult's law in terms of the lowering of the vapor pressure of the solvent, ΔP_A.

$$\Delta P_A = P_A^{\circ} - \chi_A P_A^{\circ} = P_A^{\circ}\ (1 - \chi_A). \ \ 1 - \chi_A = \chi_B ,\ \text{the mole fraction of the } \textit{solute} \text{ particles}$$

$\Delta P_A^{\circ} = \chi_B P_A^{\circ}$; the vapor pressure of the solvent (A) is lowered according to the mole fraction of solute (B) particles present.

$$P_{H_2O} \text{ at } 40°C = 55.3\ torr; \quad \frac{500\ g\ H_2O}{18.02\ g/mol} = 27.747 = 27.7\ mol\ H_2O$$

$$\chi_{C_3H_8O_2} = \frac{4.60\ torr}{55.3\ torr} = \frac{y\ mol\ C_3H_8O_2}{y\ mol\ C_3H_8O_2 + 27.747\ mol\ H_2O} = 0.08318 = 0.0832$$

$$0.08318 = \frac{y}{y + 27.747};\ 0.08318\ y + 2.308 = y;\ 0.9168\ y = 2.308,$$

$$y = 2.517 = 2.52\ mol\ C_3H_8O_2$$

This result has 3 sig figs because (27.7 × 0.0832 = 2.31) has 3 sig figs.

$$2.517\ mol\ C_3H_8O_2 \times \frac{76.09\ g\ C_3H_8O_2}{mol\ C_3H_8O_2} = 191.52 = 192\ g\ C_3H_8O_2$$

13.47   At 63.5°C, $P^{\circ}_{H_2O}$ = 175 torr, P°_{Eth} = 400 torr

Let G = the mass of H_2O and/or C_2H_5OH.

   (a) $$\chi_{Eth} = \frac{\dfrac{G}{46.07\ g\ C_2H_5OH}}{\dfrac{G}{46.07\ g\ C_2H_5OH} + \dfrac{G}{18.02\ g\ H_2O}}$$

Multiplying top and bottom of the right side of the equation by 1/G gives:

$$\chi_{Eth} = \frac{1/46.07}{1/46.07 + 1/18.02} = \frac{0.02171}{0.02171 + 0.05549} = 0.2812$$

   (b) $P_T = P_{Eth} + P_{H_2O}$; $P_{Eth} = \chi_{Eth}$; $P^{\circ}_{Eth}\ P_{H_2O} = \chi_{H_2O}\ P^{\circ}_{H_2O}$

χ_{Eth} = 0.2812, P_{Eth} = 0.2812 (400 torr) = 112.48 = 112 torr

χ_{H_2O} = 1 − 0.2812 = 0.7188; P_{H_2O} = 0.7188(175 torr) = 125.8 =126 torr

P_T = 112.5 torr + 125.8 torr = 238.3 = 238 torr

   (c) $$\chi_{Eth} \text{ in vapor} = \frac{P_{Eth}}{P_{total}} = \frac{112.5\ torr}{238.3\ torr} = 0.4721 = 0.472$$

13.49 $\Delta T = K(m)$; first, calculate the **molality** of each solution

(a)   0.35 m (b)   14.2 mol CHCl$_3$ × $\dfrac{119.4 \text{ g CHCl}_3}{\text{mol CHCl}_3}$ = 1.6955 = 1.70 kg;

$\dfrac{1.58 \text{ mol C}_{10}\text{H}_8}{1.6955 \text{ kg CHCl}_3}$ = 0.9319 = 0.932 m

(c)   5.13 g KBr × $\dfrac{1 \text{ mol KBr}}{119.0 \text{ g KBr}}$ × $\dfrac{2 \text{ mol particles}}{1 \text{ mol KBr}}$ = 0.08622 = 0.0862 mol particles

6.85 g C$_6$H$_{12}$O$_6$ × $\dfrac{1 \text{ mol C}_6\text{H}_{12}\text{O}_6}{180.2 \text{ g C}_6\text{H}_{12}\text{O}_6}$ = 0.03801 = 0.0380 mol particles

$m = \dfrac{(0.08622 + 0.03801) \text{ mol particles}}{0.255 \text{ kg H}_2\text{O}}$ = 0.48718 = 0.487 m

Then, f.p. = T_f - $K_f(m)$; b.p. = T_b + $K_b(m)$; T in °C

	m	T_f	-$K_f(m)$	f.p.	T_b	+$K_b(m)$	b.p.
(a)	0.35	-114.6	-1.99(0.35) = -0.70	-115.3	78.4	1.22(0.35) = 0.43	78.8
(b)	0.932	-63.5	-4.68(0.932) = -4.36	-67.9	61.2	3.63(0.932) = 3.38	64.6
(c)	0.487	0.0	-1.86(0.487) = -0.906	-0.91	100.0	0.52(0.487) = 0.25	100.3

13.51   0.030 m phenol < 0.040 m glycerin = 0.020 m KBr. Phenol is very slightly ionized in water, but not enough to match the number of particles in a 0.040 m glycerin solution. The KBr solution is 0.040 m in particles, so it has the same boiling point as 0.040 glycerin, which is a nonelectrolyte.

13.53 $\pi = MRT$; T = 25°C + 273 = 298 K

$M = \dfrac{\text{mol C}_9\text{H}_8\text{O}_4}{\text{L soln}} = \dfrac{50.0 \text{ mg C}_9\text{H}_8\text{O}_4}{0.250 \text{ L}}$ × $\dfrac{1 \text{ g}}{1000 \text{ mg}}$ × $\dfrac{1 \text{ mol C}_9\text{H}_8\text{O}_4}{180.2 \text{ g C}_9\text{H}_8\text{O}_4}$ = 1.1099×10^{-3}

= 1.11×10^{-3} M

$\pi = \dfrac{1.1099 \times 10^{-3} \text{ mol}}{\text{L}}$ × $\dfrac{0.08206 \text{ L} \cdot \text{atm}}{\text{K} \cdot \text{mol}}$ × 298 K = 0.02714 = 0.0271 atm

13.55 ΔT_f = 5.5 - 4.1 = 1.4; $m = \dfrac{\Delta T_f}{K_f} = \dfrac{1.4}{5.12}$ = 0.273 = 0.27 m

$\mathcal{M}$ lauryl alcohol = $\dfrac{\text{g lauryl alcohol}}{m \times \text{kg C}_6\text{H}_6} = \dfrac{5.00 \text{ g lauryl alcohol}}{0.273 \times 0.100 \text{ kg C}_6\text{H}_6}$

= 1.8×10^2 g/mol lauryl alcohol

13.57 $\pi = MRT$; $M = \dfrac{\pi}{RT}$;   T = 25°C + 273 = 298 K

M = 0.953 torr × $\dfrac{1 \text{ atm}}{760 \text{ torr}}$ × $\dfrac{\text{K} \cdot \text{mol}}{0.08206 \text{ L} \cdot \text{atm}}$ × $\dfrac{1}{298 \text{ K}}$ = 5.128×10^{-5} = 5.13×10^{-5} M

mol = M × L = 5.128×10^{-5} × 0.210 L = 1.077×10^{-5} = 1.08×10^{-5} mol lysozyme

$\mathcal{M} = \dfrac{\text{g}}{\text{mol}} = \dfrac{0.150 \text{ g}}{1.077 \times 10^{-5} \text{ mol}}$ = 1.39×10^4 g/mol lysozyme

13.59   (a) $i = \pi$ (measured) $/\pi$ (calculated for a nonelectrolyte)

π (calculated) $= MRT = 0.010\ \dfrac{mol}{L} \times \dfrac{0.08206\ L\bullet atm}{mol\bullet K} \times 298\ K = 0.2445 = 0.24$ atm

$i = 0.674$ atm$/0.2445$ atm $= 2.756 = 2.76$

(b)   The van't Hoff factor is the effective number of particles per mole of solute. The closer the measured i value is to a theoretical integer value, the more ideal the solution. Ion-pairing and other interparticle attractive forces reduce the effective number of particles in solution and reduce the measured value of i. The more concentrated the solution, the greater the ion-pairing and the smaller the measured value of i.

Colloids

13.61   The outline of a light beam passing through a colloid is visible, whereas light passing through a true solution is invisible unless collected on a screen. This is the Tyndall effect. To determine whether Faraday's (or anyone's) apparently homogeneous dispersion is a true solution or a colloid, shine a beam of light on it and see if the light is scattered.

13.63   (a) hydrophobic   (b) hydrophilic   (c) hydrophobic

13.65   Colloid particles are stabilized by attractive intermolecular forces with the dispersing medium (solvent) and do not coalesce because of electrostatic repulsions between groups at the surface of the dispersed particles. Colloids can be coagulated by heating (more collisions, greater chance that particles will coalesce); hydrophilic colloids can be coagulated by adding electrolytes, which neutralize surface charges allowing the colloid particles to collide more freely.

Additional Exercises

13.67   The outer periphery of the BHT molecule is mostly hydrocarbon-like groups, such as $-CH_3$. The one $-OH$ group is rather buried inside, and probably does little to enhance solubility in water. Thus, BHT is more likely to be soluble in the nonpolar hydrocarbon hexane, C_6H_{14}, than in polar water.

13.70 $P_{Rn} = \chi_{Rn}P_{total}$; $P_{Rn} = 3.5 \times 10^{-6} (36\ atm) = 1.26 \times 10^{-4} = 1.3 \times 10^{-4}$ atm

$C_{Rn} = k P_{Rn}$; $C_{Rn} = \dfrac{7.27 \times 10^{-3}\ M}{1\ atm} \times 1.26 \times 10^{-4}\ atm = 9.2 \times 10^{-7}\ M$

13.73   (a) $\dfrac{1.80\ mol\ LiBr}{1\ L\ soln} \times \dfrac{86.85\ g\ LiBr}{1\ mol\ LiBr} = 156.3 = 156$ g LiBr

1 L soln $= 826$ g soln; g $CH_3CN = 826 - 156.3 = 669.7 = 670$ g CH_3CN

m LiBr $= \dfrac{1.80\ mol\ LiBr}{0.6697\ kg\ CH_3CN} = 2.69\ m$

(b) $\dfrac{669.7\ g\ CH_3CN}{41.05\ g/mol} = 16.31 = 16.3$ mol CH_3CN; $\chi_{LiBr} = \dfrac{1.80}{1.80 + 16.31} = 0.0994$

(c) $\text{mass \%} = \dfrac{669.7 \text{ g } CH_3CN}{826 \text{ g soln}} \times 100 = 81.1\% \; CH_3CN$

13.75   (a) $m = \dfrac{\text{mol Na(s)}}{\text{kg Hg(l)}}; \; 1.0 \text{ cm}^3 \text{ Na(s)} \times \dfrac{0.97 \text{ g}}{1 \text{ cm}^3} \times \dfrac{1 \text{ mol}}{23.0 \text{ g Na}} = 0.0422 = 0.042 \text{ mol Na}$

$20.0 \text{ cm}^3 \text{ Hg(l)} \times \dfrac{13.6 \text{ g}}{1 \text{ cm}^3} \times \dfrac{1 \text{ kg}}{1000 \text{ g}} = 0.272 \text{ kg Hg(l)};$

$m = \dfrac{0.0422 \text{ mol Na}}{0.272 \text{ kg Hg(l)}} = 0.155 = 0.16 \; m \text{ Na}$

(b) $M = \dfrac{\text{mol Na(s)}}{\text{L soln}} = \dfrac{0.0422 \text{ mol Na}}{0.021 \text{ L soln}} = 2.01 = 2.0 \; M \text{ Na}$

(c)   Clearly, molality and molarity are not the same for this amalgam. Only in the instance that one kg solvent and the mass of one liter solution are nearly equal do the two concentration units have similar values. In this example, one kg Hg has a volume much less than one liter.

13.78   (a) $0.100 \; m \; K_2SO_4$ is $0.300 \; m$ in particles. H_2O is the solvent.

$\Delta T_f = K_f m = -1.86(0.300) = -0.558; \; T_f = 0.0 - 0.558 = -0.558°C = -0.6°C$

(b) $\Delta T_f \text{ (nonelectrolyte)} = -1.86(0.100) = -0.186; \; T_f = 0.0 - 0.186 = -0.186°C = -0.2°C$

$T_f \text{ (measured)} = i \times T_f \text{ (nonelectrolyte)}$

From Table 13.5, i for $0.100 \; m \; K_2SO_4 = 2.32$

$T_f \text{ (measured)} = 2.32(-0.186°C) = -0.432°C = -0.4°C$

13.81   (a) $K_b = \dfrac{\Delta T_b}{m}; \; \Delta T_b = 47.46°C - 46.30°C = 1.16°C$

$m = \dfrac{\text{mol solute}}{\text{kg } CS_2} = \dfrac{0.250 \text{ mol}}{400.0 \text{ mL } CS_2} \times \dfrac{1 \text{ mL } CS_2}{1.261 \text{ g } CS_2} \times \dfrac{1000 \text{ g}}{1 \text{ kg}} = 0.4956 = 0.496 \; m$

$K_b = \dfrac{1.16°C}{0.4956 \; m} = 2.34°C/m$

(b) $m = \dfrac{\Delta T_b}{K_b} = \dfrac{(47.08 - 46.30)°C}{2.34°C/m} = 0.333 = 0.33 \; m$

$m = \dfrac{\text{mol unknown}}{\text{kg } CS_2}; \; m \times \text{kg } CS_2 = \dfrac{\text{g unknown}}{\mathcal{M} \text{ unknown}}; \; \mathcal{M} = \dfrac{\text{g unknown}}{m \times \text{kg } CS_2}$

$50.0 \text{ mL } CS_2 \times \dfrac{1.261 \text{ g } CS_2}{1 \text{ mL}} \times \dfrac{1 \text{ kg}}{1000 \text{ g}} = 0.06305 = 0.0631 \text{ kg } CS_2$

$\mathcal{M} = \dfrac{5.39 \text{ g unknown}}{0.333 \; m \times 0.06305 \text{ kg } CS_2} = 257 = 2.6 \times 10^2 \text{ g/mol}$

Integrative Exercises

13.84   Since these are very dilute solutions, assume that the density of the solution $\approx$ the density of $H_2O \approx 1.0$ g/mL at 25°C. Then, 100 g solution = 100 g H_2O = 0.100 kg H_2O.

(a) CF_4: $\dfrac{0.0015 \text{ g } CF_4}{0.100 \text{ kg } H_2O} \times \dfrac{1 \text{ mol } CF_4}{88.00 \text{ g } CF_4} = 1.7 \times 10^{-4}\ m$

   $CClF_3$: $\dfrac{0.009 \text{ g } CClF_3}{0.100 \text{ kg } H_2O} \times \dfrac{1 \text{ mol } CClF_3}{104.46 \text{ g } CClF_3} = 8.6 \times 10^{-4}\ m = 9 \times 10^{-4}\ m$

   CCl_2F_2: $\dfrac{0.028 \text{ g } CCl_2F_2}{0.100 \text{ kg } H_2O} \times \dfrac{1 \text{ mol } CCl_2F_2}{120.9 \text{ g } CCl_2F_2} = 2.3 \times 10^{-3}\ m$

   $CHClF_2$: $\dfrac{0.30 \text{ g } CHClF_2}{0.100 \text{ kg } H_2O} \times \dfrac{1 \text{ mol } CHClF_2}{86.47 \text{ g } CHClF_2} = 3.5 \times 10^{-2}\ m$

(b) $m = \dfrac{\text{mol solute}}{\text{kg solvent}}$; $M = \dfrac{\text{mol solute}}{\text{L solution}}$

   Molality and molarity are numerically similar when kilograms solvent and liters solution are nearly equal. This is true when solutions are dilute, so that the density of the solution is essentially the density of the solvent, and when the density of the solvent is nearly 1 g/mL. That is, for dilute aqueous solutions such as the ones in this problem, $M \approx m$.

(c)   Water is a polar solvent; the solubility of solutes increases as their polarity increases. All the fluorocarbons listed have tetrahedral molecular structures. CF_4, a symmetrical tetrahedron, is nonpolar and has the lowest solubility. As more different atoms are bound to the central carbon, the electron density distribution in the molecule becomes less symmetrical and the molecular polarity increases. The most polar fluorocarbon, $CHClF_2$, has the greatest solubility in H_2O. It may act as a weak hydrogen bond acceptor for water.

(d) $C_g = k P_g$. Assume $M = m$ for $CHClF_2$. $P_g = 1$ atm

   $k = \dfrac{C_g}{P_g} = \dfrac{M}{P_g}$; $k = \dfrac{3.5 \times 10^{-2}\ M}{1.0 \text{ atm}} = 3.5 \times 10^{-2}$ mol/L • atm

   This value is greater than the Henry's law constant for $N_2(g)$, because $N_2(g)$ is nonpolar and of lower molecular mass than $CHClF_2$. In fact, the Henry's law constant for nonpolar CF_4, 1.7×10^{-4} mol/L • atm is similar to the value for N_2, 6.8×10^{-4} mol L • atm.

13.87 (a)

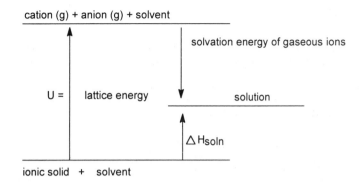

(b)   If the lattice energy (U) of the ionic solid (ion-ion forces) is too large relative to the solvation energy of the gaseous ions (ion-dipole forces), ΔH_{soln} will be too large and positive (endothermic) for solution to occur. This is the case for solutes like NaBr.

Lattice energy is inversely related to the distance between ions, so salts with large cations like $(CH_3)_4N^+$ have smaller lattice energies than salts with simple cations like Na^+. The smaller lattice energy of $(CH_4)_3NBr$ causes it to be more soluble in nonaqueous polar solvents. Also, the -CH_3 groups in the large cation are capable of dispersion interactions with the -CH_3 (or other nonpolar groups) of the solvent molecules. This produces a more negative solvation energy for the salts with large cations.

Overall, for salts with larger cations, U is smaller (less positive), the solvation energy of the gaseous ions is more negative, and ΔH_{soln} is less endothermic. These salts are more soluble in polar nonaqueous solvents.

13.90 Strategy: Assume 100 g sample. Calculate empirical formula from mass % data. Calculate molar mass from osmotic pressure. Deduce molecular formula.

$$61.00 \text{ g C} \times \frac{1 \text{ mol C}}{12.01 \text{ g C}} = 5.079 \text{ mol C}; \ 5.079/0.8467 = 6.0$$

$$6.83 \text{ g H} \times \frac{1 \text{ mol H}}{1.008 \text{ g H}} = 6.776 \text{ mol H}; \ 6.776/0.8467 = 8.0$$

$$11.86 \text{ g N} \times \frac{1 \text{ mol N}}{14.007 \text{ g N}} = 0.8467 \text{ mol N}; \ 0.8467/0.8467 = 1$$

$$20.32 \text{ g O} \times \frac{1 \text{ mol O}}{16.00 \text{ g O}} = 1.270 \text{ mol O}; \ 1.270/0.8467 = 1.5$$

Multiplying by 2 to obtain an integer ratio, the empirical formula is $C_{12}H_{16}N_2O_3$. The formula weight is 236.3 g.

$$\pi = M\text{RT}; \ M = \text{mol/L}; \ \text{mol} = g/\mathcal{M}; \ M = \frac{g}{\mathcal{M} \times L}; \ \pi = \frac{g}{\mathcal{M} \times L} \times \text{RT}; \ \mathcal{M} = \frac{g\,\text{RT}}{\pi \times L}$$

$$\mathcal{M} = \frac{2.505 \times 10^{-3} \text{ g}}{0.01000 \text{ L}} \times \frac{0.08206 \text{ L} \cdot \text{atm}}{\text{mol} \cdot \text{K}} \times \frac{298 \text{ K}}{19.7 \text{ torr}} \times \frac{760 \text{ torr}}{1 \text{ atm}} = 236 \text{ g/mol}$$

Since the formula weight and molar mass are equal, the empirical and molecular formula is $C_{12}H_{16}N_2O_3$.

14 Chemical Kinetics

Reaction Rates

14.1 (a) *Reaction rate* is the change in the amount of products or reactants in a given amount of time; it is the speed of a chemical reaction.

(b) Rates depend on concentration of reactants, surface area of reactants, temperature and presence of catalyst.

(c) The stoichiometry of the reaction (mole ratios of reactants and products) must be known to relate rate of disappearance of reactants to rate of appearance of products.

14.3

Time(min)	Mol A	(a) Mol B	Δ Mol A	(b) Rate (Δ mol A/s)
0	0.065	0.000		
10	0.051	0.014	-0.014	2.3×10^{-5}
20	0.042	0.023	-0.009	1.5×10^{-5}
30	0.036	0.029	-0.006	1.0×10^{-5}
40	0.031	0.034	-0.005	0.8×10^{-5}

(c) $\dfrac{\Delta M_B}{\Delta t} = \dfrac{(0.029 - 0.014)\ \text{mol}/0.100\ \text{L}}{(30 - 10)\ \text{min}} \times \dfrac{1\ \text{min}}{60\ \text{s}} = 1.25 \times 10^{-4} = 1.3 \times 10^{-4}\ M/\text{s}$

14.5

Time (sec)	Time Interval (sec)	Concentration (M)	ΔM	Rate (M/s)
0		0.0165		
2,000	2,000	0.0110	-0.0055	28×10^{-7}
5,000	3,000	0.00591	-0.0051	17×10^{-7}
8,000	3,000	0.00314	-0.00277	9.23×10^{-7}
12,000	4,000	0.00137	-0.00177	4.43×10^{-7}
15,000	3,000	0.00074	-0.00063	2.1×10^{-7}

14.7 From the slopes of the lines in the figure at right, the rates are $-1.6 \times 10^{-6}\ M/\text{s}$ at 4000 s, $-7.9 \times 10^{-7}\ M/\text{s}$ at 10,000 s.

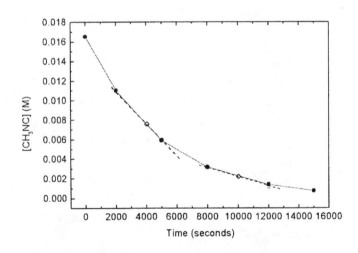

14.9   (a) $-\Delta[H_2O_2]/\Delta t = \Delta[H_2]/\Delta t = \Delta[O_2]/\Delta t$

      (b) $-\Delta[N_2O]/2\Delta t = \Delta[N_2]/2\Delta t = \Delta[O_2]/\Delta t$
              $-\Delta[N_2O]/\Delta t = \Delta[N_2]/\Delta t = 2\Delta[O_2]/\Delta t$

      (c) $-\Delta[N_2]/\Delta t = \Delta[NH_3]/2\Delta t;\ -\Delta[H_2]/3\Delta t = \Delta[NH_3]/2\Delta t$
              $-2\Delta[N_2]/\Delta t = \Delta[NH_3]/\Delta t;\quad -\Delta[H_2]/\Delta t = 3\Delta[NH_3]/2\Delta t$

14.11   (a) $\Delta[H_2O]/2\Delta t = -\Delta[H_2]/2\Delta t = -\Delta[O_2]/\Delta t$

              H_2 is burning, $-\Delta[H_2]/\Delta t = 4.6$ mol/s

              O_2 is consumed, $-\Delta[O_2]/\Delta t = -\Delta[H_2]/2\Delta t = 4.6$ mol/s/2 = 2.3 mol/s

              H_2O is produced, $+\Delta[H_2O]/\Delta t = -\Delta[H_2]/\Delta t = 4.6$ mol/s

      (b)   The change in total pressure is the sum of the changes of each partial pressure. NO and Cl_2 are disappearing and NOCl is appearing.

              $-\Delta P_{NO}/\Delta t = -30$ torr/min

              $-\Delta P_{Cl_2}/\Delta t = \Delta P_{NO}/2\Delta t = -15$ torr/min

              $+\Delta P_{NOCl}/\Delta t = -\Delta P_{NO}/\Delta t = +30$ torr/min

              $\Delta P_T/\Delta t = -30$ torr/min $- 15$ torr/min $+ 30$ torr/min $= -15$ torr/min

Rate Laws

14.13   (a)   If [A] changes, the rate will change, but the rate constant, k, will remain the same. The rate law is a general algebraic expression for the rate of a reaction (dependent variable) at any reactant concentration (independent variables); there are an infinite number of combinations of [A] and rate. The rate constant, k, is the proportionality constant that does not change (unless temperature changes).

      (b)   The reaction is first order in A, second order in B, and third order overall.

      (c)   Units of $k = \dfrac{M/s}{M^3} = M^{-2}s^{-1}$

14.15   (a)   rate $= k[H_2][NO]^2$

      (b)   rate $= (6.0 \times 10^4\ M^{-2}s^{-1})(0.050\ M)^2(0.010\ M) = 1.5\ M/s$

      (c)   rate $= (6.0 \times 10^4\ M^{-2}s^{-1})(0.10\ M)^2(0.010\ M) = 6.0\ M/s$

      (Note that doubling [NO] causes a quadrupling in rate.)

14.17   (a, b)   rate $= k[CH_3Br][OH^-];\ k = \dfrac{\text{rate}}{[CH_3Br][OH^-]}$

             at 298 K, $k = \dfrac{0.0432\ M/s}{(5.0 \times 10^{-3}\ M)(0.050\ M)} = 1.7 \times 10^2\ M^{-1}s^{-1}$

      (c)   Since the rate law is first order in [OH⁻], if [OH⁻] is tripled, the rate triples.

14.19   (a)   rate $= k[A][C]^2$

      (b)   new rate $= (1/2)(1/2)^2 = 1/8$ of old rate

14.21 (a) Doubling [NO] while holding $[O_2]$ constant increases the rate by a factor of 4 (experiments 1 and 3). Reducing $[O_2]$ by a factor of 2 while holding [NO] constant reduces the rate by a factor of 2 (experiments 2 and 3). The rate is second order in [NO] and first order in $[O_2]$. rate = $k[NO]^2[O_2]$

(b, c) From experiment 1: $k_1 = \dfrac{1.41 \times 10^{-2} \ M/s}{(0.0126 \ M)^2(0.0125 \ M)} = 7105 = 7.11 \times 10^3 \ M^{-2}s^{-1}$

$k_2 = 0.113/(0.0252)^2(0.0250) = 7118 = 7.12 \times 10^3 \ M^{-2}s^{-1}$

$k_3 = 5.64 \times 10^{-2}/(0.0252)^2(0.125) = 7105 = 7.11 \times 10^3 \ M^{-2}s^{-1}$

$k_{avg} = (7105 + 7118 + 7105)/3 = 7109 = 7.11 \times 10^3 \ M^{-2}s^{-1}$

14.23 (a) Increasing [NO] by a factor of 2.5 while holding $[Br_2]$ constant (experiments 1 and 2) increases the rate by a factor 6.25 or $(2.5)^2$. Increasing $[Br_2]$ by a factor of 2.5 while holding [NO] constant increases the rate by a factor of 2.5. The rate law for the appearance of NOBr is: rate = $\Delta[NOBr]/\Delta t = k[NO]^2[Br_2]$.

(b) From experiment 1: $k_1 = \dfrac{24 \ M/s}{(0.10 \ M)^2(0.20 \ M)} = 1.20 \times 10^4 = 1.2 \times 10^4 \ M^{-2}s^{-1}$

$k_2 = 150/(0.25)^2(0.20) = 1.20 \times 10^4 = 1.2 \times 10^4 \ M^{-2}s^{-1}$

$k_3 = 60/(0.10)^2(0.50) = 1.20 \times 10^4 = 1.2 \times 10^4 \ M^{-2}s^{-1}$

$k_4 = 735/(0.35)^2(0.50) = 1.2 \times 10^4 = 1.2 \times 10^4 \ M^{-2}s^{-1}$

$k_{avg} = (1.2 \times 10^4 + 1.2 \times 10^4 + 1.2 \times 10^4 + 1.2 \times 10^4)/4 = 1.2 \times 10^4 \ M^{-2}s^{-1}$

(c) $\Delta[NOBr]/2\Delta t = -\Delta[Br_2]/\Delta t$; the rate of disappearance of Br_2 is half the rate of appearance of NOBr.

(d) $\dfrac{-\Delta[Br_2]}{\Delta t} = \dfrac{k[NO]^2[Br_2]}{2} = \dfrac{1.2 \times 10^4}{2 \ M^2 s} \times (0.075 \ M)^2 \times (0.185 \ M) = 6.2 \ M/s$

Change of Concentration with Time

14.25 (a) A *first-order reaction* depends on the concentration, raised to the first power, of only one reactant; rate = $k[A]^1$.

(b) A graph of ln[A] vs time yields a straight line for a first-order reaction.

(c) The half-life of a first-order reaction **does not** depend on initial concentration; it is determined by the value of the rate constant, k.

14.27 For a first order reaction, $t_{1/2} = 0.693/k$, $k = 5.1 \times 10^{-4}s^{-1}$

$t_{1/2} = \dfrac{0.693}{5.1 \times 10^{-4} s^{-1}} = 1.4 \times 10^3 \ s$ or 23 min

14.29   (a)   Rearranging Equation [14.14] for a first order reaction:

$\ln[A]_t = -kt + \ln[A]_0$

2.5 min = 150 s; $[N_2O_5]_0$ = (0.0300 mol/2.50 L) = 0.0120 M

$\ln[N_2O_5]_{150} = -(6.82 \times 10^{-3}\,s^{-1})(150\,s) + \ln(0.0120)$

$\ln[N_2O_5]_{150} = -1.0230 + (-4.4228) = -5.4458 = -5.45$

$[N_2O_5]_{150} = 4.314 \times 10^{-3} = 4.3 \times 10^{-3}\,M$;   mol $N_2O_5 = 4.314 \times 10^{-3}\,M \times 2.50\,L$

$= 0.0108$ mol

(b) $[N_2O_5]_t$ = 0.0050 mol/2.50 L = 0.0020 M; $[N_2O_5]_0$ = 0.0120 M

$\ln(0.0020) = -(6.82 \times 10^{-3}\,s^{-1})\,(t) + \ln(0.0120)$

$t = \dfrac{-[\ln(0.0020) - \ln(0.0120)]}{(6.82 \times 10^{-3}\,s^{-1})} = 262.7 = 263\,s \times \dfrac{1\,\text{min}}{60\,s} = 4.38$ min

(c) $t_{1/2} = 0.693/k = 0.693/6.82 \times 10^{-3}\,s^{-1} = 101.6 = 102\,s$ or 1.69 min

14.31

t(s)	$P_{SO_2Cl_2}$	$\ln P_{SO_2Cl_2}$
0	1.000	0
2500	0.947	-0.0545
5000	0.895	-0.111
7500	0.848	-0.165
10000	0.803	-0.219

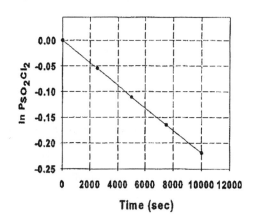

Graph $\ln P_{SO_2Cl_2}$ vs. time.   (Pressure is a satisfactory unit for a gas, since the concentration in moles /liter is proportional to P.) The graph is linear with slope $-2.19 \times 10^{-5}\,s^{-1}$ as shown on the figure.   The rate constant k = -slope = $2.19 \times 10^{-5}\,s^{-1}$.

14.33   (a)   Make both first- and second-order plots to see which is linear.

time(min)	mol A	[A] (M)	ln[A]	1/mol A
0	0.065	0.65	-0.43	1.5
10	0.051	0.51	-0.67	2.0
20	0.042	0.42	-0.87	2.4
30	0.036	0.36	-1.02	2.8
40	0.031	0.31	-1.17	3.2

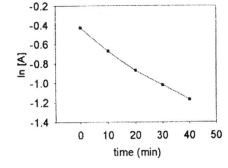
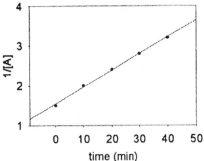

The plot of 1/[A] vs time is linear, so the reaction is second-order in [A].

(b)   k = slope = (3.2 - 2.0) M^{-1} / 30 min = 0.040 M^{-1} min^{-1}

(The best fit to the line yields slope = 0.042 $M^{-1}min^{-1}$.)

(c) $t_{1/2}$ = 1/k[A]$_o$ = 1/(0.040 M^{-1} min^{-1})(0.65 M) = 38.46 = 38 min

(Using the "best-fit" slope, $t_{1/2}$ = 37 min.)

14.35   (a)   Make both first and second order plots to see which is linear.

time(s)	[NO$_2$](M)	ln[NO$_2$]	1/[NO$_2$]
0.0	0.100	-2.303	10.0
5.0	0.017	-4.08	59
10.0	0.0090	-4.71	110
15.0	0.0062	-5.08	160
20.0	0.0047	-5.36	210

The plot of 1/[NO$_2$] vs time is linear, so the reaction is second order in NO$_2$.

(b)   The slope of the line is (210 - 59) M^{-1} / 15.0 s = 10.07 = 10 $M^{-1}s^{-1}$ = k.
(The slope of the best-fit line is 10.02 = 10 $M^{-1}s^{-1}$.)

Temperature and Rate

14.37   (a)   The central idea of the *collision model* is that molecules must collide to react.

(b)   The energy of the collision and the orientation of the molecules when they collide determine whether a reaction will occur.

(c)   According to the Kinetic Molecular Theory (Chapter 10), the higher the temperature, the greater the speed and kinetic energy of the molecules. Therefore, at a higher temperature, there are more total collisions and each collision is more energetic.

14.39 $f = e^{-E_a/RT}$ E_a = 12.5 kJ/mol = 1.25 × 10^4 J/mol; T = 400 K (127°C)

$-E_a/RT = - \dfrac{1.25 \times 10^4 \text{ J/mol}}{400 \text{ K}} \times \dfrac{\text{mol} \cdot \text{K}}{8.314 \text{ J}}$ = -3.7587 = -3.76

$f = e^{-3.7587}$ = 2.33 × 10^{-2}

At 400 K, approximately 1 out of 43 molecules has this kinetic energy.

14.41 (a)

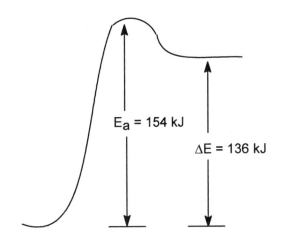

$E_a = 154$ kJ

$\Delta E = 136$ kJ

(b) E_a(reverse) = 18 kJ/mol

14.43 Assuming all collision factors (A) to be the same, reaction rate depends only on E_a; it is independent of ΔE. Based on the magnitude of E_a, reaction (c) is fastest and reaction (b) is slowest.

14.45 No. The value of A, which is related to frequency and effectiveness of collisions, can be different for each reaction and k is proportional to A.

14.47 $T_1 = 20°C + 273 = 293$ K; $T_2 = 60°C + 273 = 333$ K; $k_1 = 1.75 \times 10^{-1}s^{-1}$

(a) $\ln\left(\dfrac{k_1}{k_2}\right) = \dfrac{E_a}{R}\left(\dfrac{1}{333} - \dfrac{1}{293}\right) = \dfrac{55.5 \times 10^3 \text{ J/mol}}{8.314 \text{ J/mol}}(-4.100 \times 10^{-4})$

$\ln(k_1/k_2) = -2.7367 = -2.74$; $k_1/k_2 = 0.0648 = 0.065$; $k_2 = \dfrac{0.175 \text{ s}^{-1}}{0.0648} = 2.7 \text{ s}^{-1}$

(b) $\ln\left(\dfrac{k_1}{k_2}\right) = \dfrac{121 \times 10^3 \text{ J/mol}}{8.314 \text{ J/mol}}\left(\dfrac{1}{333} - \dfrac{1}{293}\right) = -5.9666 = -5.97$

$k_1/k_2 = 2.563 \times 10^{-3} = 2.6 \times 10^{-3}$; $k_2 = \dfrac{0.175 \text{ s}^{-1}}{2.563 \times 10^{-3}} = 68 \text{ s}^{-1}$

14.49

k	ln k	T(K)	1/T(× 10^3)
0.0521	-2.955	288	3.47
0.101	-2.293	298	3.36
0.184	-1.693	308	3.25
0.332	-1.103	318	3.14

The slope, -5.71× 10^3, equals -E_a/R. Thus, $E_a = 5.71 \times 10^3 \times 8.314$ J/mol = 47.5 kJ/mol.

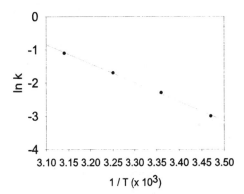

14.51 $T_1 = 50°C + 273 = 323\ K;\ T_2 = 0°C + 273 = 273\ K$

$$\ln\left(\frac{k_1}{k_2}\right) = \frac{E_a}{R}\left[\frac{1}{T_2} - \frac{1}{T_1}\right] = \frac{76.7\ kJ/mol}{8.314\ J/mol} \times \frac{1000\ J}{1\ kJ}\left[\frac{1}{273} - \frac{1}{323}\right]$$

$\ln(k_1/k_2) = 9.225 \times 10^3\ (5.670 \times 10^{-4}) = 5.231 = 5.23;\ k_1/k_2 = 187 = 1.9 \times 10^2$

The reaction will occur 190 times faster at 50°C, assuming equal initial concentrations.

Reaction Mechanisms

14.53 (a)   An *elementary step* is a process that occurs in a single event; the order is given by the coefficients in the balanced equation for the step.

(b)   A *unimolecular* elementary step involves only one reactant molecule; the activated complex is derived from a single molecule. A *bimolecular* elementary step involves two reactant molecules in the activated complex and the overall process.

(c)   A *reaction mechanism* is a series of elementary steps that describe how an overall reaction occurs and explain the experimentally determined rate law.

14.55 (a)   bimolecular, rate = $k[N_2O][Cl]$
(b)   unimolecular, rate = $k[Cl_2]$
(c)   bimolecular, rate = $k[NO][Cl_2]$

14.57 (a)
$$NO(g) + NO(g) \rightarrow N_2O_2(g)$$
$$N_2O_2(g) + H_2(g) \rightarrow N_2O(g) + H_2O(g)$$
$$\overline{2NO(g) + N_2O_2(g) + H_2(g) \rightarrow N_2O_2(g) + N_2O(g) + H_2O(g)}$$
$$2NO(g) + H_2(g) \rightarrow N_2O(g) + H_2O(g)$$

(b)   First step: $-\Delta[NO]/\Delta t = k[NO][NO] = k[NO]^2$

Second step: $-\Delta[H_2]/\Delta t = k[H_2][N_2O_2]$

(c) N_2O_2 is the intermediate; it is produced in the first step and consumed in the second.

(d)   Since $[H_2]$ appears in the rate law, the second step must be slow relative to the first.

14.59 (a)   rate = $k[NO][Cl_2]$

(b)   Since the observed rate law is second-order in [NO], the second step must be slow relative to the first step; the second step is rate determining.

Catalysis

14.61 (a)   A catalyst increases the rate of reaction by decreasing the activation energy, E_a, or increasing the frequency factor A. Lowering the activation energy is more common and more dramatic.

(b)   A *homogeneous catalyst* is in the same phase as the reactants; a *heterogeneous catalyst* is in a different phase and is usually a solid.

14.63   (a) $2[NO_2(g) + SO_2(g) \rightarrow NO(g) + SO_3(g)]$

              $2NO(g) + O_2(g) \rightarrow 2NO_2(g)$

              —————————————————————

              $2SO_2(g) + O_2(g) \rightarrow 2SO_3(g)$

  (b) $NO_2(g)$ is a catalyst because it is consumed and then reproduced in the reaction sequence. ($NO(g)$ is an intermediate because it is produced and then consumed.)

  (c)   Since NO_2 is in the same state as the other reactants, this is homogeneous catalysis.

14.65   Use of chemically stable supports such as alumina and silica makes it possible to obtain very large surface areas per unit mass of the precious metal catalyst. This is so because the metal can be deposited in a very thin, even monomolecular, layer on the surface of the support.

14.67   As illustrated in Figure 14.22, the two C-H bonds that exist on each carbon of the ethylene molecule before adsorption are retained in the process in which a D atom is added to each C (assuming we use D_2 rather than H_2). To put two deuteriums on a single carbon, it is necessary that one of the already existing C-H bonds in ethylene be broken while the molecule is adsorbed, so the H atom moves off as an adsorbed atom, and is replaced by a D. This requires a larger activation energy than simply adsorbing C_2H_4 and adding one D atom to each carbon.

14.69   (a)   Living organisms operate efficiently in a very narrow temperature range; heating to increase reaction rate is not an option. Therefore, the role of enzymes as homogeneous catalysts that speed up desirable reactions without heating and undesirable side-effects is crucial for biological systems.

  (b)   *catalase*: $2H_2O_2 \rightarrow 2H_2O + O_2$; *nitrogenase*: $N_2 \rightarrow 2NH_3$ (nitrogen fixation)

14.71   Let k = the rate constant for the uncatalyzed reaction,

     k_c = the rate constant for the catalyzed reaction

According to Equation 14.23, $\ln k = -E_a/RT + \ln A$

Subtracting $\ln k$ from $\ln k_c$,

$$\ln k_c - \ln k = -\left[\frac{55 \text{ kJ/mol}}{RT} + \ln A\right] - \left[-\frac{85 \text{ kJ/mol}}{RT} + \ln A\right]$$

  (a)   RT = 8.314 J/K•mol × 298 K × 1 kJ/1000 J = 2.478 kJ/mol; ln A is the same for both reactions.

$$\ln (k_c/k) = \frac{85 \text{ kJ/mol} - 55 \text{ kJ/mol}}{2.478 \text{ kJ/mol}}; \quad k_c/k = 1.8 \times 10^5$$

The catalyzed reaction is approximately 180,000 times faster at 25°C.

  (b)   RT = 8.314 J/K•mol × 398 K × 1 kJ/1000 J = 3.309 kJ/mol

$$\ln (k_c/k) = \frac{30 \text{ kJ/mol}}{3.309 \text{ kJ/mol}}; \quad k_c/k = 8.7 \times 10^3$$

The catalyzed reaction is 8700 times faster at 125°C.

Additional Exercises

14.73   rate = $\dfrac{-\Delta[H_2S]}{\Delta t} = \dfrac{\Delta[Cl^-]}{2\Delta t} = k[H_2S][Cl_2]$

$\dfrac{-\Delta[H_2S]}{\Delta t} = (3.5 \times 10^{-2} \ M^{-1}s^{-1})(1.6 \times 10^{-4} \ M)(0.070 \ M) = 3.92 \times 10^{-7} = 3.9 \times 10^{-7} \ M/s$

$\dfrac{\Delta[Cl^-]}{\Delta t} = \dfrac{2\Delta[H_2S]}{\Delta t} = 2(3.92 \times 10^{-7} \ M/s) = 7.8 \times 10^{-7} \ M/s$

14.75   (a) $k = (8.56 \times 10^{-5} \ M/s)/(0.200 \ M) = 4.28 \times 10^{-4} \ s^{-1}$

(b) $\ln[urea] = -(4.28 \times 10^{-4}s^{-1} \times 5.00 \times 10^3 \ s) + \ln(0.500)$

$\ln[urea] = -2.14 - 0.693 = -2.833 = -2.83; \ [urea] = 0.0588 = 0.059 \ M$

(c) $t_{1/2} = 0.693/k = 0.693/4.28 \times 10^{-4} \ s^{-1} = 1.62 \times 10^3 \ s$

14.78

ln k	1/T
-24.17	3.33×10^{-3}
-20.72	3.13×10^{-3}
-17.32	2.94×10^{-3}
-15.24	2.82×10^{-3}

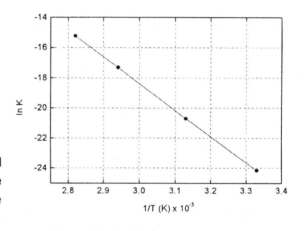

The calculated slope is -1.751×10^4. The activation energy E_a, equals - (slope) × (8.314 J/mol). Thus, $E_a = 1.8 \times 10^4 (8.314) = 1.5 \times 10^5$ J/mol $= 1.5 \times 10^2$ kJ/mol. (The best-fit slope is $-1.76 \times 10^4 = -1.8 \times 10^4$ and the value of E_a is 1.5×10^2 kJ/mol.)

14.83   Enzyme: carbonic anhydrase; substrate: carbonic acid (H_2CO_3); turnover number: 1×10^7 molecules/s.

14.85   (a)   The fact that the rate doubles with a doubling of the concentration of sugar tells us that the fraction of enzyme tied up in the form of an enzyme-substrate complex is small. A doubling of the substrate concentration leads to a doubling of the concentration of enzyme-substrate complex, because most of the enzyme molecules are available to bind substrates.

(b)   The behavior of inositol suggests that it acts as a competitor with sucrose for binding at the active sites of the enzyme system. Such a competition results in a lower effective concentration of active sites for binding of sucrose, and thus results in a lower reaction rate.

Integrative Exercises

14.88   In the lock and key model of enzyme action, the active site is the specific location in the enzyme where reaction takes place. The precise geometry (size and shape) of the active site both accommodates and activates the substrate (reactant). Proteins are large biopolymers, with the same structural flexibility as synthetic polymers (Chapter 12). The three-dimensional shape of the protein in solution, including the geometry of the active site, is determined by many intermolecular forces of varying strengths.

    Changes in temperature change the kinetic energy of the various groups on the enzyme and their tendency to form intermolecular associations or break free from them. Thus, changing the temperature changes the overall shape of the protein and specifically the shape of the active site. At the operating temperature of the enzyme, the competition between kinetic energy driving groups apart and intermolecular attraction pulling them together forms an active site that is optimum for a specific substrate. At temperatures above the temperature of maximum activity, sufficient kinetic energy has been imparted so that the forces driving groups apart win the competition, and the three-dimensional structure of the enzyme is destroyed. This is the process of *denaturation*. The activity of the enzyme is destroyed because the active site has collapsed. The protein or enzyme is denatured, because it is no longer capable of its "natural" activity.

15 Chemical Equilibrium

The Concept of Equilibrium; Equilibrium-Constant Expressions

15.1   Yes. The first box is pure reactant A. As the reaction proceeds, some A changes to B. In the fourth and fifth boxes, the relative amounts (concentrations) of A and B are constant. Although the reaction is ongoing the rates of A → B and B → A are equal, and the relative amounts of A and B are constant.

15.3   (a) $K = \dfrac{k_f}{k_r}$, Equation [15.3]; $K = \dfrac{3.8 \times 10^2 \text{ s}^{-1}}{8.6 \times 10^{-1} \text{ s}^{-1}} = 4.4 \times 10^2$

         (b) $rate_f = rate_r$; $k_f[A] = k_r[B]$

                 Since $k_f > k_r$, in order for the two rates to be equal, [B] must be greater than [A].

15.5   (a)   The *law of mass action* expresses the relationship between the concentrations of reactants and products at equilibrium for any reaction. The law of mass action is a generic equilibrium expression.

                 $$K_c = \dfrac{[H_2O_2]}{[H_2][O_2]}$$

         (b)   The *equilibrium expression* is an algebraic equation where the variables are the equilibrium concentrations of the reactants and products for a specific chemical reaction. The *equilibrium constant* is a number; it is the ratio calculated from the equilibrium expression for a particular chemical reaction. For any reaction, there are an infinite number of sets of equilibrium concentrations, depending on initial concentrations, but there is only one equilibrium constant.

         (c)   Introduce a known quantity of $H_2O_2(g)$ into a vessel of known volume at constant (known) temperature. After equilibrium has been established, measure the total pressure in the flask. Using an equilibrium table, such as the one in Sample Exercise 15.8, calculate equilibrium pressures and concentrations of $H_2(g)$, $O_2(g)$ and $H_2O_2(g)$ and calculate K_c.

15.7   (a) $K_c = \dfrac{[N_2O][NO_2]}{[NO]^3}$; $K_p = \dfrac{P_{N_2O} \times P_{NO_2}}{P_{NO}^3}$ (b) $K_c = \dfrac{[CS_2][H_2]^4}{[CH_4][H_2S]^2}$; $K_p = \dfrac{P_{CS_2} \times P_{H_2}^4}{P_{CH_4} \times P_{H_2S}^2}$

         (c) $K_c = \dfrac{[CO]^4}{[Ni(CO)_4]}$; $K_p = \dfrac{P_{CO}^4}{P_{Ni(CO)_4}}$ (d) $K_c = \dfrac{[H_2O]^3}{[H_2]^3}$; $K_p = \dfrac{P_{H_2O}^3}{P_{H_2}^3}$

(e) $K_c = \dfrac{[NO_2]^4[O_2]}{[N_2O_5]^2}$; $K_p = \dfrac{P_{NO_2}^4 \times P_{O_2}}{P_{N_2O_5}^2}$

homogeneous: (a), (b), (e); heterogeneous: (c), (d)

15.9   (a)   mostly reactants ($K_c \ll 1$)

     (b)   mostly products ($K_c \gg 1$)

15.11 $K_p = K_c(RT)^{\Delta n}$ (Equation 15.11)

$\Delta n = (1\ mol\ PCl_5 - (1\ mol\ PCl_3 - 1\ mol\ Cl_2)) = -1$
$K_p = 0.042\,(0.08206 \times 500)^{-1} = 1.024 \times 10^{-3} = 1.0 \times 10^{-3}$

15.13   (a) $2SO_2(g) + O_2(g) \rightleftharpoons 2SO_3(g)$ is the reverse of the reaction given.
             $K_c' = (K_c)^{-1} = 1/2.4 \times 10^{-3} = 4.2 \times 10^2$

     (b)   Since $K_c < 1$ (when SO_3 is the reactant) and $K_c > 1$ (when SO_3 is the product), the equilibrium favors SO_3 at this temperature.

15.15   (a) $K_c' = 1/K_c = 1/20.4 = 0.049077$

     (b) $K_c' = K_c^2 = (20.4)^2 = 416.16 = 416$

     (c) $K_p = K_c(RT)^{\Delta n}$; $\Delta n = -1$; $T = 700 + 273 = 973$

             $K_p = 416.16/(0.08206)(973) = 5.21$

15.17   (a) $K_c = \dfrac{[Hg]^4[O_2]}{[Hg_2O]^2}$

     (b)   The molar concentration, the ratio of moles of a substance to volume occupied by the substance, is a constant for pure solids and liquids.

     (c)   constant 1 $= [Hg]^4$;   constant 2 $= [Hg_2O]^2$

             $K_c = \dfrac{\text{constant 1}\,[O_2]}{\text{constant 2}}$; $K_c' = K_c\,\dfrac{\text{constant 2}}{\text{constant 1}} = [O_2]$

Calculating Equilibrium Constants

15.19 $K_c = \dfrac{[H_2][I_2]}{[HI]^2} = \dfrac{(4.79 \times 10^{-4})(4.79 \times 10^{-4})}{(3.53 \times 10^{-3})^2} = 1.84 \times 10^{-2}$

15.21 $2NO(g) + Cl_2(g) \rightleftharpoons 2NOCl(g)$

     $K_p = \dfrac{P_{NOCl}^2}{P_{NO}^2 \times P_{Cl_2}} = \dfrac{(0.28)^2}{(0.095)^2(0.171)} = 50.80 = 51$

15.23 (a) Since the reaction is carried out in a 1.00 L vessel, the moles of each component are equal to the molarity.

	2NO	+	2H_2	⇌	N_2	+	2H_2O
initial	0.100 *M*		0.050 *M*		0 *M*		0.100 *M*
change	-0.038 *M*		-0.038 *M*		+0.019 *M*		+0.038 *M*
equil.	0.062 *M*		0.012 *M*		0.019 *M*		0.138 *M*

First calculate the change in [NO], 0.100 - 0.062 = 0.038 *M*. From the stoichiometry of the reaction, calculate the change in the other concentrations. Finally, calculate the equilibrium concentrations.

(b) $K_c = \dfrac{[N_2][H_2O]^2}{[NO]^2[H_2]^2} = \dfrac{(0.019)(0.138)^2}{(0.062)^2(0.012)^2} = 6.5 \times 10^2$

15.25 (a) M = mol/L; M = mol/2.00 L. [CO_2] = 0.2000 mol/2.000 L = 0.1000 *M*; [H_2] = 0.05000 *M*; [H_2O] = 0.0800 *M*.

	CO_2	+	H_2	⇌	CO	+	H_2O
initial	0.1000 *M*		0.05000 *M*		0 *M*		0.08000 *M*
change	-0.0056 *M*		-0.0056 *M*		+0.0056 *M*		+0.0056 *M*
equil	0.0944 *M*		0.04440 *M*		0.0056 *M*		0.0856 *M*

First calculate the change in [H_2O], 0.0856 - 0.0800 = 0.0056 *M*.
From the stoichiometry of the reaction, calculate the change in the other concentrations. Finally, calculate the equilibrium concentrations.

(b) $K_c = \dfrac{[CO][H_2O]}{[CO_2][H_2]} = \dfrac{(0.0056)(0.0856)}{(0.0944)(0.0444)} = 0.1144 = 0.11$

(c)   Yes. Since Δn = 0, $K_p = K_c = 0.11$.

Applications of Equilibrium Constants

15.27 (a) A *reaction quotient* is the result of the law of mass action for a general set of concentrations, whereas the equilibrium constant requires equilibrium concentrations.

(b)   In the direction of more products, to the right.

(c)   If Q = K, the system is at equilibrium; the concentrations used to calculate Q must be equilibrium concentrations.

15.29 $K_c = \dfrac{[CO][Cl_2]}{[COCl_2]} = 2.19 \times 10^{-10}$ at 100°C

(a) $Q = \dfrac{(3.31 \times 10^{-6})(6.62 \times 10^{-6})}{(2.00 \times 10^{-3})} = 1.10 \times 10^{-8}$; Q > K_c

The reaction will proceed to the left to attain equilibrium.

(b) $Q = \dfrac{(1.10 \times 10^{-7})(2.25 \times 10^{-6})}{(4.50 \times 10^{-2})} = 5.50 \times 10^{-12}$; $Q < K_c$

The reaction will proceed to the right to attain equilibrium.

(c) $Q = \dfrac{(1.48 \times 10^{-6})(1.48 \times 10^{-6})}{(0.0100)} = 2.19 \times 10^{-10}$, $Q = K_c$

The mixture is at equilibrium.

15.31 $K_c = \dfrac{[SO_2][Cl_2]}{[SO_2Cl_2]}$; $[Cl_2] = \dfrac{K_c[SO_2Cl_2]}{[SO_2]} = \dfrac{(0.078)(0.108)}{(0.052)} = 0.16\ M$

15.33   (a) $K_c = 1.04 \times 10^{-3} = \dfrac{[Br]^2}{[Br_2]}$; $[Br_2] = \dfrac{0.245\ g\ Br_2}{159.8\ g\ Br_2/mol \times 0.200\ L} = 7.666 \times 10^{-3}$

$= 7.67 \times 10^{-3}\ M$

$[Br] = (1.04 \times 10^{-3}\ [Br_2])^{1/2} = (1.04 \times 10^{-3}\ (7.666 \times 10^{-3}))^{1/2} = 2.824 \times 10^{-3}$

$= 2.82 \times 10^{-3}\ M$

$g\ Br = \dfrac{2.824 \times 10^{-3}\ mol\ Br}{1\ L} \times \dfrac{79.90\ g\ Br}{1\ mol\ Br} \times 0.200\ L = 0.04513 = 0.0451\ g\ Br$

$[Br_2] = 7.67 \times 10^{-3}\ M$; $[Br] = 2.82 \times 10^{-3}\ M$; $0.0451\ g\ Br$

(b) $PV = nRT$; $P = gRT/(\mathcal{M} \times V)$

$P_{H_2} = \dfrac{0.056\ g\ H_2}{2.016\ g/mol} \times \dfrac{0.08206\ L \cdot atm}{K \cdot mol} \times \dfrac{700\ K}{2.000\ L} = 0.7978 = 0.80\ atm$

$P_{I_2} = \dfrac{4.36\ g\ I_2}{253.8\ g/mol} \times \dfrac{0.08206\ L \cdot atm}{K \cdot mol} \times \dfrac{700\ K}{2.000\ L} = 0.4934 = 0.494\ atm$

$K_p = 55.3 = $; $\dfrac{P_{HI}^2}{P_{H_2} \times_{I_2}}$ $P_{HI} = [55.3\ (P_{H_2})(P_{I_2})]^{1/2} = [55.3(0.7978)(0.4934)]^{1/2}$

$= 4.666 = 4.7\ atm$

$g_{HI} = \dfrac{\mathcal{M}_{HI}P_{HI}V}{RT} = \dfrac{128.0\ g\ HI}{mol\ HI} \times \dfrac{K \cdot mol}{0.08206\ L \cdot atm} \times \dfrac{4.666\ atm \times 2.000\ L}{700\ K}$

$= 20.79 = 21\ g\ HI$

15.35 $2NO(g) \rightleftharpoons N_2(g) + O_2(g)$ $K_c = \dfrac{[N_2][O_2]}{[NO]^2} = 2.4 \times 10^3$

initial	0.200 *M*	0	0
change	-2x	+x	+x
equil.	0.200-2x	+x	+x

$2.4 \times 10^3 = \dfrac{x^2}{(0.200-2x)^2}$; $(2.4 \times 10^3)^{1/2} = \dfrac{x}{0.200 - 2x}$

$x = (2.4 \times 10^3)^{1/2}\ (0.200 - 2x)$; $x = 9.798 - 97.98x$; $98.98x = 9.798$, $x = 0.09899 = 0.099$

$[N_2] = [O_2] = 0.099\ M$; $[NO] = 0.200 - 2(0.09899) = 0.00202 = 0.002\ M$

15.37 $K_p = \dfrac{P_{NO}^2 P_{Br_2}}{P_{NOBr}^2}$

When $P_{NOBr} = P_{NO}$, these terms cancel and $P_{Br_2} = K_p = 0.416$ atm. This is true for all cases where $P_{NOBr} = P_{NO}$.

15.39   (a)   Starting with only $PH_3BCl_3(s)$, the equation requires that the equilibrium concentrations of $PH_3(g)$ and $BCl_3(g)$ are equal.

           $K_c = [PH_3][BCl_3]$; $1.87 \times 10^{-3} = x^2$; $x = 0.04324 = 0.0432$ M PH_3 and BCl_3

      (b)   Since the mole ratios are 1:1:1, mol $PH_3BCl_3(s)$ required = mol PH_3 or BCl_3 produced.

$$\dfrac{0.04324 \text{ mol } PH_3}{1 \text{ L}} \times 0.500 \text{ L} \times \dfrac{151.2 \text{ g } PH_3BCl_3}{1 \text{ mol } PH_3BCl_3} = 3.27 \text{ g } PH_3BCl_3$$

           In fact, some $PH_3BCl_3(s)$ must remain for the system to be in equilibrium, so a bit more than 3.27 g PH_3BCl_3 is needed.

15.41 $K_c = 280 = \dfrac{[IBr]^2}{[I_2][Br_2]}$;   [Br] initial $= \dfrac{0.500 \text{ mol}}{1.000 \text{ L}} = 0.500$ M

	I_2	$+$	Br_2	$\rightleftharpoons$	$2IBr$
initial	0 M		0 M		0.500 M
change	+x		+x		-2x
equil.	x		x		0.500-2x

Since no I_2 or Br_2 were present initially, the amounts present at equilibrium are produced by the reverse reaction and stoichiometrically equal. Let these amounts equal x. The amount of HBr that reacts is then 2x. Substitute the equilibrium concentrations (in terms of x) into the equilibrium expression and solve for x.

$K_c = 280 = \dfrac{(0.500 - 2x)^2}{x^2}$; taking the square root of both sides

$16.733 = \dfrac{0.500 - 2x}{x}$; $16.733x + 2x = 0.500$; $18.733x = 0.500$

$x = 0.0267$ M; $[I_2] = 0.0267$ M, $[Br_2] = 0.0267$ M

$[IBr] = 0.500 - 2x = 0.500 - 0.0534 = 0.447$ M

LeChâtelier's Principle

15.43   (a)   Shift equilibrium to the right; more $SO_3(g)$ is formed, the amount of $SO_2(g)$ decreases.

      (b)   Heating an exothermic reaction decreases the value of K. More SO_2 and O_2 will form, the amount of SO_3 will decrease.

(c) Since, Δn = -1, a change in volume will affect the equilibrium position and favor the side with more moles of gas. The amounts of SO_2 and O_2 increase and the amount of SO_3 decreases.

(d) No effect. Speeds up the forward and reverse reactions equally.

(e) No effect. Does not appear in the equilibrium expression.

(f) Shift equilibrium to the right; amounts of SO_2 and O_2 decrease.

15.45 (a) No effect (b) no effect (c) increase equilibrium constant (d) no effect

15.47 (a) $\Delta H° = \Delta H°_f \, NO_2(g) + \Delta H°_f \, N_2O(g) - 3\Delta H°_f \, NO(g)$

$\Delta H° = 33.84 \text{ kJ} + 81.6 \text{ kJ} - 3(90.37 \text{ kJ}) = -155.7 \text{ kJ}$

(b) The reaction is exothermic ($-\Delta H°$), so the equilibrium constant will decrease with increasing temperature.

(c) Δn does not equal zero, so a change in volume at constant temperature will affect the fraction of products in the equilibrium mixture. An increase in container volume would favor reactants, while a decrease in volume would favor products.

Additional Exercises

15.49 (a) Since both the forward and reverse processes are elementary steps, we can write the rate laws directly from the chemical equation.

$rate_f = k_f \, [CO][Cl_2] = rate_r = k_r \, [COCl][Cl]$

$$\frac{k_f}{k_r} = \frac{[COCl][Cl]}{[CO][Cl_2]} = K$$

$$K = \frac{k_f}{k_r} = \frac{1.4 \times 10^{-28} \, M^{-1}s^{-1}}{9.3 \times 10^{10} \, M^{-1}s^{-1}} = 1.5 \times 10^{-39}$$

(b) Since the K is quite small, reactants are much more plentiful than products at equilibrium.

15.51 $[SO_2Cl_2] = 2.00 \text{ mol}/2.00 \text{ L} = 1.00 \, M$. The change in $[SO_2Cl_2]$, x, = 0.56(1.00 M) = 0.56 M

	$SO_2Cl_2(g)$	⇌	$SO_2(g)$	+	$Cl_2(g)$
initial	1.00 M		0		0
change	-0.56 M		+0.56 M		+0.56 M
equil.	0.44 M		+0.56 M		+0.56 M

$$K_c = \frac{[SO_2][Cl_2]}{[SO_2Cl_2]} = \frac{(0.56)^2}{0.44} = 0.7127 = 0.71$$

15.54 (a)

	A(g)	⇌	2B(g)
initial	0.55 atm		0
change	-0.19 atm		+0.38 atm
equil.	0.36 atm		0.38 atm

$P_T = P_A + P_B = 0.36$ atm $+ 0.38$ atm $= 0.74$ atm

(b) $K_p = \dfrac{(P_B)^2}{P_A} = \dfrac{(0.38)^2}{0.36} = 0.4011 = 0.40$

(c) $K_c = \dfrac{K_p}{(RT)^{\Delta n}}$; $\Delta n = +1$, $T = 0°C + 273 = 273$ K

$K_c = \dfrac{0.4011}{(0.08206 \times 273)^{+1}} = 0.01790 = 0.018$

15.57 (a) $K_p = K_c(RT)^{\Delta n}$; $K_c = \dfrac{K_p}{(RT)^{\Delta n}} = \dfrac{0.052}{(0.08206 \times 333)^2} = 6.964 \times 10^{-5} = 7.0 \times 10^{-5}$

(b) $[BCl_3] = 0.0128$ mol$/0.500$ L $= 0.0256$ M

PH_3BCl_3 is a solid and its concentration is taken as a constant, C.

	PH_3BCl_3	⇌	PH_3	+	BCl_3
initial	C		0 M		0.0256 M
change			+x M		+x M
equil.	C		x M		0.0256+x M

$K_c = [PH_3][BCl_3]$; $7.0 \times 10^{-5} = x(0.0256 + x)$

$x^2 + 0.0256x - 7.0 \times 10^{-5} = 0$

$x = \dfrac{-0.0256 \pm [(0.0256)^2 - 4(-7.0 \times 10^{-5})]^{1/2}}{2} = 0.00249 = 2.5 \times 10^{-3}$ M $= [PH_3]$

Check: $(2.5 \times 10^{-3} + 0.0256)(2.5 \times 10^{-3}) = 7.0 \times 10^{-5}$; the solution is correct to two significant figures.

15.60   In general, the reaction quotient is of the form $Q = \dfrac{[NOCl]^2}{[NO]^2[Cl_2]}$.

(a) $Q = \dfrac{(0.11)^2}{(0.15)^2(0.31)} = 1.7$

Q > K_p. Therefore, the reaction will shift toward reactants, to the left, in moving toward equilibrium.

(b) $Q = \dfrac{(0.050)^2}{(0.12)^2(0.10)} = 1.7$

Q > K_p. Therefore, the reaction will shift toward reactants, to the left, in moving toward equilibrium.

(c) $Q = \dfrac{(5.10 \times 10^{-3})^2}{(0.15)^2 (0.20)} = 5.8 \times 10^{-3}$

$Q < K_p$. Therefore, the reaction mixture will shift in the direction of more product, to the right, in moving toward equilibrium.

15.63 $K_c = K_p = \dfrac{P_{CO_2}}{P_{CO}} = 6.0 \times 10^2$

If P_{CO} is 150 torr, P_{CO_2} can never exceed 760 - 150 = 610 torr. Then Q = 610/150 = 4.1. Since this is far less than K, the reaction will shift in the direction of more product. Reduction will therefore occur.

15.66   First calculate K_c for the equilibrium

$$H_2 + I_2 \rightleftharpoons 2HI$$

$$K_c = \dfrac{[HI]^2}{[H_2][I_2]} = \dfrac{(0.155)^2}{(2.24 \times 10^{-2})(2.24 \times 10^{-2})} = 47.88 = 47.9$$

The added HI represents a concentration of $\dfrac{0.100 \text{ mol}}{5.00 \text{ L}} = 0.0200 \ M$.

	H_2	+	I_2	$\rightleftharpoons$	$2HI$
initial	$2.24 \times 10^{-2}\ M$		$2.24 \times 10^{-2}\ M$		$0.155 + 0.0200\ M$
change	$+ x\ M$		$+ x\ M$		$-2x\ M$
equil.	$2.24 \times 10^{-2}\ M + x\ M$		$2.24 \times 10^{-2}\ M + x\ M$		$0.175 - 2x\ M$

$\dfrac{(0.175 - 2x)^2}{(2.24 \times 10^{-2} + x)^2} = 47.88$.   Take the square root of both sides:

$\dfrac{0.175 - 2x}{2.24 \times 10^{-2} + x} = (47.88)^{1/2} = 6.920 = 6.92$

$0.175 - 2x = 0.155 + 6.92x$; $x = 2.242 \times 10^{-3} = 2.24 \times 10^{-3}$

$[I_2] = [H_2] = 2.24 \times 10^{-2} + 2.24 \times 10^{-3} = 2.464 \times 10^{-2} = 2.46 \times 10^{-2}\ M$

$[HI] = 0.175 - 2x = 0.1705 = 0.171\ M$

15.69   The patent claim is false. A catalyst does not alter the position of equilibrium in a system, only the rate of approach to the equilibrium condition.

Integrative Exercises

15.70   (a)   (i) $K_c = [Na^+]/[Ag^+]$ (ii) $K_c = [Hg^{2+}]^3 / [Al^{3+}]^2$

(iii) $K_c = [Zn^{2+}][H_2] / [H^+]^2$

(b) According to Table 4.5, the activity series of the metals, a metal can be oxidized by any metal cation below it on the table.

    (i) Ag^+ is far below Na, so the reaction will proceed to the right and K_c will be large.

    (ii) Al^{3+} is above Hg, so the reaction will not proceed to the right and K_c will be small.

    (iii) H^+ is below Zn, so the reaction will proceed to the right and K_c will be large.

(c) $K_c < 1$ for this reaction, so Fe^{2+} (and thus Fe) is above Cd on the table. In other words, Cd is below Fe. The value of K_c, 0.06, is small but not extremely small, so Cd will be only a few rows below Fe.

15.72   (a)   At equilibrium, the forward and reverse reactions occur at **equal** rates.

    (b)   One expects the reactants to be favored at equilibrium since they are lower in energy.

    (c)   A catalyst lowers the activation energy for both the forward and reverse reactions; the "hill" would be lower.

    (d)   Since the activation energy is lowered for both processes, the new rates would be equal and the ratio of the rate constants, k_f / k_r, would remain unchanged.

    (e)   Since the reaction is endothermic (the energy of the reactants is lower than that of the products, ΔE is positive), the value of K should increase with increasing temperature.

15.75 $K_c = [CO]^2 / [CO_2]$. To calculate K_c, find concentrations in units of moles/L from the ideal-gas equation, $n/V = P/RT$. Since the total pressure is 1 atm in all cases, n/V for CO_2 and CO at each temperature can be calculated. For example, at 850°C (1123 K):

$$[CO_2] = \frac{0.0623 \text{ atm}}{\left[\dfrac{0.08206 \text{ L} \cdot \text{atm}}{\text{mol} \cdot \text{K}}\right](1123 \text{ K})} = 6.76 \times 10^{-4} \ M$$

$$[CO] = \frac{0.9377 \text{ atm}}{\left[\dfrac{0.08206 \text{ L} \cdot \text{atm}}{\text{mol} \cdot \text{K}}\right](1123 \text{ K})} = 1.018 \times 10^{-2} \ M$$

Temp (K)	$[CO_2]$	[CO]	K_c
1123	6.76×10^{-4}	1.018×10^{-2}	0.153
1223	1.32×10^{-4}	9.833×10^{-3}	0.732
1323	$3.4 \ \times 10^{-5}$	9.177×10^{-3}	2.5
1473	$5 \ \ \ \times 10^{-6}$	8.268×10^{-3}	14 (1×10^1 to 1 sig fig)

Because K_c grows larger with increasing temperature, the reaction must be endothermic in the forward direction.

16 Acid-Base Equilibria

Arrhenius and Brønsted-Lowry Acids and Bases

16.1   Solutions of HCl and H_2SO_4 taste sour, turn litmus paper red (are acidic), neutralize solutions of bases, react with active metals to form $H_2(g)$ and conduct electricity. The two solutions have these properties in common because both solutes are strong acids. That is, they both ionize completely in H_2O to form $H^+(aq)$ and an anion. (The first ionization step for H_2SO_4 is complete, but the second is not.) The presence of ions enables the solutions to conduct electricity; the presence of $H^+(aq)$ in excess of 1×10^{-7} M accounts for all the other properties listed.

16.3   (a)   According to the Arrhenius definition, an acid when dissolved in water increases $[H^+]$. According to the Brønsted-Lowry definition, an acid is capable of donating H^+, regardless of physical state. The Arrhenius definition of an acid is confined to an aqueous solution; the Brønsted-Lowry definition applies to any physical state.

(b) $HCl(g) + NH_3(g) \rightarrow NH_4^+Cl^-(s)$ HCl is the B-L (Brønsted-Lowry) acid; it donates an H^+ to NH_3 to form NH_4^+. NH_3 is the B-L base; it accepts the H^+ from HCl.

16.5   A conjugate base has one less H^+ than its conjugate acid.

(a) HSO_3^- (b) $C_2H_3O_2^-$ (c) $HAsO_4^{2-}$ (d) NH_3

16.7

B-L acid	+	B-L base	$\rightleftharpoons$	Conjugate acid	+	Conjugate base
(a) $NH_4^+(aq)$		$CN^-(aq)$		$HCN(aq)$		$NH_3(aq)$
(b) $H_2O(l)$		$(CH_3)_3N(aq)$		$(CH_3)_3NH^+(aq)$		$OH^-(aq)$
(c) $HCHO_2(aq)$		$PO_4^{3-}(aq)$		$HPO_4^{2-}(aq)$		$CHO_2^-(aq)$

16.9   (a)   Acid: $HC_2O_4^-(aq) + H_2O(l) \rightleftharpoons C_2O_4^{2-}(aq) + H_3O^+(aq)$
                       B-L acid   B-L base   conj. base   conj. acid

Base: $HC_2O_4^-(aq) + H_2O(l) \rightleftharpoons H_2C_2O_4(aq) + OH^-(aq)$
           B-L base   B-L acid   conj. acid   conj. base

(b) $H_2C_2O_4$ is the conjugate acid of $HC_2O_4^-$.

$C_2O_4^{2-}$ is the conjugate base of $HC_2O_4^-$.

16.11   (a) weak, NO_2^- (b) strong, HSO_4^- (c) weak, PO_4^{3-}

(d) negligible, CH_3^- (e) weak, CH_3NH_2

16.13 (a) HBr. It is one of the seven strong acids (Section 16.5).

(b) F^-. HCl is a stronger acid than HF, so F^- is the stronger conjugate base.

16.15 Acid-base equilibria favor formation of the weaker acid and base. Compare the substances acting as acids on opposite sides of the equation. (Bases can also be compared; the conclusion should be the same.)

Base	+	**Acid**	$\rightleftharpoons$	**Conjugate acid**	+	**Conjugate base**

(a) $F^-(aq)$ + $HCO_3^-(aq)$ $\rightleftharpoons$ $HF(aq)$ + $CO_3^{2-}(aq)$

HF is a stronger acid than HCO_3^-, so the equilibrium lies to the left.

(b) $O^{2-}(aq)$ + $H_2O(l)$ $\rightleftharpoons$ $OH^-(aq)$ + $OH^-(aq)$

H_2O is a stronger acid than OH^-, so the equilibrium lies to the right.

(c) $HS^-(aq)$ + $HC_2H_3O_2(aq)$ $\rightleftharpoons$ $H_2S(aq)$ + $C_2H_3O_2^-(aq)$

$HC_2H_3O_2$ is a stronger acid than H_2S, so the equilibrium lies to the right.

Autoionization of Water

16.17 (a) *Autoionization* is the ionization of a neutral molecule (in the absence of any other reactant) into an anion and a cation. The equilibrium expression for the autoionization of water is $H_2O(l) \rightleftharpoons H^+(aq) + OH^-(aq)$.

(b) Pure water is a poor conductor of electricity because it contains very few ions. Ions, mobile charged particles, are required for the conduction of electricity in liquids.

(c) If a solution is *acidic*, it contains more H^+ than OH^- ($[H^+] > [OH^-]$).

16.19 In pure water at 25°C, $[H^+] = [OH^-] = 1 \times 10^{-7}$ M. If $[H^+] > 1 \times 10^{-7}$ M, the solution is acidic; if $[H^+] < 1 \times 10^{-7}$ M, the solution is basic.

(a) $[H^+] = \dfrac{K_w}{[OH^-]} = \dfrac{1.0 \times 10^{-14}}{5 \times 10^{-5}\ M} = \mathbf{2 \times 10^{-10}}$ $M < 1 \times 10^{-7}$ M; basic

(b) $[H^+] = \dfrac{K_w}{[OH^-]} = \dfrac{1.0 \times 10^{-14}}{3.2 \times 10^{-9}\ M} = \mathbf{3.1 \times 10^{-6}}$ $M > 1 \times 10^{-7}$ M; acidic

(c) $[OH^-] = 100[H^+]$; $K_w = [H^+] \times 100[H^+] = 100[H^+]^2$;

$[H^+] = (K_w/100)^{1/2} = \mathbf{1.0 \times 10^{-8}}$ $M < 1 \times 10^{-7}$ M; basic

16.21 At 37°C, $K_w = 2.4 \times 10^{-14} = [H^+][OH^-]$.

In pure water, $[H^+] = [OH^-]$; $2.4 \times 10^{-14} = [H^+]^2$; $[H^+] = (2.4 \times 10^{-14})^{1/2}$

$[H^+] = [OH^-] = 1.5 \times 10^{-7}$ M

The pH Scale

16.23   A change of one pH unit (in either direction) is:

$\Delta pH = pH_2 - pH_1 = -(\log[H^+]_2 - \log[H^+]_1) = -\log \dfrac{[H^+]_2}{[H^+]_1} = \pm 1$.   The antilog of +1 is 10; the antilog of -1 is 1×10^{-1}. Thus, a ΔpH of one unit represents an increase or decrease in $[H^+]$ by a factor of 10.

(a) $\Delta pH = \pm 2.00$ is a change of $10^{2.00}$; $[H^+]$ changes by a factor of 100.

(b) $\Delta pH = \pm 0.5$ is a change of $10^{0.50}$; $[H^+]$ changes by a factor of 3.2.

16.25   (a) $K_w = [H^+][OH^-]$. If NaOH is added to water, it dissociates into $Na^+(aq)$ and $OH^-(aq)$. This increases $[OH^-]$ and necessarily decreases $[H^+]$. When $[H^+]$ decreases, pH increases.

(b) $pH = -\log [H^+] = -\log (0.0003) = 3.5$ If pH < 7, the solution is acidic.

(c)   pH = 7.8   pOH = 14.0 - 6.3 = 6.2

$[H^+] = 10^{-pH} = 10^{-7.8} = 2 \times 10^{-8} M$ $[OH^-] = 10^{-pOH} = 10^{-6.2} = 6 \times 10^{-7} M$

16.27

$[H^+]$	$[OH^-]$	pH	pOH	acidic or basic
$7.5 \times 10^{-3} M$	$1.3 \times 10^{-12} M$	2.12	11.88	acidic
$2.8 \times 10^{-5} M$	$3.6 \times 10^{-10} M$	4.56	9.44	acidic
$5.6 \times 10^{-9} M$	$1.8 \times 10^{-6} M$	8.25	5.75	basic
$5.0 \times 10^{-9} M$	$2.0 \times 10^{-6} M$	8.30	5.70	basic

Strong Acids and Bases

16.29   (a)   A *strong* acid is completely ionized in aqueous solution; a strong acid is a strong electrolyte.

(b)   For a strong acid such as HCl, $[H^+]$ = initial acid concentration. $[H^+] = 0.500 M$

(c)   HCl, HBr, HI

16.31   For a strong acid, $[H^+]$ = initial acid concentration.

(a) $8.5 \times 10^{-3} M$ HBr = $8.5 \times 10^{-3} M$ H^+; pH = -log (8.5×10^{-3}) = 2.07

(b) $\dfrac{1.52 \text{ g } HNO_3}{0.575 \text{ L soln}} \times \dfrac{1 \text{ mol } HNO_3}{63.02 \text{ g } HNO_3} = 0.041947 = 0.0419\ M\ HNO_3$

$[H^+] = 0.0419\ M$; pH = -log (0.041947) = 1.377

(c) $M_c \times V_c = M_d \times V_d$;   0.250 M × 0.00500 L = ? M × 0.0500 L

$$M_d = \frac{0.250\ M \times 0.00500\ L}{0.0500\ L} = 0.0250\ M\ HCl$$

[H⁺] = 0.0250 M; pH = -log (0.0250) = 1.602

(d) $$[H^+]_{total} = \frac{mol\ H^+\ from\ HBr + mol\ H^+\ from\ HCl}{total\ L\ solution}$$

$$[H^+]_{total} = \frac{(0.100\ M\ HBr \times 0.0100\ L) + (0.200\ M \times 0.0200\ L)}{0.0300\ L}$$

$$[H^+]_{total} = \frac{1.00 \times 10^{-3}\ mol\ H^+ + 4.00 \times 10^{-3}\ mol\ H^+}{0.0300\ L} = 0.1667 = 0.167\ M$$

pH = -log (0.1667 M) = 0.778

16.33 (a)   [OH⁻] = 2[Sr(OH)₂] = 2(1.5 × 10⁻³ M) = 3.0 × 10⁻³ M OH⁻ (see Exercise 16.30(b))

pOH = -log (3.0 × 10⁻³) = 2.52; pH = 14 - pOH = 11.48

(b) $$\frac{2.250\ g\ LiOH}{0.2500\ L\ soln} \times \frac{1\ mol\ LiOH}{23.948\ g\ LiOH} = 0.37581 = 0.3758\ M\ LiOH = [OH^-]$$

pOH = -log (0.37581) = 0.4250; pH = 14 - pOH = 13.5750

(c) $M_c \times V_c = M_d \times V_d$;   0.175 M × 0.00100 L = ? M × 2.00 L

$$M_d = \frac{0.0175\ M \times 0.00100\ L}{2.00\ L} = 8.75 \times 10^{-5}\ M\ NaOH = [OH^-]$$

pOH = -log (8.75 × 10⁻⁵) = 4.058; pH = 14 - pOH = 9.942

(d) $$[OH^-]_{total} = \frac{mol\ OH^-\ from\ KOH + mol\ OH^-\ from\ Ca(OH)_2}{total\ L\ soln}$$

$$[OH^-]_{total} = \frac{(0.105\ M \times 0.00500\ L) + 2(9.5 \times 10^{-2} \times 0.0150\ L)}{0.0200\ L}$$

$$[OH^-]_{total} = \frac{0.525 \times 10^{-3}\ mol\ OH^- + 2.85 \times 10^{-3}\ mol\ OH^-}{0.0200\ L} = 0.16875 = 0.17\ M$$

pOH = -log (0.16875) = 0.77; pH = 14 - pOH = 13.23

(9.5 × 10⁻² M has 2 sig figs, so the [OH⁻] has 2 sig figs and pH and pOH have 2 decimal places.)

16.35   pOH = 14 - pH = 14.00 - 11.50 = 2.50

pOH = 2.50 = -log[OH⁻]; [OH⁻] = 10⁻²·⁵⁰ = 3.2 × 10⁻³ M

[OH⁻] = [NaOH] = 3.2 × 10⁻³ M

16.37   Upon dissolving, Li_2O dissociates to form Li^+ and O^{2-}. According to Equation 16.19, O^{2-} is completely protonated in aqueous solution.

Thus, initial $[Li_2O] = [O_2^-]$; $[OH^-] = 2[O^{2-}] = 2[Li_2O]$

$$[Li_2O] = \frac{mol\ Li_2O}{L\ solution} = 2.00\ g\ Li_2O \times \frac{1\ mol\ Li_2O}{29.88\ g\ Li_2O} \times \frac{1}{0.600\ L} = 0.1116 = 0.112\ M$$

$[OH^-] = 0.2232 = 0.223\ M$; pOH = 0.651   pH = 14.00 - pOH = 13.349

Weak Acids

16.39   (a) $HBrO_2(aq) \rightleftharpoons H^+(aq) + BrO_2^-(aq)$; $K_a = \dfrac{[H^+][BrO_2^-]}{[HBrO_2]}$

$HBrO_2(aq) + H_2O(l) \rightleftharpoons H_3O^+(aq) + BrO_2^-(aq)$; $K_a = \dfrac{[H_3O^+][BrO_2^-]}{[HBrO_2]}$

(b) $HC_3H_5O_2(aq) \rightleftharpoons H^+(aq) + C_3H_5O_2^-(aq)$; $K_a = \dfrac{[H^+][C_3H_5O_2^-]}{[HC_3H_5O_2]}$

$HC_3H_5O_2(aq) + H_2O(l) \rightleftharpoons H_3O^+(aq) + C_3H_5O_2^-(aq)$; $K_a = \dfrac{[H_3O^+][C_3H_5O_2^-]}{[HC_3H_5O_2]}$

16.41 $HC_3H_5O_3(aq) \rightleftharpoons H^+(aq) + C_3H_5O_3^-(aq)$; $K_a = \dfrac{[H^+][C_3H_5O_3^-]}{[HC_3H_5O_3]}$

$[H^+] = [C_3H_5O_3^-] = 10^{-2.44} = 3.63 \times 10^{-3} = 3.6 \times 10^{-3}\ M$

$[HC_3H_5O_3] = 0.10 - 3.63 \times 10^{-3} = 0.0964 = 0.096\ M$

$$K_a = \frac{(3.63 \times 10^{-3})^2}{(0.0964)} = 1.4 \times 10^{-4}$$

16.43 $[H^+] = 0.094 \times [HX]_{initial} = 0.0188 = 0.019\ M$

	HX(aq) $\rightleftharpoons$	H$^+$(aq) +	X$^-$(aq)
initial	0.200 *M*	0	0
equil.	(0.200 - 0.019) *M*	0.019 *M*	0.019 *M*

$$K_a = \frac{[H^+][X^-]}{[HX]} = \frac{(0.0188)^2}{0.181} = 2.0 \times 10^{-3}$$

16.45 $[H^+] = 10^{-pH} = 10^{-2.90} = 1.26 \times 10^{-3} = 1.3 \times 10^{-3}\ M$

$$K_a = 1.8 \times 10^{-5} = \frac{[H^+][C_2H_3O_2^-]}{[HC_2H_3O_2]} = \frac{(1.26 \times 10^{-3})^2}{(x - 1.26 \times 10^{-3})}$$

$1.8 \times 10^{-5} (x - 1.26 \times 10^{-3}) = (1.26 \times 10^{-3})^2$;

$1.8 \times 10^{-5} x = 1.585 \times 10^{-6} + 2.266 \times 10^{-8} = 1.608 \times 10^{-6}$;

$x = 0.08931 = 0.089\ M\ HC_2H_3O_2$

16.47 $HC_7H_5O_2(aq)$ $H^+(aq)$ + $C_7H_5O_2^-(aq)$

initial   0.050 M 0   0

equil.   (0.050 - x) M x M x M

$$K_a = \frac{[H^+][C_7H_5O_2^-]}{[HC_7H_5O_2]} = \frac{x^2}{(0.050 - x)} \approx \frac{x^2}{0.050} = 6.3 \times 10^{-5}$$

$x^2 = 0.050\,(6.3 \times 10^{-5})$; $x = 1.8 \times 10^{-3}$ M = $[H^+] = [H_3O^+] = [C_7H_5O_2^-]$

$[HC_7H_5O_2] = 0.050 - 0.0018 = 0.048$ M

$$\frac{1.8 \times 10^{-3}\, M\, H^+}{0.050\, M\, HC_7H_5O_2} \times 100 = 3.6\% \text{ ionization; the assumption is valid}$$

16.49 (a) $HC_3H_5O_2(aq)$ $\rightleftharpoons$ $H^+(aq)$ + $C_3H_5O_2^-$ (aq)

initial   0.095 M 0   0

equil   (0.095 - x) M x M x M

$$K_a = \frac{[H^+][C_3H_5O_2^-]}{[HC_3H_5O_2]} = \frac{x^2}{(0.095 - x)} \approx \frac{x^2}{0.095} = 1.3 \times 10^{-5}$$

$x^2 = 0.095(1.3 \times 10^{-5})$; $x = 1.111 \times 10^{-3} = 1.1 \times 10^{-3}$ M H^+; pH = 2.95

$$\frac{1.1 \times 10^{-3}\, M\, H^+}{0.095\, M\, HC_3H_5O_2} \times 100 = 1.2\% \text{ ionization; the assumption is valid}$$

(b) $$K_a = \frac{[H^+][CrO_4^{2-}]}{[HCrO_4^-]} = \frac{x^2}{(0.100 - x)} \approx \frac{x^2}{0.100} = 3.0 \times 10^{-7}$$

$x^2 = 0.100(3.0 \times 10^{-7})$; $x = 1.732 \times 10^{-4} = 1.7 \times 10^{-4}$ M H^+

pH = -log(1.732 × 10^{-4}) = 3.7614 = 3.76

$$\frac{1.7 \times 10^{-4}\, M\, H^+}{0.100\, M\, HCrO_4^-} \times 100 = 0.17\% \text{ ionization; the assumption is valid}$$

(c) $C_5H_5N(aq) + H_2O(l)$ $\rightleftharpoons$ $C_5H_5NH^+(aq)$ + OH^-

initial   0.120 M 0   0

equil   (0.120 - x) M x M x M

$$K_b = \frac{[C_5H_5NH^+][OH^-]}{[C_5H_5N]} = \frac{x^2}{(0.120 - x)} \approx \frac{x^2}{0.120} = 1.7 \times 10^{-9}$$

$x^2 = 0.120(1.7 \times 10^{-9})$; $x = 1.428 \times 10^{-5} = 1.4 \times 10^{-5}$ M OH^-; pH = 9.15

$$\frac{1.4 \times 10^{-5}\, M\, OH^-}{0.120\, M\, C_5H_5N} \times 100 = 0.011\% \text{ ionization; the assumption is valid}$$

16.51   Let $[H^+] = [NC_7H_4SO_3^-] = z$. $K_a = $ antilog $(-2.32) = 4.79 \times 10^{-3} = 4.8 \times 10^{-3}$

$\dfrac{z^2}{0.10 - z} = 4.79 \times 10^{-3}$.   Since K_a is relatively large, solve the quadratic.

$z^2 = 4.79 \times 10^{-3} z - 4.79 \times 10^{-4} = 0$

$z = \dfrac{-4.79 \times 10^{-3} \pm \sqrt{(4.79 \times 10^{-3})^2 - 4(1)(-4.79 \times 10^{-4})}}{2(1)} = \dfrac{-4.79 \times 10^{-3} \pm \sqrt{1.937 \times 10^{-3}}}{2}$

$z = 1.96 \times 10^{-2} = 2.0 \times 10^{-2} \; M \; H^+$; $pH = -\log (1.96 \times 10^{-2}) = 1.71$

16.53   (a) $HN_3(aq) \; \rightleftharpoons \; H^+(aq) + N_3^-(aq)$

        initial $0.400 \; M$ 0 0

        equil $(0.400 - x) \; M$ $x \; M$ $x \; M$

$K_a = \dfrac{[H^+][N_3^-]}{[HN_3]} = 1.9 \times 10^{-5}; \; \dfrac{x^2}{(0.400 - x)} \approx \dfrac{x^2}{0.400} = 1.9 \times 10^{-5}$

$x = 0.00276 = 2.8 \times 10^{-3} \; M = [H^+]; \;$ % ionization $= \dfrac{2.76 \times 10^{-3}}{0.400} \times 100 = 0.69\%$

(b) $1.9 \times 10^{-5} \approx \dfrac{x^2}{0.100}; \; x = 0.00138 = 1.4 \times 10^{-3} \; M \; H^+$

% ionization $= \dfrac{1.38 \times 10^{-3} \, M \, H^+}{0.100 \, M \, HN_3} \times 100 = 1.4\%$

(c) $1.9 \times 10^{-5} \approx \dfrac{x^2}{0.0400}; \; x = 8.72 \times 10^{-4} = 8.7 \times 10^{-4} \; M \; H^+$

% ionization $= \dfrac{8.72 \times 10^{-4} \, M \, H^+}{0.0400 \, M \, HN_3} \times 100 = 2.2\%$

Notice that a tenfold dilution [part (a) versus part (c)] leads to a slightly more than threefold increase in percent ionization.

16.55   Let the weak acid be HX. $HX(aq) \rightleftharpoons H^+(aq) + X^-(aq)$

$K_a = \dfrac{[H^+][X^-]}{[HX]}; \; [H^+] = [X^-] = y; \; K_a = \dfrac{y^2}{[HX] - y}; \;$ assume that % ionization is small

$K_a = \dfrac{y^2}{[HX]}; \; y = K_a^{1/2} [HX]^{1/2}$

% ionization $= \dfrac{y}{[HX]} \times 100 = \dfrac{K_a^{1/2} [HX]^{1/2}}{[HX]} \times 100 = \dfrac{K_a^{1/2}}{[HX]^{1/2}} \times 100$

That is, percent ionization varies inversely as the square root of concentration HX.

16.57 $H_3C_6H_5O_7(aq) \rightleftharpoons H^+(aq) + H_2C_6H_5O_7^-(aq)$ $K_{a1} = 7.4 \times 10^{-4}$

      $H_2C_6H_5O_7^-(aq) \rightleftharpoons H^+(aq) + HC_6H_5O_7^{2-}(aq)$ $K_{a2} = 1.7 \times 10^{-5}$

      $HC_6H_5O_7^{2-}(aq) \rightleftharpoons H^+(aq) + C_6H_5O_7^{3-}(aq)$ $K_{a3} = 4.0 \times 10^{-7}$

To calculate the pH of a 0.050 *M* solution, assume initially that only the first ionization is important:

$$H_3C_6H_5O_7(aq) \rightleftharpoons H^+(aq) + H_2C_6H_5O_7^-(aq)$$

initial   0.050 *M*   0   0

equil.   (0.050 - x) *M*   x *M*   x *M*

$$K_{a1} = \frac{[H^+][H_2C_6H_5O_7^-]}{[H_3C_6H_5O_7]} = \frac{x^2}{(0.050 - x)} = 7.4 \times 10^{-4}$$

$x^2 = (0.050 - x)(7.4 \times 10^{-4}); \quad x^2 \approx (0.050)(7.4 \times 10^{-4}); \quad x = 0.00608 = 6.1 \times 10^{-3} \ M$

Since this value for x is rather large in relation to 0.050, a better approximation for x can be obtained by substituting this first estimate into the expression for x^2, then solving again for x:

$$x^2 = (0.050 - x)(7.4 \times 10^{-4}) = (0.050 - 6.08 \times 10^{-3})(7.4 \times 10^{-4})$$
$$x^2 = 3.2 \times 10^{-5}; \quad x = 5.7 \times 10^{-3} \ M$$

The correction to the value of x, though not large, is significant. (This is the same result obtained from the quadratic formula.) Does the second ionization produce a significant additional concentration of H^+?

$$H_2C_6H_5O_7^-(aq) \rightleftharpoons H^+(aq) + HC_6H_5O_7^{2-}(aq)$$

initial $5.7 \times 10^{-5} \ M$ $5.7 \times 10^{-3} \ M$ 0

equil. $(5.7 \times 10^{-3} - y)$ $(5.7 \times 10^{-3} + y)$ y

$$K_{a2} = \frac{[H^+][HC_6H_5O_7^{2-}]}{[H_2C_6H_5O_7^-]} = 1.7 \times 10^{-5}; \quad \frac{(5.7 \times 10^{-3} + y)(y)}{(5.7 \times 10^{-3} - y)} = 1.7 \times 10^{-5}$$

Assume that y is small relative to 5.7×10^{-3}; that is, that additional ionization of $H_2C_6H_5O_7^-$ is small, then

$$\frac{(5.7 \times 10^{-3})y}{(5.7 \times 10^{-3})} = 1.7 \times 10^{-5} \ M; \quad y = 1.7 \times 10^{-5} \ M$$

This value is indeed small compared to $5.7 \times 10^{-3} \ M$. This indicates that the second ionization can be neglected. pH is therefore $-\log [5.7 \times 10^{-3}] = 2.24$.

Weak Bases

16.59   All Brønsted-Lowry bases contain at least one nonbonded (lone) pair of electrons to attract H^+.

16.61   (a) $(CH_3)_2NH(aq) + H_2O(l) \rightleftharpoons (CH_3)_2NH_2^+(aq) + OH^-(aq); \quad K_b = \dfrac{[(CH_3)_2NH_2^+][OH^-]}{[(CH_3)_2NH]}$

         (b) $CO_3^{2-}(aq) + H_2O(l) \rightleftharpoons HCO_3^-(aq) + OH^-(aq); \quad K_b = \dfrac{[HCO_3^-][OH^-]}{[CO_3^{2-}]}$

         (c) $CHO_2^-(aq) + H_2O(l) \rightleftharpoons HCHO_2(aq) + OH^-(aq); \quad K_b = \dfrac{[HCHO_2][OH^-]}{[CHO_2^-]}$

16.63 $C_2H_5NH_2(aq) + H_2O(l) \rightleftharpoons C_2H_5NH_3^+(aq) + OH^-(aq)$

initial   0.075 M 0   0

equil.   (0.075 - x) M x M x M

$$K_b = \frac{[C_2H_5NH_3^+][OH^-]}{[C_2H_5NH_2]} = \frac{(x)(x)}{(0.075 - x)} \approx \frac{x^2}{0.075} = 6.4 \times 10^{-4}$$

$x^2 = 0.075 (6.4 \times 10^{-4})$; $x = [OH^-] = 6.9 \times 10^{-3}\ M$; pH = 11.84

$$\frac{6.9 \times 10^{-3}\ M\ OH^-}{0.075\ M\ C_2H_5NH_2} \times 100 = 9.2\% \text{ ionization};\ \text{the assumption is \textbf{not} valid}$$

To obtain a more precise result, the K_b expression is rewritten in standard quadratic form and solved via the quadratic formula.

$$\frac{x^2}{0.075 - x} = 6.4 \times 10^{-4};\ x^2 + 6.4 \times 10^{-4}\ x - 4.8 \times 10^{-5} = 0$$

$$x = \frac{b \pm \sqrt{b^2 - 4ac}}{2a} = \frac{-6.4 \times 10^{-4} \pm \sqrt{(6.4 \times 10^{-4})^2 - 4(1)(-4.8 \times 10^{-5})}}{2}$$

$x = 6.61 \times 10^{-3} = 6.6 \times 10^{-3}\ M\ OH^-$; pOH = 2.18, pH = 14.00 - pOH = 11.82

Note that the pH values obtained using the two algebraic techniques are very similar.

16.65   (a) $[OH^-] = 10^{-pOH}$; pOH = 14 - pH = 14.00 - 11.33 = 2.67

$[OH^-] = 10^{-2.67} = 2.138 \times 10^{-3} = 2.1 \times 10^{-3}\ M$

$C_{10}H_{15}ON(aq) + H_2O(l) \rightleftharpoons C_{10}H_{15}ONH^+(aq) + OH^-(aq)$

initial   0.035 M 0   0

equil.   0.033 M $2.1 \times 10^{-3}\ M$ $2.1 \times 10^{-3}\ M$

(b) $K_b = \dfrac{[C_{10}H_{15}ONH^+][OH^-]}{[C_{10}H_{15}ON]} = \dfrac{(2.138 \times 10^{-3})^2}{(0.03286)} = 1.4 \times 10^{-4}$

The K_a - K_b Relationship; Acid-Base Properties of Salts

16.67   (a)   For a conjugate acid/conjugate base pair such as $C_6H_5OH/C_6H_5O^-$, K_b for the conjugate base is always K_w / K_a for the conjugate acid. K_b for the conjugate base can always be calculated from K_a for the conjugate acid, so a separate list of K_b values is not necessary.

(b) $K_b = K_w / K_a = 1.0 \times 10^{-14} / 1.3 \times 10^{-10} = 7.7 \times 10^{-5}$

(c) K_b for phenolate (7.7×10^{-5}) > K_b for ammonia (1.8×10^{-5}).
Phenolate is a stronger base than NH_3.

16.69 (a) Acetic acid is stronger, because it has the larger K_a value.

     (b) Hypochlorite ion is the stronger base because the weaker acid, hypochlorous acid, has the stronger conjugate base.

     (c) K_b for $C_2H_3O_2^-$ = K_w/K_a for $HC_2H_3O_2$ = $1.0 \times 10^{-14}/1.8 \times 10^{-5}$ = 5.6×10^{-10}

          K_b for ClO^- = K_w/K_a for $HClO$ = $1 \times 10^{-14}/3.0 \times 10^{-8}$ = 3.3×10^{-7}

          Note that K_b for ClO^- is greater than K_b for $C_2H_3O_2^-$.

16.71 When the solute in an aqueous solution is a salt, evaluate the acid/base properties of the component ions.

     (a) NaCN is a soluble salt and thus a strong electrolyte. When it is dissolved in H_2O, it dissociates completely into Na^+ and CN^-. $[NaCN] = [Na^+] = [CN^-] = 0.10$ M. Na^+ is the conjugate acid of the strong base NaOH and thus does not influence the pH of the solution. CN^-, on the other hand, is the conjugate base of the weak acid HCN and **does** influence the pH of the solution. Like any other weak base, it hydrolyzes water to produce $OH^-(aq)$. Solve the equilibrium problem to determine $[OH^-]$.

$$CN^-(aq) + H_2O(l) \rightleftharpoons HCN(aq) + OH^-(aq)$$

initial	0.10 M	0	0
equil.	(0.10 - x) M	x M	x M

$$K_b \text{ for } CN^- = \frac{[HCN][OH^-]}{[CN^-]} = \frac{K_w}{K_a \text{ for HCN}} = \frac{1 \times 10^{-14}}{4.9 \times 10^{-10}} = 2.04 \times 10^{-5} = 2.0 \times 10^{-5}$$

$$2.04 \times 10^{-5} = \frac{(x)(x)}{(0.10 - x)}; \text{ assume the percent of } CN^- \text{ that hydrolyzes is small}$$

$$x^2 = 0.10 \,(2.04 \times 10^{-5}); \; x = [OH^-] = 0.00143 = 1.4 \times 10^{-3} \, M$$

$$pOH = 2.85; \; pH = 14 - 2.85 = 11.15$$

     (b) $Na_2CO_3(aq) \rightarrow 2Na^+(aq) + CO_3^{2-}(aq)$

          CO_3^{2-} is the conjugate base of HCO_3^- and its hydrolysis reaction will determine the $[OH^-]$ and pH of the solution (see similar explanation for NaCN in part (a)). We will assume the process $HCO_3^-(aq) + H_2O(l) \rightleftharpoons H_2CO_3(aq) + OH^-$ will not add significantly to the $[OH^-]$ in solution because $[HCO_3^-(aq)]$ is so small. Solve the equilibrium problem for $[OH^-]$.

$$CO_3^{2-}(aq) + H_2O(l) \rightleftharpoons HCO_3^-(aq) + OH^-(aq)$$

initial	0.080 M	0	0
equil.	(0.080 - x) M	x	x

$$K_b = \frac{[HCO_3^-][OH^-]}{[CO_3^{2-}]} = \frac{K_w}{K_a \text{ for } HCO_3^-} = \frac{1.0 \times 10^{-14}}{5.6 \times 10^{-11}} = 1.79 \times 10^{-4} = 1.8 \times 10^{-4}$$

$1.8 \times 10^{-4} = \dfrac{x^2}{(0.080 - x)}$; $x^2 = 0.080\,(1.79 \times 10^{-4})$; $x = 0.00378 = 3.8 \times 10^{-3}\ M\ OH^-$

(Assume x is small compared to 0.080); pOH = 2.42; pH = 14 - 2.42 = 11.58

$\dfrac{3.8 \times 10^{-3}\ M\ OH^-}{0.080\ M\ CO_3^{2-}} \times 100 = 4.75\%$ hydrolysis; the assumption is valid

(c)   For the two salts present, Na^+ and Ca^{2+} are negligible acids. NO_2^- is the conjugate base of HNO_2 and will determine the pH of the solution.

Calculate total $[NO_2^-]$ present initially.

$[NO_2^-]_{total} = [NO_2^-]$ from $NaNO_2$ + $[NO_2^-]$ from $Ca(NO_2)_2$

$[NO_2^-]_{total} = 0.10\ M + 2(0.20\ M) = 0.50\ M$

The hydrolysis equilibrium is:

$$NO_2^-(aq) + H_2O(l) \rightleftharpoons HNO_2 + OH^-(aq)$$

initial   0.50 M   0   0

equil.   (0.50 - x) M   x M   x M

$K_b = \dfrac{[HNO_2][OH^-]}{[NO_2^-]} = \dfrac{K_w}{K_a\ \text{for}\ HNO_2} = \dfrac{1.0 \times 10^{-14}}{4.5 \times 10^{-4}} = 2.22 \times 10^{-11} = 2.2 \times 10^{-11}$

$2.2 \times 10^{-11} = \dfrac{x^2}{(0.50 - x)} \approx \dfrac{x^2}{0.50}$; $x^2 = 0.50\,(2.22 \times 10^{-11})$

$x = 3.33 \times 10^{-6} = 3.3 \times 10^{-6}\ M\ OH^-$; pOH = 5.48; pH = 14 - 5.48 = 8.52

16.73 (a)   acidic; NH_4^+ is a weak acid, Br^- is negligible.

(b)   acidic; Fe^{3+} is a highly charged metal cation and a Lewis acid; Cl^- is negligible.

(c)   basic; CO_3^{2-} is the conjugate base of HCO_3^-; Na^+ is negligible.

(d)   neutral; both K^+ and ClO_4^- are negligible.

(e)   acidic; $HC_2O_4^-$ is amphoteric, but K_a for the acid dissociation (6.4×10^{-5}) is much greater than K_b for the base hydrolysis ($1.0 \times 10^{-14} / 5.9 \times 10^{-2} = 1.7 \times 10^{-13}$).

16.75 Strategy: estimate using relative base strength and then calculate to confirm prediction. NaCl is a neutral salt, so it is not the unknown. The unknown is a relatively weak base, because a pH of 8.08 is not very basic. Since F^- is a weaker base than OCl^-, the unknown is probably NaF. Calculate K_b for the unknown from the data provided.

$[OH^-] = 10^{-pOH}$; pOH = 14.00 - pH = 14.00 - 8.08 = 5.92

$[OH^-] = 10^{-5.92} = 1.202 \times 10^{-6} = 1.2 \times 10^{-6}\ M = [HX]$

$[NaX] = [X^-] = 0.050$ mol salt/0.500 L = 0.10 M

$K_b = \dfrac{[OH^-][HX]}{[X^-]} = \dfrac{(1.202 \times 10^{-6})^2}{(0.10 - 1.2 \times 10^{-6})} \approx \dfrac{(1.202 \times 10^{-6})^2}{0.10} = 1.4 \times 10^{-11}$

K_b for $F^- = K_w/K_a$ for HF = $1.0 \times 10^{-14}/6.8 \times 10^{-4} = 1.5 \times 10^{-11}$

The unknown is NaF.

16.77 The solution will be basic because of the hydrolysis of the sorbate anion, $C_6H_7O_2^-$. Calculate the initial molarity of $C_6H_7O_2^-$.

$$\frac{4.93 \text{ g } KC_6H_7O_2}{0.500 \text{ L}} \times \frac{1 \text{ mol } KC_6H_7O_2}{150.2 \text{ g } KC_6H_7O_2} = 0.065646 = 0.0656 \text{ M } KC_6H_7O_2$$

$[C_6H_7O_2^-] = [KC_6H_7O_2] = 0.0656 \text{ M}$

$$C_6H_7O_2^-(aq) + H_2O(l) \rightleftharpoons HC_6H_7O_2(aq) + OH^-(aq)$$

initial	0.0656 M		0	0
equil.	(0.0656 - x) M		x M	x M

$$K_b = \frac{[HC_6H_7O_2][OH^-]}{[C_6H_7O_2^-]} = \frac{K_w}{K_a \text{ for } HC_6H_7O_2} = \frac{1.0 \times 10^{-14}}{1.7 \times 10^{-5}} = 5.88 \times 10^{-10} = 5.9 \times 10^{-10}$$

$$5.88 \times 10^{-10} = \frac{x^2}{0.0656 - x} \approx \frac{x^2}{0.0656}; \quad x^2 = 0.0656 \,(5.88 \times 10^{-10})$$

$x = [OH^-] = 6.21 \times 10^{-6} = 6.2 \times 10^{-6} \text{ M}; \quad pOH = 5.21; \quad pH = 14 - pOH = 8.79$

Acid-Base Character and Chemical Structure

16.79 (a) As the electronegativity of the central atom (X) increases, more electron density is withdrawn from the X-O and O-H bonds, respectively. In water, the O-H bond is ionized to a greater extent and the strength of the oxyacid increases.

(b) As the number of nonprotonated oxygen atoms in the molecule increases, they withdraw electron density from the other bonds in the molecule and the strength of the oxyacid increases.

16.81 (a) HNO_3 is a stronger acid than HNO_2 because it has one more nonprotonated oxygen atom, and thus a higher oxidation number on N.

(b) For binary hydrides, acid strength increases going down a family, so H_2S is a stronger acid than H_2O.

(c) H_2SO_4 is a stronger acid because H^+ is much more tightly held by the anion HSO_4^-.

(d) For oxyacids, the greater the electronegativity of the central atom, the stronger the acid, so H_2SO_4 is a stronger acid than H_2SeO_4.

(e) CCl_3COOH is stronger because the electronegative Cl atoms withdraw electron density from other parts of the molecule, which weakens the O-H bond and makes H^+ easier to remove.

16.83 (a) BrO^- (HClO is the stronger acid due to a more electronegative central atom, so BrO^- is the stronger base.)

(b) BrO^- ($HBrO_2$ has more nonprotonated O atoms and is the stronger acid, so BrO^- is the stronger base.)

(c) HPO_4^{2-} (larger negative charge, greater attraction for H^+)

16.85　(a)　True

　　　　(b)　False. In a series of acids that have the same central atom, acid strength increases with the number of nonprotonated oxygen atoms bonded to the central atom.

　　　　(c)　False. H_2Te is a stronger acid than H_2S because the H-Te bond is longer, weaker and more easily dissociated than the H-S bond.

Lewis Acids and Bases

16.87　**Theory**　　　　　　**Acid**　　　　　　　　　　**Base**

Arrhenius　　　　　forms H^+ ions in water　　　produces OH^- in water

Brønsted-Lowry　　proton (H^+) donor　　　　proton acceptor

Lewis　　　　　　electron pair acceptor　　　electron pair donor

The Brønsted-Lowry theory is more general than Arrhenius's definition, because it is based on a unified model for the processes responsible for acidic or basic character, and it shows the relationships between these processes. The Lewis theory is more general still because it does not restrict the acidic species to compounds having ionizable hydrogen. Any substance that can be viewed as an electron-pair acceptor is defined as a Lewis acid.

16.89　　　　　　　**Lewis Acid**　　　**Lewis Base**

　　　　(a)　$Fe(ClO_4)_3$ or Fe^{3+}　　　H_2O

　　　　(b)　H_2O　　　　　　　　　CN^-

　　　　(c)　BF_3　　　　　　　　　$(CH_3)_3N$

　　　　(d)　HIO　　　　　　　　　NH_2^-

16.91　(a)　Cu^{2+}, higher cation charge

　　　　(b)　Fe^{3+}, higher cation charge

　　　　(c)　Al^{3+}, smaller cation radius, same charge

Additional Exercises

16.93　(a)　$HC_4H_7O_2(aq) + H_2O(l) \rightleftharpoons H_3O^+(aq) + C_4H_7O_2^-(aq)$
　　　　　　　acid　　　　　　　　　　　　　　　　　　conj. base

　　　　(b)　$CN^-(aq) + H_2O(l) \rightleftharpoons OH^-(aq) + HCN(aq)$
　　　　　　　base　　　　　　　　　　　　　conj. acid

16.95　$pK_w = 13.76$,　$K_w = 10^{-13.76} = 1.738 \times 10^{-14} = 1.7 \times 10^{-14}$

　　　　$[H^+] = [OH^-]$;　$K_w = [H^+]^2$;　$1.738 \times 10^{-14} = [H^+]^2$;　$[H^+] = 1.3 \times 10^{-7}\ M$

19.98　No. K_a and K_b (thus pK_a and pK_b) values assume Brønsted-Lowery behavior of acids and bases in aqueous solutions. $[H_2O]$ does not appear in the K expressions because H_2O is a pure liquid, but it is a required reactant in the chemical equilibria described by K_a and K_b values.

16.99 The solution with the higher pH has the lower $[H^+]$.

    (a)   For solutions with equal concentrations, the weaker acid will have a lower $[H^+]$ and higher pH.

    (b)   The acid with $K_a = 8 \times 10^{-6}$ is the weaker acid, so it has the higher pH.

    (c)   The base with $pK_b = 4.5$ is the stronger base, has greater $[OH^-]$ and smaller $[H^+]$, so higher pH.

16.101 (a) $H_2X \rightarrow H^+ + HX^-$

            Assuming HX^- does not ionize, $[H^+] = 0.050\ M$, pH = 1.30

    (b) $H_2X \rightarrow 2H^+ + X^-$; $0.050\ M\ H_2X = 0.10\ M\ H^+$; pH = 1.00

    (c)   The observed pH of a $0.050\ M$ solution of H_2X is only slightly less than 1.30, the pH assuming no ionization of HX^-. HX^- is not completely ionized; H_2X, which is completely ionized, is a stronger acid than HX^-.

    (d)   Since H_2X is a strong acid, HX^- has no tendency to act like a base. HX^- does act like a weak acid, so a solution of NaHX would be acidic.

16.104 Call each compound in the neutral form Q.

Then, $Q(aq) + H_2O(l) \rightleftharpoons QH^+(aq) + OH^-$. $K_b = [QH^+][OH^-]/[Q]$

The ratio in question is $[QH^+]/[Q]$, which equals $K_b/[OH^-]$ for each compound. At pH = 2.5, pOH = 11.5, $[OH^-]$ = antilog $(-11.5) = 3.16 \times 10^{-12} = 3 \times 10^{-12}\ M$. Now calculate $K_b/[OH^-]$ for each compound:

Nicotine $\dfrac{[QH^+]}{[Q]} = 7 \times 10^{-7}/3.16 \times 10^{-12} = 2 \times 10^5$

Caffeine $\dfrac{[QH^+]}{[Q]} = 4 \times 10^{-14}/3.16 \times 10^{-12} = 1 \times 10^{-2}$

Strychnine $\dfrac{[QH^+]}{[Q]} = 1 \times 10^{-6}/3.16 \times 10^{-12} = 3 \times 10^5$

Quinine $\dfrac{[QH^+]}{[Q]} = 1 \times 10^{-6}/3.16 \times 10^{-12} = 3.5 \times 10^5$

For all the compounds except caffeine the protonated form has a much higher concentration than the neutral form. However, for caffeine, a very weak base, the neutral form dominates.

Integrative Exercises

16.107 At 25°C, $[H^+] = [OH^-] = 1.0 \times 10^{-7}\ M$

$$\frac{1.0 \times 10^{-7}\ \text{mol}\ H^+}{1\ L\ H_2O} \times 0.0010\ L \times \frac{6.022 \times 10^{23}\ H^+\ \text{ions}}{\text{mol}\ H^+} = 6.0 \times 10^{13}\ H^+\ \text{ions}$$

16.109 Strategy: Use $PV = nRT$ to calculate mol SO_2, and thus mol H_2SO_3 and M H_2SO_3. Solve the equilibrium problem to find $[H^+]$ and pH.

$$n = \frac{PV}{RT} = \frac{1.0 \text{ atm} \times 3.9 \text{ L } SO_2}{293 \text{ K}} \times \frac{K \cdot mol}{0.08206 \text{ L} \cdot atm} = 0.162 = 0.16 \text{ mol } SO_2$$

From the given reaction, mol SO_2 = mol H_2SO_3. 0.16 mol H_2SO_3/1.0 L = 0.16 M H_2SO_3

$$H_2SO_3(aq) \rightleftharpoons H^+(aq) + HSO_3^-(aq) \qquad K_{a1} = 1.7 \times 10^{-2}$$

$$HSO_3^-(aq) \rightleftharpoons H^+(aq) + SO_3^{2-}(aq) \qquad K_{a2} = 6.4 \times 10^{-8}$$

$$K_{a1} = 1.7 \times 10^{-2} = \frac{[H^+][HSO_3^-]}{[H_2SO_3]} = \frac{x^2}{0.162 - x}; \text{ since } K_{a1} \text{ is relatively large, use the quadratic.}$$

$$x^2 + 1.7 \times 10^{-2} x - 2.75 \times 10^{-3} = 0; \quad x = \frac{-1.7 \times 10^{-2} \pm \sqrt{(1.7 \times 10^{-2})^2 - 4(1)(-2.75 \times 10^{-3})}}{2}$$

$x = 0.0447 = 0.045 \, M \, H^+; \quad pH = 1.35$

16.112 Calculate M of the solution from osmotic pressure, and K_b using the equilibrium expression for the hydrolysis of cocaine. Let Coc = cocaine and CocH$^+$ be the conjugate acid of cocaine.

$$\pi = MRT; \quad M = \pi/RT = \frac{52.7 \text{ torr}}{288 \text{ K}} \times \frac{1 \text{ atm}}{760 \text{ torr}} \times \frac{mol \cdot K}{0.08206 \text{ L} \cdot atm}$$

$$= 0.002934 = 2.93 \times 10^{-3} \, M \, Coc$$

pH = 8.53; pOH = 14 - pH = 5.47; $[OH^-] = 10^{-5.47} = 3.39 \times 10^{-6} = 3.4 \times 10^{-6} \, M$

$$Coc(aq) + H_2O(l) \rightleftharpoons CocH^+(aq) + OH^-(aq)$$

initial $2.93 \times 10^{-3} \, M$ 0   0

equil. $(2.93 \times 10^{-3} - 3.4 \times 10^{-6}) \, M$ $3.4 \times 10^{-6} \, M$ $3.4 \times 10^{-6} \, M$

$$K_b = \frac{[CocH^+][OH^-]}{[Coc]} = \frac{(3.39 \times 10^{-6})^2}{(2.934 \times 10^{-3} - 3.39 \times 10^{-6})} = 3.9 \times 10^{-9}$$

Note that % hydrolysis is small in this solution, so "x", $3.4 \times 10^{-6} \, M$, is small compared to $2.93 \times 10^{-3} \, M$ and could be ignored in the denominator of the calculation.

16.114 (a)   (i) $HCO_3^-(aq) \rightleftharpoons H^+(aq) + CO_3^{2-}(aq)$ $K_1 = K_{a2}$ for $H_2CO_3 = 5.6 \times 10^{-11}$

$H^+(aq) + OH^-(aq) \rightleftharpoons H_2O(l)$ $K_2 = 1/K_w = 1 \times 10^{14}$

$HCO_3^-(aq) + OH^-(aq) \rightleftharpoons CO_3^{2-}(aq) + H_2O(l)$ $K = K_1 \times K_2 = 5.6 \times 10^3$

(ii) $NH_4^+(aq) \rightleftharpoons H^+(aq) + NH_3(aq)$ $K_1 = K_a$ for $NH_4^+ = 5.6 \times 10^{-10}$

$CO_3^{2-}(aq) + H^+(aq) \rightleftharpoons HCO_3^-(aq)$ $K_2 = 1/K_{a2}$ for $H_2CO_3 = 1.8 \times 10^{10}$

$NH_4^+(aq) + CO_3^{2-}(aq) \rightleftharpoons HCO_3^-(aq) + NH_3(aq)$ $K = K_1 \times K_2 = 10$

(b)   Both (i) and (ii) have K > 1, although K = 10 is not **much** greater than 1. Both could be written with a single arrow. (This is true in general when a strong acid or strong base, $H^+(aq)$ or $OH^-(aq)$, is a reactant.)

17 Additional Aspects of Aqueous Equilibria

Common-Ion Effect

17.1 (a) The extent of ionization of a weak electrolyte is decreased when a strong electrolyte containing an ion in common with the weak electrolyte is added to it.

(b) NaOCl

17.3 In general, when an acid is added to a solution, pH decreases; when a base is added to a solution, pH increases.

(a) pH increases; NO_2^- decreases the ionization of HNO_2 and decreases $[H^+]$.

(b) pH decreases; $CH_3NH_3^+$ decreases the ionization (hydrolysis) of CH_3NH_2 and decreases $[OH^-]$.

(c) pH increases; CHO_2^- decreases the ionization of $HCHO_2$ and decreases $[H^+]$.

(d) no change; Br^- is a negligible base and does not affect the 100% ionization of the strong acid HBr.

(e) pH decreases; the pertinent equilibrium is
$C_2H_3O_2^-(aq) + H_2O(l) \rightleftharpoons HC_2H_3O_2 + OH^-(aq)$.
HCl reacts with $OH^-(aq)$, decreasing $[OH^-]$ and pH.

17.5 (a)

$$HC_3H_5O_2(aq) \rightleftharpoons H^+(aq) + C_3H_5O_2^-(aq)$$

i	0.085 M		0.060 M
c	-x	+x	+x
e	(0.085 - x) M	+x M	(0.060 + x) M

$$K_a = 1.3 \times 10^{-5} = \frac{[H^+][C_3H_5O_2^-]}{[HC_3H_5O_2]} = \frac{(x)(0.060 + x)}{(0.085 - x)}$$

Assume x is small compared to 0.060 and 0.085.

$$1.3 \times 10^{-5} = \frac{0.060\,x}{0.085}; \quad x = 1.8 \times 10^{-5} = [H^+], \quad pH = 4.73$$

(b)

$$(CH_3)_3N(aq) + H_2O(l) \rightleftharpoons (CH_3)_3NH^+(aq) + OH^-(aq)$$

i	0.075 M	0.10 M	
c	-x	+x	+x
e	(0.075 - x) M	(0.10 + x) M	+x M

$$K_b = 6.4 \times 10^{-5} = \frac{[OH^-][(CH_3)_3NH^+]}{[(CH_3)_3N]} = \frac{(x)(0.10 + x)}{(0.075 - x)} \approx \frac{0.10\,x}{0.075}$$

$$x = 4.8 \times 10^{-5} = [OH^-], \quad pOH = 4.32, \quad pH = 14.00 - 4.32 = 9.68$$

17.7 $\quad\quad\quad\quad\quad$ HBu(aq) $\rightleftharpoons$ H$^+$(aq) + Bu$^-$(aq) $\quad\quad\quad\quad$ $K_a = \dfrac{[H^+][Bu^-]}{[HBu]} = 1.5 \times 10^{-5}$

$\quad$ equil (a) $\quad$ 0.050 - x M $\quad\quad$ x M $\quad\quad$ x M

$\quad$ equil (b) $\quad$ 0.050 - x M $\quad\quad$ x M $\quad\quad$ 0.070 + x M

(a) $\quad$ $K_a = 1.5 \times 10^{-5} = \dfrac{x^2}{0.050 - x} \approx \dfrac{x^2}{0.050}$; x = [H$^+$] = 8.66 × 10^{-4} = 8.7 × 10^{-4} M H$^+$

$\quad\quad$ % ionization = $\dfrac{8.7 \times 10^{-4}\,M\,H^+}{0.050\,M\,HBu}$ × 100 = 1.7% ionization

(b) $\quad$ $K_a = 1.5 \times 10^{-5} = \dfrac{(x)(0.070 + x)}{0.050 - x} \approx \dfrac{0.070\,x}{0.050}$; x = 1.1 × 10^{-5} M H$^+$

$\quad\quad$ % ionization = $\dfrac{1.1 \times 10^{-5}\,M\,H^+}{0.050\,M\,HBu}$ × 100 = 0.022% ionization

Buffers

17.9 $\quad$ HC$_2$H$_3$O$_2$ and NaC$_2$H$_3$O$_2$ are a weak conjugate acid/conjugate base pair which act as a buffer because unionized HC$_2$H$_3$O$_2$ reacts with added base, while C$_2$H$_3$O$_2^-$ combines with added acid, leaving [H$^+$] relatively unchanged. Although HCl and KCl are a conjugate acid/conjugate base pair, Cl$^-$ is a negligible base. That is, it has no tendency to combine with added acid to form unionized HCl. Any added acid simply increases [H$^+$] in an HCl/KCl mixture. In general, the conjugate bases of strong acids are negligible and mixtures of strong acids and their conjugate salts do not act as buffers.

17.11 $\quad$ Assume that % ionization is small in these buffers (Exercises 7.7 and 7.8).

(a) $\quad$ $K_a = \dfrac{[H^+][Lac^-]}{[HLac]}$; $[H^+] = \dfrac{[K_a][HLac]}{[Lac^-]} = \dfrac{1.4 \times 10^{-4}\,(0.12)}{(0.11)}$

$\quad\quad$ [H$^+$] = 1.53 × 10^{-4} = 1.5 × 10^{-4}; pH = 3.82

(b) $\quad$ mol = M × L; total volume = 85 mL + 95 mL = 180 mL

$\quad\quad$ $[H^+] = \dfrac{K_a[HLac]}{[Lac^-]} = \dfrac{1.4 \times 10^{-4}\,(0.13\,M \times 0.085\,L)/0.180\,L}{(0.15\,M \times 0.095\,L)/0.180\,L} = \dfrac{1.4 \times 10^{-4}\,(0.13 \times 0.085)}{(0.15 \times 0.095)}$

$\quad\quad$ [H$^+$] = 1.086 × 10^{-4} = 1.1 M H$^+$; pH = 3.96

17.13 (a) $\quad$ HC$_2$H$_3$O$_2$(aq) $\rightleftharpoons$ H$^+$(aq) + C$_2$H$_3$O$_2^-$(aq); $K_a = 1.8 \times 10^{-5} = \dfrac{[H^+][C_2H_3O_2^-]}{[HC_2H_3O_2]}$

$\quad\quad$ $[HC_2H_3O_2] = \dfrac{20.0\,g\,HC_2H_3O_2}{2.00\,L\,soln} \times \dfrac{1\,mol\,HC_2H_3O_2}{60.05\,g\,HC_2H_3O_2} = 0.167\,M$

$\quad\quad$ $[C_2H_3O_2^-] = \dfrac{20.0\,g\,NaC_2H_3O_2}{2.00\,L\,soln} \times \dfrac{1\,mol\,NaC_2H_3O_2}{82.04\,g\,NaC_2H_3O_2} = 0.122\,M$

$\quad\quad$ $[H^+] = \dfrac{K_a[HC_2H_3O_2]}{[C_2H_3O_2^-]} = \dfrac{1.8 \times 10^{-5}\,(0.167 - x)}{(0.122 + x)} \approx \dfrac{1.8 \times 10^{-5}\,(0.167)}{(0.122)}$

$\quad\quad$ [H$^+$] = 2.4843 × 10^{-5} = 2.5 × 10^{-5} M, pH = 4.60

(b) $Na^+(aq) + C_2H_3O_2^-(aq) + H^+(aq) + Cl^-(aq) \rightarrow HC_2H_3O_2(aq) + Na^+(aq) + Cl^-(aq)$

(c) $HC_2H_3O_2(aq) + Na^+(aq) + OH^-(aq) \rightarrow C_2H_3O_2^-(aq) + H_2O(l) + Na^+(aq)$

17.15   In this problem, $[BrO^-]$ is the unknown.

pH = 8.80, $[H^+] = 10^{-8.80} = 1.585 \times 10^{-9} = 1.6 \times 10^{-9}$ M

$[HBrO] = 0.050 - 1.6 \times 10^{-9} \approx 0.050$ M

$K_a = 2.5 \times 10^{-9} = \dfrac{1.585 \times 10^{-9}\,[BrO^-]}{0.050}$; $[BrO^-] = 0.07887 = 0.079$ M

For 1.00 L, 0.079 mol NaBrO are needed.

17.17   (a) $K_a = \dfrac{[H^+][C_2H_3O_2^-]}{[HC_2H_3O_2]}$; $[H^+] = \dfrac{K_a[HC_2H_3O_2]}{[C_2H_3O_2^-]}$

$[H^+] \approx \dfrac{1.8 \times 10^{-5}\,(0.10)}{(0.13)} = 1.385 \times 10^{-5} = 1.4 \times 10^{-5}$ M; pH = 4.86

(b) $HC_2H_3O_2(aq) + KOH(aq) \rightarrow C_2H_3O_2^-(aq) + H_2O(l) + K^+(aq)$

0.10 mol	0.02 mol	0.13 mol
-0.02 mol	-0.02 mol	+0.02 mol
0.08 mol	0 mol	0.15 mol

$[H^+] = \dfrac{1.8 \times 10^{-5}\,(0.08\ \text{mol}/0.100\ \text{L})}{(0.15\ \text{mol}/0.100\ \text{L})} = 9.60 \times 10^{-6} = 1 \times 10^{-5}$ M; pH = 5.02 = 5.0

(c) $C_2H_3O_2^-(aq) + HNO_3(aq) \rightarrow HC_2H_3O_2(aq) + Cl^-(aq)$

0.13 mol	0.02 mol	0.10 mol
-0.02 mol	-0.02 mol	+0.02 mol
0.11 mol	0 mol	0.12 mol

$[H^+] = \dfrac{1.8 \times 10^{-5}\,(0.12\ \text{mol}/0.100\ \text{L})}{(0.11\ \text{mol}/0.100\ \text{L})} = 1.96 \times 10^{-5} = 2.0 \times 10^{-5}$ M; pH = 4.71

17.19 $H_2CO_3(aq) \rightleftharpoons H^+(aq) + HCO_3^-(aq)$ $K_a = \dfrac{[H^+][HCO_3^-]}{[H_2CO_3]}$; $\dfrac{[HCO_3^-]}{[H_2CO_3]} = \dfrac{K_a}{[H^+]}$

(a)   at pH = 7.4, $[H^+] = 10^{-7.4} = 4.0 \times 10^{-8}$ M; $\dfrac{[HCO_3^-]}{[H_2CO_3]} = \dfrac{4.3 \times 10^{-7}}{4.0 \times 10^{-8}} = 11$

(b)   at pH = 7.1, $[H^+] = 7.9 \times 10^{-8}$ M; $\dfrac{[HCO_3^-]}{[H_2CO_3]} = 5.4$

Acid-Base Titrations

17.21   (a)   Curve B. The initial pH is lower and the equivalence point region is steeper.

(b)   pH at the approximate equivalence point of curve A = 8.0
pH at the approximate equivalence point of curve B = 7.0

(c)   Volume of base required to reach the equivalence point depends only on moles of acid present; it is independent of acid strength. Since acid B requires 40 mL and acid A requires only 30 mL, more moles of acid B are being titrated. For equal volumes of A and B, the concentration of acid B is greater.

17.23 (a)   HX is weaker. The pH at the equivalence point is determined by the identity and concentration of the conjugate base, X^- or Y^-. The higher the pH at the equivalence point, the stronger the conjugate base (X^-) and the weaker the conjugate acid (HX).

(b)   Phenolphthalein, which changes color in the pH 8-10 range, is perfect for HX and probably appropriate for HY. Bromthymol blue changes from 6-7.5, and thymol blue between from 8-9.5, but these are two-color indicators. One-color indicators such as phenolphthalein are preferred because detection of the color change is more reproducible.

17.25 (a) $40.0 \text{ mL HNO}_3 \times \dfrac{0.0900 \text{ mol HNO}_3}{1000 \text{ mL soln}} \times \dfrac{1 \text{ mol NaOH}}{1 \text{ mol HNO}_3} \times \dfrac{1000 \text{ mL soln}}{0.0850 \text{ mol NaOH}}$

$= 42.353 = 42.4 \text{ mL NaOH soln}$

(b) $35.0 \text{ mL HBr} \times \dfrac{0.0720 \ M \text{ HBr}}{1000 \text{ mL soln}} \times \dfrac{1 \text{ mol NaOH}}{1 \text{ mol HBr}} \times \dfrac{1000 \text{ mL soln}}{0.0850 \text{ mol NaOH}}$

$= 29.645 = 29.6 \text{ mL NaOH soln}$

(c) $\dfrac{1.85 \text{ g HCl}}{1 \text{ L soln}} \times \dfrac{1 \text{ mol HCl}}{36.46 \text{ g HCl}} = 0.05074 = 0.0507 \ M \text{ HCl}$

$50.0 \text{ mL HCl} \times \dfrac{0.05074 \text{ mol HCl}}{1000 \text{ mL}} \times \dfrac{1 \text{ mol NaOH}}{1 \text{ mol HCL}} \times \dfrac{1000 \text{ mL soln}}{0.0850 \text{ mol NaOH}}$

$= 29.847 = 29.8 \text{ mL NaOH soln}$

17.27   moles $H^+ = M_{HBr} \times L_{HBr} = 0.200 \ M \times 0.0200 \text{ L} = 4.00 \times 10^{-3} \text{ mol}$

moles $OH^- = M_{NaOH} \times L_{NaOH} = 0.200 \ M \times L_{NaOH}$

	mL_{HBr}	mL_{NaOH}	Total Volume	Moles H^+	Moles OH^-	Molarity Excess Ion	pH
(a)	20.0	15.0	35.0	4.00×10^{-3}	3.00×10^{-3}	$0.0286(H^+)$	1.544
(b)	20.0	19.9	39.9	4.00×10^{-3}	3.98×10^{-3}	$5 \times 10^{-4}(H^+)$	3.3
(c)	20.0	20.0	40.0	4.00×10^{-3}	4.00×10^{-3}	$1 \times 10^{-7}(H^+)$	7.0
(d)	20.0	20.1	40.1	4.00×10^{-3}	4.02×10^{-3}	$5 \times 10^{-4}(H^+)$	10.7
(e)	20.0	35.0	55.0	4.00×10^{-3}	7.00×10^{-3}	$0.0545(OH^-)$	12.737

molarity of excess ion = moles ion / total vol in L

(a) $\dfrac{4.00 \times 10^{-3} \text{ mol H}^+ - 3.00 \times 10^{-3} \text{ mol OH}^-}{0.0350 \text{ L}} = 0.0286 \ M \text{ H}^+$

(b) $\dfrac{4.00 \times 10^{-3} \text{ mol H}^+ - 3.98 \times 10^{-3} \text{ mol OH}^-}{0.0339 \text{ L}} = 5.01 \times 10^{-4} = 5 \times 10^{-4} \ M \text{ H}^+$

(c)　equivalence point, mol H^+ = mol OH^-

NaBr does not hydrolyze, so $[H^+]$ = $[OH^-]$ = 1×10^{-7} M

(d)　$\dfrac{4.02 \times 10^{-3} \text{ mol } H^+ - 4.00 \times 10^{-3} \text{ mol } OH^-}{0.041 \text{ L}}$ = 4.88×10^{-4} = 5×10^{-4} M OH^-

(e)　$\dfrac{7.00 \times 10^{-3} \text{ mol } H^+ - 4.00 \times 10^{-3} \text{ mol } OH^-}{0.0550 \text{ L}}$ = 0.054545 = 0.0545 M OH^-

17.29　(a)　At 0 mL, only weak acid, $HC_2H_3O_2$, is present in solution. Using the acid ionization equilibrium

$$HC_2H_3O_2(aq) \rightleftharpoons H^+(aq) + C_2H_3O_2^-(aq)$$

initial	0.150 M	0	0
equil	0.150 - x M	x M	x M

$$K_a = \dfrac{[H^+][C_2H_3O_2^-]}{[HC_2H_3O_2]} = 1.8 \times 10^{-5} \text{ (Appendix D)}$$

1.8×10^{-5} = $\dfrac{x^2}{(0.150 - x)}$ $\approx$ $\dfrac{x^2}{0.150}$; $x^2 = 2.7 \times 10^{-6}$; x = $[H^+]$ = 0.001643

$= 1.6 \times 10^{-3}$; pH = 2.78

(b)-(f)　Calculate the moles of each component after the acid-base reaction takes place. Moles $HC_2H_3O_2$ originally present = $M \times L$ = 0.150 M × 0.0350 L = 5.25×10^{-3} mol. Moles NaOH added = $M \times L$ = 0.150 M × y mL.

$$NaOH(aq) \; + \; HC_2H_3O_2(aq) \; \rightarrow \; Na^+C_2H_3O_2^-(aq) + H_2O(l)$$

		(0.150 M × 0.0175 L) =		
(b)	before rx	2.625×10^{-3} mol	5.25×10^{-3} mol	
	after rx	**0**	**2.625×10^{-3} mol**	**2.63×10^{-3} mol**
		(0.150 M × 0.0345 L) =		
(c)	before rx	5.175×10^{-3} mol	5.25×10^{-3} mol	
	after rx	**0**	**0.075×10^{-3} mol**	**5.18×10^{-3} mol**
		(0.150 M × 0.0350 L) =		
(d)	before rx	5.25×10^{-3} mol	5.25×10^{-3} mol	
	after rx	**0**	**0**	**5.25×10^{-3} mol**
		(0.150 M × 0.0355 L) =		
(e)	before rx	5.325×10^{-3} mol	5.25×10^{-3} mol	
	after rx	**0.075×10^{-3} mol**	**0**	**5.25×10^{-3} mol**
		(0.150 M × 0.0500 L) =		
(f)	before rx	7.50×10^{-3} mol	5.25×10^{-3} mol	
	after rx	**2.25×10^{-3} mol**	**0**	**5.25×10^{-3} mol**

Calculate the molarity of each species (M = mol/L) and solve the appropriate equilibrium problem in each part.

(b) V_T = 35.0 mL $HC_2H_3O_2$ + 17.5 mL NaOH = 52.5 mL = 0.0525 L

$$[HC_2H_3O_2] = \frac{2.625 \times 10^{-3} \text{ mol}}{0.0525} = 0.0500 \, M$$

$$[C_2H_3O_2^-] = \frac{2.625 \times 10^{-3} \text{ mol}}{0.0525} = 0.0500 \, M$$

$$HC_2H_3O_2(aq) \rightleftharpoons H^+(aq) + C_2H_3O_2^-(aq)$$

equil   0.0500 - x M x M 0.0500 + x M

$$K_a = \frac{[H^+][C_2H_3O_2^-]}{[HC_2H_3O_2]}; \quad [H^+] = \frac{K_a[HC_2H_3O_2]}{[C_2H_3O_2^-]}$$

$$[H^+] = \frac{1.8 \times 10^{-5}(0.0500 - x)}{(0.0500 + x)} = 1.8 \times 10^{-5} \, M \, H^+; \quad pH = 4.74$$

(c) $$[HC_2H_3O_2] = \frac{7.5 \times 10^{-5} \text{ mol}}{0.0695 \text{ L}} = 0.001079 = 1.1 \times 10^{-3} \, M$$

$$[C_2H_3O_2^-] = \frac{5.175 \times 10^{-3} \text{ mol}}{0.0695 \text{ L}} = 0.07446 = 0.074 \, M$$

$$[H^+] = \frac{1.8 \times 10^{-5}(1.079 \times 10^{-3} - x)}{(0.07446 + x)} \approx 2.6 \times 10^{-7} \, M \, H^+; \quad pH = 6.58$$

(d)   At the equivalence point, only $C_3H_5O_2^-$ is present.

$$[C_2H_3O_2^-] = \frac{5.25 \times 10^{-3} \text{ mol}}{0.0700 \text{ L}} = 0.0750 \, M$$

The pertinent equilibrium is the base hydrolysis of $C_2H_3O_2^-$.

$$C_2H_3O_2^-(aq) + H_2O(l) \rightleftharpoons HC_2H_3O_2(aq) + OH^-(aq)$$

initial   0.0750 M 0   0

equil   0.0750 - x M x   x

$$K_b = \frac{K_w}{K_a \text{ for } HC_2H_3O_2} = \frac{1.0 \times 10^{-14}}{1.8 \times 10^{-5}} = 5.56 \times 10^{-10} = 5.6 \times 10^{-10} = \frac{[HC_2H_3O_2][OH^-]}{[C_2H_3O_2^-]}$$

$$5.56 \times 10^{-10} = \frac{x^2}{0.0750 - x}; \quad x^2 \approx 5.56 \times 10^{-10}(0.0750); \quad x = 6.458 \times 10^{-6}$$

$$= 6.5 \times 10^{-10} \, M \, OH^-$$

pOH = -log(6.458 × 10⁻⁶) = 5.19; pH = 14.00 - pOH = 8.81

(e)   After the equivalence point, the excess strong base determines the pOH and pH. The $[OH^-]$ from the hydrolysis of $C_2H_3O_2^-$ is small and can be ignored.

$$[OH^-] = \frac{0.075 \times 10^{-3} \text{ mol}}{0.0705 \text{ L}} = 1.064 \times 10^{-3} = 1.1 \times 10^{-3} \, M; \quad pOH = 2.97$$

$$pH = 14.00 - 2.97 = 11.03$$

(f) $$[OH^-] = \frac{2.25 \times 10^{-3} \text{ mol}}{0.0850 \text{ L}} = 0.0265 \, M \, OH^-; \quad pOH = 1.577; \quad pH = 14.00 - 1.577 = 12.423$$

17.31 The volume of 0.200 M HBr required in all cases equals the volume of base and the final volume = $2V_{base}$. The concentration of the salt produced at the equivalence point =

$$\frac{0.200\,M \times V_{base}}{2V_{base}} = 0.100\,M.$$

(a) 0.100 M NaBr, pH = 7.00

(b) 0.100 M $HONH_3^+Br^-$; $\qquad\qquad HONH_3^+(aq) \rightleftharpoons H^+(aq) + HONH_2$

[equil] $\qquad$ 0.100 − x $\qquad\qquad$ x $\qquad$ x

$$K_a = \frac{[H^+][HONH_2]}{[HONH_3^+]} = \frac{K_w}{K_b} = \frac{1.0 \times 10^{-14}}{1.1 \times 10^{-8}} = 9.09 \times 10^{-7} = 9.1 \times 10^{-7}$$

Assume x is small with respect to [salt].

$K_a = x^2 / 0.100$; $x = [H^+] = 3.02 \times 10^{-4} = 3.0 \times 10^{-4}\,M$, pH = 3.52

(c) 0.100 M $C_6H_5NH_3^+Br^-$. Proceeding as in (b):

$$K_a = \frac{[H^+][C_6H_5NH_2]}{[C_6H_5NH_3^+]} = \frac{K_w}{K_b} = 2.33 \times 10^{-5} = 2.3 \times 10^{-5}$$

$[H^+]^2 = 0.100(2.33 \times 10^{-5})$; $[H^+] = 1.52 \times 10^{-3} = 1.5 \times 10^{-3}\,M$, pH = 2.82

Solubility Equilibria and Factors Affecting Solubility

17.33 (a) The concentration of undissolved solid does not appear in the solubility product expression because it is constant as long as there is solid present. Concentration is a ratio of moles solid to volume of the solid; solids occupy a specific volume not dependent on the solution volume. As the amount (moles) of solid changes, the volume changes proportionally, so that the ratio of moles solid to volume solid is constant.

(b) $K_{sp} = [Ag^+][I^-]$; $\quad K_{sp} = [Sr^{2+}][SO_4^{2-}]$; $\quad K_{sp} = [Fe^{2+}][OH^-]^2$; $\quad K_{sp} = [Hg_2^{2+}][Br^-]^2$

17.35 (a) $CaF_2(s) \rightleftharpoons Ca^{2+}(aq) + 2F^-(aq)$; $\quad K_{sp} = [Ca^{2+}][F^-]^2$

The molar solubility is the moles of CaF_2 that dissolve per liter of solution. Each mole of CaF_2 produces **1** mol $Ca^{2+}(aq)$ and **2** mol $F^-(aq)$.
$[Ca^{2+}] = 1.24 \times 10^{-3}\,M$; $[F^-] = 2 \times 1.24 \times 10^{-3}\,M = 2.48 \times 10^{-3}\,M$
$K_{sp} = (1.24 \times 10^{-3})(2.48 \times 10^{-3})^2 = 7.63 \times 10^{-9}$

(b) $SrF_2(s) \rightleftharpoons Sr^{2+}(aq) + 2F^-(aq)$; $\quad K_{sp} = [Sr^{2+}][F^-]^2$

Transform the gram solubility to molar solubility.

$$\frac{1.1 \times 10^{-2}\,g\;SrF_2}{0.100\,L} \times \frac{1\;mol\;SrF_2}{125.6\,g\;SrF_2} = 8.76 \times 10^{-4} = 8.8 \times 10^{-4}\,mol\;SrF_2/L$$

$[Sr^{2+}] = 8.76 \times 10^{-4}\,M$; $[F^-] = 2(8.76 \times 10^{-4}\,M)$

$K_{sp} = (8.76 \times 10^{-4})(2(8.76 \times 10^{-4}))^2 = 2.7 \times 10^{-9}$

(c) $Ba(IO_3)_2(s) \rightleftharpoons Ba^{2+}(aq) + 2IO_3^-(aq);\quad K_{sp} = [Ba^{2+}][IO_3^-]^2$

Since 1 mole of dissolved $Ba(IO_3)_2$ produces 1 mole of Ba^{2+}, the molar solubility of

$Ba(IO_3)_2 = [Ba^{2+}]$.   Let $x = [Ba^{2+}]$; $[IO_3^-] = 2x$

$K_{sp} = 6.0 \times 10^{-10} = (x)(2x)^2$; $4x^3 = 6.0 \times 10^{-10}$; $x^3 = 1.5 \times 10^{-10}$; $x = 5.3 \times 10^{-4}\ M$

The molar solubility of $Ba(IO_3)_2$ is 5.3×10^{-4} mol/L.

17.37 $CaC_2O_4(s) \rightleftharpoons Ca^{2+}(aq) + C_2O_4^{2-}(aq);\quad K_{sp} = [Ca^{2+}][C_2O_4^{2-}]$

$[Ca^{2+}] = [C_2O_4^{2-}] = \dfrac{0.0061\ g\ CaC_2O_4}{1.00\ L\ soln} \times \dfrac{1\ mol\ CaC_2O_4}{128.1\ g\ CaC_2O_4} = 4.76 \times 10^{-5} = 4.8 \times 10^{-5}\ M$

$K_{sp} = (4.76 \times 10^{-5}\ M)(4.76 \times 10^{-5}\ M) = 2.3 \times 10^{-9}$

17.39 (a) $AgBr(s) \rightleftharpoons Ag^+(aq) + Br^-(aq);\quad K_{sp} = [Ag^+][Br^-] = 5.0 \times 10^{-13}$

molar solubility $= x = [Ag^+] = [Br^-];\quad K_{sp} = x^2$

$x = (5.0 \times 10^{-13})^{1/2}$; $x = 7.1 \times 10^{-7}$ mol AgBr/L

(b)   Molar solubility $= x = [Br^-]$; $[Ag^+] = 0.030\ M + x$

$K_{sp} = (0.030 + x)(x) \approx 0.030(x)$

$5.0 \times 10^{-13} = 0.030(x)$; $x = 1.7 \times 10^{-11}$ mol AgBr/L

(c)   Molar solubility $= x = [Ag^+]$

There are two sources of Br^-: $NaBr(0.10\ M)$ and $AgBr(x\ M)$

$K_{sp} = (x)(0.10 + x)$; Assuming x is small compared to 0.10 M

$5.0 \times 10^{-13} = 0.10\ (x)$; $x \approx 5.0 \times 10^{-12}$ mol AgBr/L

17.41 $Mn(OH)_2(s) \rightleftharpoons Mn^{2+}(aq) + 2OH^-(aq);\ K_{sp} = 1.6 \times 10^{-13}$

Since $[OH^-]$ is set by the pH of the solution, the solubility of $Mn(OH)_2$ is just $[Mn^{2+}]$.

(a)   pH = 7.0, pOH = 14 - pH = 7.0, $[OH^-] = 10^{-pOH} = 1.0 \times 10^{-7}\ M$

$K_{sp} = 1.6 \times 10^{-13} = [Mn^{2+}](1.0 \times 10^{-7})^2$; $[Mn^{2+}] = \dfrac{1.6 \times 10^{-13}}{1.0 \times 10^{-14}} = 16\ M$

$\dfrac{16\ mol\ Mn(OH)_2}{1\ L} \times \dfrac{89.95\ g\ Mn(OH)_2}{1\ mol\ Mn(OH)_2} = 1423 = 1.4 \times 10^3\ g\ Mn(OH)_2/L$

Note that the solubility of $Mn(OH)_2$ in pure water is $3.6 \times 10^{-5}\ M$, and the pH of the resulting solution is 9.0. The relatively low pH of a solution buffered to pH 7.0 actually increases the solubility of $Mn(OH)_2$.

(b)   pH = 9.5, pOH = 4.5, $[OH^-] = 3.16 \times 10^{-5} = 3.2 \times 10^{-5}\ M$

$K_{sp} = 1.6 \times 10^{-13} = [Mn^{2+}](3.16 \times 10^{-5})^2$; $[Mn^{2+}] = \dfrac{1.6 \times 10^{-13}}{1.0 \times 10^{-9}} = 1.6 \times 10^{-4}\ M$

$1.6 \times 10^{-4}\ M\ Mn(OH)_2 \times 88.95\ g/mol = 0.0142 = 0.014\ g/L$

(c)   pH = 11.8, pOH = 2.2, $[OH^-] = 6.31 \times 10^{-3} = 6.3 \times 10^{-3}$ M

$$K_{sp} = 1.6 \times 10^{-13} = [Mn^{2+}](6.31 \times 10^{-3})^2; \quad [Mn^{2+}] = \frac{1.6 \times 10^{-13}}{3.98 \times 10^{-5}} = 4.0 \times 10^{-9} \text{ M}$$

4.02×10^{-9} M $Mn(OH)_2 \times 88.95$ g/mol $= 3.575 \times 10^{-7} = 3.6 \times 10^{-7}$ g/L

17.43   If the anion of the salt is the conjugate base of a weak acid, it will combine with H^+, reducing the concentration of the free anion in solution, thereby causing more salt to dissolve.
More soluble in acid: (a) $ZnCO_3$ (b) ZnS   (d) AgCN   (e) $Ba_3(PO_4)_2$

17.45   The formation equilibrium is

$$Cu^{2+}(aq) + 4NH_3(aq) \rightleftharpoons Cu(NH_3)_4{}^{2+}(aq) \quad K_f = \frac{[Cu(NH_3)_4{}^{2+}]}{[Cu^{2+}][NH_3]^4} = 5 \times 10^{12}$$

Assuming that nearly all the Cu^{2+} is in the form $Cu(NH_3)_4{}^{2+}$

$[Cu(NH_3)_4{}^{2+}] = 1 \times 10^{-3}$ M; $[Cu^{2+}] = x$; $[NH_3] = 0.10$ M

$$5 \times 10^{12} = \frac{(1 \times 10^{-3})}{x(0.10)^4}; \quad x = 2 \times 10^{-12} \text{ M} = [Cu^{2+}]$$

17.47 $Ag I(s) \rightleftharpoons Ag^+(aq) + I^-(aq)$

$\underline{Ag^+(aq) + 2CN^-(aq \rightleftharpoons Ag(CN)_2{}^-(aq)}$

$Ag I(s) + 2CN^-(aq) \rightleftharpoons Ag(CN)_2{}^-(aq) + I^-(aq)$

$$K = K_{sp} \times K_f = [Ag^+][I^-] \times \frac{[Ag(CN)_2{}^-]}{[Ag^+][CN^-]^2} = (8.3 \times 10^{-17})(1 \times 10^{21}) = 8 \times 10^4$$

Precipitation; Qualitative Analysis

17.49   Precipitation conditions: will Q (see Chapter 15) exceed K_{sp} for the compound?

(a)   In base, Ca^{2+} can form $Ca(OH)_2(s)$.

$Ca(OH)_2(s) \rightleftharpoons Ca^{2+}(aq) + 2OH^-(aq)$; $K_{sp} = [Ca^{2+}][OH^-]^2$

$Q = [Ca^{2+}][OH^-]^2$; $[Ca^{2+}] = 0.050$ M; pOH = 6; $[OH^-] = 10^{-6} = 1 \times 10^{-6}$ M

$Q = (0.050)(1 \times 10^{-6})^2 = 5 \times 10^{-14}$; $K_{sp} = 6.5 \times 10^{-6}$ (Appendix D)

$Q < K_{sp}$, no $Ca(OH)_2$ precipitates.

(b) $Ag_2SO_4(s) \rightleftharpoons 2Ag^+(aq) + SO_4{}^{2-}(aq)$; $K_{sp} = [Ag^+]^2[SO_4{}^{2-}]$

$$[Ag^+] = \frac{0.050 \text{ M} \times 100 \text{ mL}}{110 \text{ mL}} = 4.545 \times 10^{-2} = 4.5 \times 10^{-2} \text{ M}$$

$$[SO_4{}^{2-}] = \frac{0.050 \text{ M} \times 10 \text{ mL}}{110 \text{ mL}} = 4.545 \times 10^{-3} = 4.5 \times 10^{-3} \text{ M}$$

$Q = (4.545 \times 10^{-2})^2(4.545 \times 10^{-3}) = 9.4 \times 10^{-6}$; $K_{sp} = 1.5 \times 10^{-5}$

$Q < K_{sp}$, no Ag_2SO_4 precipitates.

17.51 $Mn(OH)_2(s) \rightleftharpoons Mn^{2+}(aq) + 2OH^-(aq)$; $K_{sp} = [Mn^{2+}][OH^-]^2 = 1.6 \times 10^{-13}$

At equilibrium, $[Mn^{2+}][OH^-]^2 = 1.6 \times 10^{-13}$. Change $[Mn^{2+}]$ to mol/L and solve for $[OH^-]$.

$$\frac{1\ \mu g\ Mn^{2+}}{1\ L} \times \frac{1 \times 10^{-6}\ g}{1\ \mu g} \times \frac{1\ mol\ Mn^{2+}}{54.94\ g\ Mn^{2+}} = 1.82 \times 10^{-8} = 2 \times 10^{-8}\ M\ Mn^{2+}$$

$1.6 \times 10^{-13} = (1.82 \times 10^{-8})[OH^-]^2$; $[OH^-]^2 = 8.79 \times 10^{-6}$; $[OH^-] = 2.96 \times 10^{-3} = 3 \times 10^{-3}\ M$

pOH = 2.53; pH = 14 - 2.53 = 11.47 = 11.5

17.53   Calculate $[I^-]$ needed to initiate precipitation of each ion. The cation that requires lower $[I^-]$ will precipitate first.

Ag^+: $K_{sp} = [Ag^+][I^-]$; $8.3 \times 10^{-17} = (2.0 \times 10^{-4})[I^-]$; $[I^-] = \dfrac{8.3 \times 10^{-17}}{2.0 \times 10^{-4}} = 4.2 \times 10^{-13}\ M\ I^-$

Pb^{2+}: $K_{sp} = [Pb^{2+}][I^-]^2$; $7.9 \times 10^{-9} = (1.5 \times 10^{-3})[I^-]^2$; $[I^-] = \left(\dfrac{7.9 \times 10^{-9}}{1.5 \times 10^{-3}}\right)^{1/2} = 2.3 \times 10^{-3}\ M\ I^-$

AgI will precipitate first, at $[I^-] = 4.2 \times 10^{-13}\ M$.

17.55   The first two experiments eliminate Group 1 and 2 ions (Figure 17.22). The fact that no insoluble carbonates form in the filtrate from the third experiment rules out Group 4 ions. The ions which might be in the sample are those of Group 3, that is, Al^{3+}, Fe^{2+}, Zn^{2+}, Cr^{3+}, Ni^{2+}, Co^{2+}, or Mn^{2+}, and those of Group 5, NH_4^+, Na^+ or K^+.

17.57   (a)   Make the solution acidic using 0.2 M HCl; saturate with H_2S. CdS will precipitate, ZnS will not.

       (b)   Add excess base; $Fe(OH)_3(s)$ precipitates, but Cr^{3+} forms the soluble complex $Cr(OH)_4^-$.

       (c)   Add $(NH_4)_2HPO_4$; Mg^{2+} precipitates as $MgNH_4PO_4$, K^+ remains in solution.

       (d)   Add 6 M HCl, precipitate Ag^+ as AgCl(s).

17.59   (a)   Because phosphoric acid is a weak acid, the concentration of free $PO_4^{3-}(aq)$ in an aqueous phosphate solution is low except in strongly basic media. In less basic media, the solubility product of the phosphates that one wishes to precipitate is not exceeded.

       (b) K_{sp} for those cations in Group 3 is much larger. Thus, to exceed K_{sp} a higher $[S^{2-}]$ is required. This is achieved by making the solution more basic.

       (c)   They should all redissolve in strongly acidic solution, e.g., in 12 M HCl (all the chlorides of Group 3 metals are soluble).

Additional Exercises

17.61 The equilibrium of interest is

$$HC_5H_3O_3(aq) \rightleftharpoons H^+(aq) + C_5H_3O_3^-(aq); \quad K_a = 6.76 \times 10^{-4} = \frac{[H^+][C_5H_3O_3^-]}{[HC_5H_3O_3]}$$

Begin by calculating $[HC_5H_3O_3]$ and $[C_5H_3O_3^-]$ for each case.

(a)
$$\frac{35.0 \text{ g } HC_5H_3O_3}{0.250 \text{ L soln}} \times \frac{1 \text{ mol } HC_5H_3O_3}{112.1 \text{ g } HC_5H_3O_3} = 1.249 = 1.25 \text{ M } HC_5H_3O_3$$

$$\frac{30.0 \text{ g } NaC_5H_3O_3}{0.250 \text{ L soln}} \times \frac{1 \text{ mol } NaC_5H_3O_3}{134.1 \text{ g } NaC_5H_3O_3} = 0.8949 = 0.895 \text{ M } C_5H_3O_3^-$$

$$[H^+] = \frac{K_a[HC_5H_3O_3]}{[C_5H_3O_3^-]} = \frac{6.76 \times 10^{-4}(1.249 - x)}{(0.8949 + x)} \approx \frac{6.76 \times 10^{-4}(1.249)}{(0.8949)}$$

$$[H^+] = 9.43 \times 10^{-4} \text{ M}, \quad pH = 3.025$$

(b)   For dilution, $M_1V_1 = M_2V_2$

$$[HC_5H_3O_3] = \frac{0.250 \text{ M} \times 30.0 \text{ mL}}{125 \text{ mL}} = 0.0600 \text{ M}$$

$$[C_5H_3O_3^-] = \frac{0.220 \text{ M} \times 20.0 \text{ mL}}{125 \text{ mL}} = 0.0352 \text{ M}$$

$$[H^+] \approx \frac{6.76 \times 10^{-4}(0.0600)}{0.0352} = 1.15 \times 10^{-3} \text{ M}, \quad pH = 2.938$$

(yes, $[H^+]$ is < 5% of 0.0352 M)

(c) $0.0850 \text{ M} \times 0.500 \text{ L} = 0.0425 \text{ mol } HC_5H_3O_3$

$1.65 \text{ M} \times 0.0500 \text{ L} = 0.0825 \text{ mol NaOH}$

$$HC_5H_3O_3(aq) + NaOH(aq) \rightarrow NaC_5H_3O_3(aq) + H_2O(l)$$

initial	0.0425 mol	0.0825 mol	
reaction	-0.0425 mol	-0.0425 mol	+0.0425 mol
after	0 mol	0.0400 mol	0.0425 mol

The strong base NaOH dominates the pH; the contribution of $C_5H_3O_3^-$ is negligible. This combination would be "after the equivalence point" of a titration. The total volume is 0.550 L.

$$[OH^-] = \frac{0.0400 \text{ mol}}{0.550 \text{ L}} = 0.0727 \text{ M}; \quad pOH = 1.138, \quad pH = 12.862$$

17.63 $K_a = \frac{[H^+][In^-]}{[HIn]}$; at pH = 4.68, [HIn] = [In^-]; $[H^+] = K_a$; pH = pK_a = 4.68

17.66   The pH of a buffer is centered around pK_a for its conjugate acid. For the bases in Table D.2, pK_a for the conjugate acids = 14 - pK_b. 14 - pK_b = 10.6; pK_b = 3.4, $K_b = 10^{-3.4} = 4 \times 10^{-4}$. Select two bases with K_b values near 4×10^{-4}.

Methylamine, dimethylamine and ethylamine have K_b values closest to 4×10^{-4}, and ammonia and trimethylamine would probably also work. We will select methylamine and dimethylamine. (We could also select very weak acids with $pK_a = 10.6$, $K_a = 10^{-10.6}$ $\approx 2.5 \times 10^{-11}$. Either HIO or HCO_3^- would be appropriate.)

In general, $BH^+(aq) \rightleftharpoons B(aq) + H^+(aq)$

$$K_a = \frac{[B][H^+]}{[BH^+]}; \quad [H^+] = \frac{K_a[BH^+]}{[B]}; \quad [H^+] = 10^{-10.6} = 2.51 \times 10^{-11} \, M$$

For methylamine, $K_a = \dfrac{1.0 \times 10^{-14}}{4.4 \times 10^{-4}} = 2.272 \times 10^{-11} = 2.3 \times 10^{-11}$;

$$\frac{[BH^+]}{[B]} = \frac{[H^+]}{K_a} = \frac{2.51 \times 10^{-11}}{2.27 \times 10^{-11}} = 1.1$$

The ratio of $[CH_3NH_3^+]$ to $[CH_3NH_2]$ is 1.1 to 1.

For dimethylamine, $K_a = \dfrac{1.0 \times 10^{-14}}{5.4 \times 10^{-4}} = 1.852 \times 10^{-11} = 1.9 \times 10^{-11}$;

$$\frac{[BH^+]}{[B]} = \frac{[H^+]}{K_a} = \frac{2.51 \times 10^{-11}}{1.85 \times 10^{-11}} = 1.4$$

The ratio of $[(CH_3)_2NH_2^+]$ to $[(CH_3)_2NH]$ is 1.4 to 1. (The stronger base requires more of its conjugate acid to achieve a buffer of the same pH.)

17.68   (a)   For a monoprotic acid (one H^+ per mole of acid), at the equivalence point
moles OH^- added = moles H^+ originally present

$$M_B \times V_B = \text{g acid/molar mass}$$

$$\mathcal{M} = \frac{\text{g acid}}{M_B \times V_B} = \frac{0.1355 \text{ g}}{0.0950 \, M \times 0.0193 \text{ L}} = 73.90 = 73.9 \text{ g/mol}$$

(b)   initial mol HA $= \dfrac{0.1355 \text{ g}}{73.9 \text{ g/mol}} = 1.834 \times 10^{-3} = 1.83 \times 10^{-3}$ mol HA

mol OH^- added to pH 5.10 $= 0.0950 \, M \times 0.0120 \text{ L} = 1.14 \times 10^{-3}$ mol OH^-

	HA(aq)	+	NaOH(aq)	→	NaA(aq) + H₂O
before rx	1.834×10^{-3} mol		1.14×10^{-3} mol		0
change	-1.14×10^{-3} mol		-1.14×10^{-3} mol		$+1.14 \times 10^{-3}$ mol
after rx	0.694×10^{-3} mol		0		1.14×10^{-3} mol

$$[HA] = \frac{0.694 \times 10^{-3} \text{ mol}}{0.0370 \text{ L}} = 0.01874 = 0.0187 \, M$$

$$[A^-] = \frac{1.14 \times 10^{-3} \text{ mol}}{0.0370 \text{ L}} = 0.03081 = 0.0308 \, M; \quad [H^+] = 10^{-5.10} = 7.94 \times 10^{-6} \, M$$

The mixture after reaction (a buffer) can be described by the acid dissociation equilibrium

	HA(aq)	$\rightleftharpoons$	H⁺(aq)	+	A⁻(aq)
initial	0.0187 M		0		0.0308 M
equil	(0.0187 - 7.94 × 10⁻⁶ M)		7.94 × 10⁻⁶ M		(0.0308 + 7.94 × 10⁻⁶) M

$$K_a = \frac{[H^+][A^-]}{[HA]} \approx \frac{(7.94 \times 10^{-6})(0.0308)}{(0.0187)} = 1.3 \times 10^{-5}$$

(Although we have carried 3 figures through the calculation to avoid rounding errors, the data indicate an answer with 2 significant figures.)

17.70 (a) $\dfrac{0.4885 \text{ g KHP}}{0.100 \text{ L}} \times \dfrac{1 \text{ mol KHP}}{204.2 \text{ g KHP}} = 0.02392 = 0.0239 \ M \ P^{2-}$ at the equivalence point

The pH at the equivalence point is determined by the hydrolysis of P^{2-}.

$$P^{2-}(aq) + H_2O(l) \rightleftharpoons HP^-(aq) + OH^-(aq)$$

$$K_b = \frac{[HP^-][OH^-]}{[P^{2-}]} = \frac{K_w}{K_a \text{ for HP}^-} = \frac{1.0 \times 10^{-14}}{3.1 \times 10^{-6}} = 3.23 \times 10^{-9} = 3.2 \times 10^{-9}$$

$$3.23 \times 10^{-9} = \frac{x^2}{(0.02392 - x)} \approx \frac{x^2}{0.2392}; \ X = [OH^-] = 8.8 \times 10^{-6} \ M$$

pH = 14 - 5.06 = 8.94. From Figure 16.4, either phenolphthalein (pH 8.2 - 10.0) or thymol blue (pH 8.0 - 9.6) could be used to detect the equivalence point.

Phenolphthalein is usually the indicator of choice because the colorless to pink change is easier to see.

(b) $0.4885 \text{ g KHP} \times \dfrac{1 \text{ mol KHP}}{204.2 \text{ g KHP}} \times \dfrac{1 \text{ mol NaOH}}{1 \text{ mol KHP}} \times \dfrac{1}{0.03855 \text{ L NaOH}}$

$$= 0.06206 \ M \text{ NaOH}$$

17.73 Assume that H_3PO_4 will react with NaOH in a stepwise fashion. (This is not unreasonable, since the three K_a values for H_3PO_4 are significantly different.)

	H_3PO_4(aq)	+	NaOH(aq)	$\rightarrow$	$H_2PO_4^-$(aq)	+	Na⁺(aq)	+	H_2O(l)
before	0.20 mol		0.30 mol		0 mol				
after	0 mol		0.10 mol		0.20 mol				

	$H_2PO_4^-$(aq)	+	NaOH(aq)	$\rightarrow$	HPO_4^-(aq)	+	Na⁺(aq)	+	H_2O(l)
before	0.20 mol		0.10 mol		0.25 mol				
after	0.10 mol		0		0.35 mol				

Thus, after all NaOH has reacted, the resulting 1.00 L solution is a buffer containing 0.10 mol $H_2PO_4^-$ and 0.35 mol HPO_4^{2-}. $H_2PO_4^-$(aq) $\rightleftharpoons$ H⁺(aq) + HPO_4^{2-}(aq)

$$K_a = 6.2 \times 10^{-8} = \frac{[HPO_4^{2-}][H^+]}{[H_2PO_4^-]}; \ [H^+] = \frac{6.2 \times 10^{-8} (0.10 \ M)}{0.35 \ M} = 1.77 \times 10^{-8} = 1.8 \times 10^{-8} \ M;$$

$$\text{pH} = 7.75$$

17.76 $C_3H_5O_3^-$ will be formed by reaction of $HC_3H_5O_3$ with NaOH.

0.1000 M × 0.05000 L = 5.000 × 10^{-3} mol $HC_3H_5O_3$; b = mol NaOH needed

	$HC_3H_5O_3$	+	NaOH	→	$C_3H_5O_3^-$	+ H_2O + Na^+
initial	5.000 × 10^{-3}		b mol			
rx	-b mol		-b mol		+b mol	
after rx	5.000 × 10^{-3} - b mol		0		b mol	

$K_a = \dfrac{[H^+][C_3H_5O_3^-]}{[HC_3H_5O_3]}$; $K_a = 1.4 \times 10^{-4}$; $[H^+] = 10^{-pH} = 10^{-3.50} = 3.16 \times 10^{-4} = 3.2 \times 10^{-4}\,M$

Since solution volume is the same for $HC_3H_5O_3$ and $C_3H_5O_3^-$, we can use moles in the equation for $[H^+]$.

$K_a = 1.4 \times 10^{-4} = \dfrac{3.16 \times 10^{-4}\,(b)}{(5.000 \times 10^{-3} - b)}$;   0.4427 (5.000 × 10^{-3} - b) = b, 2.214 × 10^{-3} = 1.4427 b,

b = 1.53 × 10^{-3} = 1.5 × 10^{-3} mol OH^-

(The precision of K_a dictates that the result has 2 sig figs.)

Substituting this result into the K_a expression gives $[H^+] = 3.27 \times 10^{-4}$. (Using 1.53 × 10^{-3} mol OH^- (3 sig figs) gives, $[H^+] = 3.16 \times 10^{-4}$, a more reassuring cross check.)

Calculate volume NaOH required from M = mol/L.

1.53 × 10^{-3} mol OH^- × $\dfrac{1\,L}{1.000\,mol}$ × $\dfrac{1\,\mu L}{1 \times 10^{-6}\,L}$ = 1.5 × 10^3 μL (1.5 mL)

17.79   After precipitation, the solution in contact with $CaF_2(s)$ is saturated. The $[Ca^{2+}]$ calculated from the K_{sp} expression gives an upper limit of $[Ca^{2+}]$ remaining in solution.

$K_{sp} = [Ca^{2+}][F^-]^2 = 3.9 \times 10^{-11}$; $[F^-] = 0.10\,M$

3.9 × 10^{-11} = $[Ca^{2+}](0.10)^2$; $[Ca^{2+}] = 3.9 \times 10^{-9}\,M$

17.82 $PbSO_4(s) \rightleftharpoons Pb^{2+}(aq) + SO_4^{2-}(aq)$; $K_{sp} = 6.3 \times 10^{-7} = [Pb^{2+}][SO_4^{2-}]$

$SrSO_4(s) \rightleftharpoons Sr^{2+}(aq) + SO_4^{2-}(aq)$; $K_{sp} = 3.2 \times 10^{-7} = [Sr^{2+}][SO_4^{2-}]$

Let x = $[Pb^{2+}]$, y = $[Sr^{2+}]$, x + y = $[SO_4^{2-}]$

$\dfrac{x(x+y)}{y(x+y)} = \dfrac{6.3 \times 10^{-7}}{3.2 \times 10^{-7}}$; $\dfrac{x}{y}$ = 1.9688 = 2.0; x = 1.969 y = 2.0 y

y(1.969 y+y) = 3.2 × 10^{-7}; 2.969 y^2 = 3.2 × 10^{-7}; y = 3.283 × 10^{-4} = 3.3 × 10^{-4}

x = 1.969 y; x = 1.969(3.283 × 10^{-4}) = 6.464 × 10^{-4} = 6.5 × 10^{-4}

$[Pb^{2+}]$ = 6.5 × $10^{-4}\,M$, $[Sr^{2+}]$ = 3.3 × $10^{-4}\,M$, $[SO_4^{2-}]$ = (3.283 + 6.464) × 10^{-4} = 9.7 × $10^{-4}\,M$

17.85

$Zn(OH)_2(s) \rightleftharpoons Zn^{2+}(aq) + 2OH^-(aq)$	$K_{sp} = 3.0 \times 10^{-16}$
$Zn^{2+}(aq) + 4OH^-(aq) \rightleftharpoons Zn(OH)_4^{2-}(aq)$	$K_f = 4.6 \times 10^{17}$

$Zn(OH)_2(s) + 2OH^-(aq) \rightleftharpoons Zn(OH)_4^{2-}(aq)$ $K = K_{sp} \times K_f = 138 = 1.4 \times 10^2$

$$K = 138 = 1.4 \times 10^2 = \frac{[Zn(OH)_4^{2-}]}{[OH^-]^2}$$

If 0.010 mol $Zn(OH)_2$ dissolves, 0.010 mol $Zn(OH)_4^{2-}$ should be present at equilibrium.

$$[OH^-]^2 = \frac{(0.010)}{138}; \quad [OH^-] = 8.5 \times 10^{-3} \, M \quad [OH^-] \geq 8.5 \times 10^{-3} \, M \text{ or pH} \geq 11.93$$

Integrative Exercises

17.86 (a) Complete ionic:

$H^+(aq) + Cl^-(aq) + Na^+(aq) + CHO_2^-(aq) \rightarrow HCHO_2(aq) + Na^+(aq) + Cl^-(aq)$

Na^+ and Cl^- are spectator ions.

Net ionic: $H^+(aq) + CHO_2^-(aq) \rightleftharpoons HCHO_2(aq)$

(b) The net ionic equation in part (a) is the reverse of the dissociation of $HCHO_2$.

$$K = \frac{1}{K_a} = \frac{1}{1.8 \times 10^{-4}} = 5.55 \times 10^3 = 5.6 \times 10^3$$

(c) For Na^+ and Cl^-, this is just a dilution problem.

$M_1V_1 = M_2V_2$; V_2 is 50.0 mL + 50.0 mL = 100.0 mL

Cl^-: $\dfrac{0.15 \, M \times 50.0 \, mL}{100.0 \, mL} = 0.075 \, M$; Na^+: $\dfrac{0.15 \, M \times 50.0 \, mL}{100.0 \, mL} = 0.075 \, M$

H^+ and CHO_2^- react to form $HCHO_2$. Since K >> 1, the reaction essentially goes to completion.

$0.15 \, M \times 0.0500 \, mL = 7.5 \times 10^{-3} \, mol \, H^+$

$0.15 \, M \times 0.0500 \, mL = 7.5 \times 10^{-3} \, mol \, CHO_2^-$

$\overline{ = 7.5 \times 10^{-3} \, mol \, HCHO_2}$

Solve the weak acid problem to determine $[H^+]$, $[CHO_2^-]$ and $[HCHO_2]$ at equilibrium.

$$K_a = \frac{[H^+][CHO_2^-]}{[HCHO_2]}; \quad [H^+] = [CHO_2^-] = x \, M; \quad [HCHO_2] = \frac{(7.5 \times 10^{-3} - x) \, mol}{0.100 \, L}$$

$$= (0.075 - x) \, M$$

$$1.8 \times 10^{-4} = \frac{x^2}{(0.075-x)} \approx \frac{x^2}{0.075}; \quad x = 3.7 \times 10^{-3} \, M \quad H^+ \text{ and } HCHO_2^-$$

$[HCHO_2] = (0.075 - 0.0037) = 0.071 \, M$

$$\frac{[H^+]}{[HNO_2]} \times 100 = \frac{3.7 \times 10^{-3}}{0.075} \times 100 = 4.9\% \text{ dissociation}$$

In summary:

$[Na^+] = [Cl^-] = 0.075 \, M$, $[HCHO_2] = 0.071 \, M$, $[H^+] = [CHO_2^-] = 0.0037 \, M$

17.88 $n = \dfrac{PV}{RT} = 735 \text{ torr} \times \dfrac{1 \text{ atm}}{760 \text{ torr}} \times \dfrac{7.5 \text{ L}}{295 \text{ K}} \times \dfrac{\text{K} \cdot \text{mol}}{0.08206 \text{ L} \cdot \text{atm}} = 0.300 = 0.30 \text{ mol NH}_3$

0.40 M × 0.50 L = 0.20 mol HCl

$$HCl(aq) \;+\; NH_3(g) \;\rightarrow\; NH_4^+(aq) \;+\; Cl^-(aq)$$

before	0.20 mol	0.30 mol		
after	0	0.10 mol	0.20 mol	0.20 mol

The solution will be a buffer because of the substantial concentrations of NH_3 and NH_4^+ present. Use K_a for NH_4^+ to describe the equilibrium.

$$NH_4^+(aq) \;\rightleftharpoons\; NH_3(aq) + H^+(aq)$$

equil.   0.20 - x   0.10 + x   x

$K_a = \dfrac{1.0 \times 10^{-14}}{1.8 \times 10^{-5}} = 5.56 \times 10^{-10} = 5.6 \times 10^{-10}$; $K_a = \dfrac{[NH_3][H^+]}{[NH_4^+]}$; $[H^+] = \dfrac{K_a[NH_4^+]}{[NH_3]}$

Since this expression contains a ratio of concentrations, volume will cancel and we can substitute moles directly. Assume x is small compared to 0.10 and 0.20.

$[H^+] = \dfrac{5.56 \times 10^{-10}(0.20)}{(0.10)} = 1.111 \times 10^{-9} = 1.1 \times 10^{-9} \, M$,   pH = 8.95

17.91 $\pi = MRT$, $M = \dfrac{\pi}{RT} = \dfrac{21 \text{ torr}}{298 \text{ K}} \times \dfrac{1 \text{ atm}}{760 \text{ torr}} \times \dfrac{\text{K} \cdot \text{mol}}{0.08206 \text{ L} \cdot \text{atm}} = 1.13 \times 10^{-3} = 1.1 \, M$

$SrSO_4(s) \rightleftharpoons Sr^{2+}(aq) + SO_4^{2-}(aq)$; $K_{sp} = [Sr^{2+}][SO_4^{2-}]$

The total particle concentration is $1.13 \times 10^{-3} \, M$. Each mole of $SrSO_4$ that dissolves produces 2 mol of ions, so $[Sr^{2+}] = [SO_4^{2-}] = 1.13 \times 10^{-3} \, M / 2 = 5.65 \times 10^{-4} = 5.7 \times 10^{-4} \, M$.

$K_{sp} = (5.65 \times 10^{-4})^2 = 3.2 \times 10^{-7}$

18 Chemistry of the Environment

Earth's Atmosphere

18.1 (a) The temperature profile of the atmosphere (Figure 18.1) is the basis of its division into regions. The center of each peak or trough in the temperature profile corresponds to a new region.

(b) Troposphere, 0-12 km; stratosphere, 12-50 km; mesosphere, 50-85 km; thermosphere, 85-110 km.

18.3 $P_{Ar} = \chi_{Ar} \cdot P_{atm}$; $P_{Ar} = 0.00934 \, (742 \text{ torr}) = 6.93 \text{ torr}$

$P_{CO_2} = \chi_{CO_2} \cdot P_{atm}$; $P_{CO_2} = 0.000355 \, (742 \text{ torr}) = 0.2634 = 0.263 \text{ torr}$

18.5 $P_{He} = \chi_{He} \cdot P_{atm}$; $P_{He} = 5.24 \times 10^{-6} \, (0.97 \text{ atm}) = 5.083 \times 10^{-6} = 5.1 \times 10^{-6} \text{ atm}$

$$n_{He} = \frac{P_{He}V}{RT} = \frac{5.083 \times 10^{-6} \text{ atm} \times 1.0 \text{ L}}{295 \text{ K}} \times \frac{K \cdot mol}{0.08206 \, L \cdot atm} = 2.100 \times 10^{-7}$$

$$= 2.1 \times 10^{-7} \text{ mol He}$$

$$2.100 \times 10^{-7} \text{ mol He} \times \frac{6.022 \times 10^{23} \text{ atoms}}{1 \text{ mol}} = 1.3 \times 10^{17} \text{ He atoms}$$

The Upper Atmosphere; Ozone

18.7 $$\frac{210 \times 10^3 \text{ J}}{1 \text{ mol}} \times \frac{1 \text{ mol}}{6.022 \times 10^{23} \text{ molecules}} = 3.487 \times 10^{-19} = 3.49 \times 10^{-19} \text{ J/molecule}$$

$\lambda = c/\nu$ We also have that $E = h\nu$, so $\nu = E/h$. Thus,

$$\lambda = \frac{hc}{E} = \frac{(6.626 \times 10^{-34} \text{ J} \cdot \text{sec})(3.00 \times 10^8 \text{ m/sec})}{3.487 \times 10^{-19} \text{ J}} = 5.70 \times 10^{-7} \text{ m} = 570 \text{ nm}$$

18.9 The bond dissociation energy of N_2, 941 kJ/mol, is much higher than that of O_2, 495 kJ/mol. Photons with a wavelength short enough to photodissociate N_2 are not as abundant as the ultraviolet photons which lead to photodissociation of O_2. Also, N_2 does not absorb these photons as readily as O_2 so even if a short-wavelength photon is available, it may not be absorbed by an N_2 molecule.

18.11 (a) Oxygen atoms exist longer at 120 km because there are fewer particles (atoms and molecules) at this altitude and thus fewer collisions and subsequent reactions that consume O atoms.

(b) Ozone is the primary absorber of high energy ultraviolet radiation in the 200-310 nm range. If this radiation were not absorbed in the stratosphere, plants and animals at the earth's surface would be seriously and adversely affected.

18.13 *CFC* stands for chlorofluorocarbon, a class of compounds that contain chlorine, fluorine and carbon. A common CFC is Freon-12, CF_2Cl_2. CFCs are harmful to the environment because their photodissociation produces Cl atoms, which catalyze the destruction of ozone.

18.15 (a) $HCl(g)$, $ClONO_2(g)$

(b) Neither HCl nor $ClONO_2$ react directly with ozone. The chlorine that is present in the "chlorine reservoir" does not participate in the destruction of ozone. Thus, the larger the "chlorine reservoir," the slower the rate of ozone depletion.

Chemistry of the Troposphere

18.17 (a) CO binds with hemoglobin in the blood to block O_2 transport to the cells; people with CO poisoning suffocate from lack of O_2.

(b) SO_2 is corrosive to lung tissue and contributes to higher levels of respiratory disease and shorter life expectancy, especially for people with other respiratory problems such as asthma. It also is a major source of acid rain, which damages forests and wildlife in natural waters.

(c) O_3 is extremely reactive and toxic because of its ability to form free radicals upon reaction with organic molecules in the body. It is particularly dangerous for asthma suffers, exercisers and the elderly. O_3 can also react with organic compounds in polluted air to form peroxyacylnitrates, which cause eye irritation and breathing difficulties.

18.19 CO in unpolluted air is typically 0.05 ppm, whereas in urban air CO is about 10 ppm. A major source is automobile exhaust. SO_2 is less than 0.01 ppm in unpolluted air and on the order of 0.08 ppm in urban air. A major source is coal and oil-burning power plants, but there is also some SO_2 in auto exhaust. NO is about 0.01 ppm in unpolluted air and about 0.05 ppm in urban air. It comes mainly from auto exhaust.

18.21 All oxides of nonmetals produce acid solutions when dissolved in water. Sulfur oxides are produced naturally during volcanic eruptions and carbon oxides are products of combustion and metabolism. These dissolved gases cause rainwater to be naturally acidic.

18.23 Among the components of coal are sulfur-containing organic compounds. Combustion (oxidation) of these molecules produces $SO_2(g)$. Formation of $SO_3(g)$ requires further oxidation of SO_2 according to the reaction

$$2SO_2(g) + O_2(g) \rightleftharpoons 2\ SO_3(g)$$

Oxidation of $SO_2(g)$ to $SO_3(g)$ is significant but not complete, perhaps because carbon consumes most of the available $O_2(g)$.

18.25 (a)   Visible (Figure 6.4)

(b) $E_{photon} = hc/\lambda = \dfrac{6.626 \times 10^{-34} \text{ J} \bullet \text{s} \times 3.00 \times 10^8 \text{ m/s}}{420 \times 10^{-9} \text{ m}} = 4.733 \times 10^{-19}$

$= 4.73 \times 10^{-19}$ J/photon

$\dfrac{4.733 \times 10^{-19} \text{ J}}{1 \text{ photon}} \times \dfrac{6.022 \times 10^{23} \text{ photons}}{1 \text{ mol}} \times \dfrac{1 \text{ kJ}}{1000 \text{ J}} = 285$ kJ/mol

18.27 A *greenhouse gas* functions like the glass in a greenhouse. In the atmosphere, greenhouse gases absorb infrared radiation given off by the earth and send it back to the earth's surface, where it is detected as heat. The main greenhouse gases are $H_2O(g)$ and $CO_2(g)$ but $CH_4(g)$ and other trace gases act similarly.

The World Ocean

18.29 A salinity of 5.3 denotes that there are 5.3 g of dry salt per kg of water.

$\dfrac{5.3 \text{ g NaCl}}{1 \text{ kg soln}} \times \dfrac{1.03 \text{ kg soln}}{1 \text{ L soln}} \times \dfrac{1 \text{ mol NaCl}}{58.44 \text{ g NaCl}} \times \dfrac{1 \text{ mol Na}^+}{1 \text{ mol NaCl}} = 0.0934 = 0.093$ M Na^+

18.31 1×10^{11} g Br $\times \dfrac{1 \times 10^3 \text{ g H}_2\text{O}}{0.067 \text{ g Br}} \times \dfrac{1 \text{ L H}_2\text{O}}{1 \times 10^3 \text{ g H}_2\text{O}} = 1.5 \times 10^{12}$ L H_2O

Because the process is only 10% efficient, ten times this much, or 1.5×10^{13} L H_2O, must be processed.

Freshwater

18.33 (a)   Decomposition of organic matter by aerobic bacteria depletes dissolved O_2. A low dissolved oxygen concentration indicates the presence of organic pollutants.

(b)   According to Section 13.3, the solubility of $O_2(g)$ (or any gas) in water decreases with increasing temperature.

18.35 1.0 g $C_{18}H_{29}O_3S^-\times \dfrac{1 \text{ mol } C_{18}H_{29}O_3S^-}{325 \text{ g } C_{18}H_{29}O_3S^-} \times \dfrac{51 \text{ mol } O_2}{2 \text{ mol } C_{18}H_{29}O_3S^-} \times \dfrac{32.0 \text{ g } O_2}{1 \text{ mol } O_2} = 2.5$ g O_2

Notice that the mass of O_2 required is 2.5 times greater than the mass of biodegradable material.

18.37 $Ca^{2+}(aq) + 2HCO_3^-(aq) \rightarrow CaCO_3(s) + CO_2(g) + H_2O(l)$

18.39 $Ca(OH)_2$ is added to remove Ca^{2+} as $CaCO_3(s)$, and Na_2CO_3 removes the remaining Ca^{2+}. $Ca^{2+}(aq) + 2HCO_3^-(aq) + [Ca^{2+}(aq) + 2OH^-(aq)] \rightarrow 2CaCO_3(s) + 2H_2O(l)$.   One mole $Ca(OH)_2$ is needed for each 2 moles of $HCO_3^-(aq)$ present. If there are 7.0×10^{-4} mol $HCO_3^-(aq)$ per liter, we must add 3.5×10^{-4} mol $Ca(OH)_2$ per liter, or a total of 0.35 mol $Ca(OH)_2$ for 10^3 L. This reaction removes 3.5×10^{-4} mol of the original Ca^{2+} from each liter of solution, leaving 1.5×10^{-4} M $Ca^{2+}(aq)$. To remove this $Ca^{2+}(aq)$, we add 1.5×10^{-4} mol Na_2CO_3 per liter, or a total of 0.15 mol Na_2CO_3, forming $CaCO_3(s)$.

Additional Exercises

18.41 (a) *Acid rain* is rain with a larger $[H^+]$ and thus a lower pH than expected. The additional H^+ is produced by the dissolution of sulfur and nitrogen oxides such as $SO_3(g)$ and $NO_2(g)$ in rain droplets to form sulfuric and nitric acid, $H_2SO_4(aq)$ and $HNO_3(aq)$.

(b) The *greenhouse effect* is warming of the atmosphere caused by heat trapping gases such as $CO_2(g)$ and $H_2O(g)$. That is, these gases absorb infrared or "heat" radiation emitted from the earth's surface and serve to maintain a relatively constant temperature on the surface. A significant increase in the amount of atmospheric CO_2 (from burning fossil fuels and other sources) could cause a corresponding increase in the average surface temperature and drastically change the global climate.

(c) *Photochemical smog* is an unpleasant collection of atmospheric pollutants initiated by photochemical dissociation of NO_2 to form NO and O atoms. The major components are NO(g), $NO_2(g)$, CO(g) and unburned hydrocarbons, all produced by automobile engines, and $O_3(g)$, ozone.

(d) The *ozone hole* is a region of depleted O_3 in the stratosphere over Antarctica. It is caused by reactions between O_3 and Cl atoms originating from chlorofluorocarbons (CFC's), CF_xCl_{4-x}. Depletion of the ozone layer would allow damaging ultraviolet radiation disruptive to the plant and animal life in our ecosystem to reach earth.

18.43 Stratospheric ozone is formed and destroyed in a cycle of chemical reactions. The decomposition of O_3 to O_2 and O produces oxygen atoms, an essential ingredient for the production of ozone. While single O_3 molecules exist for only a few seconds, new O_3 molecules are constantly reformed. This cyclic process ensures a finite concentration of O_3 in the stratosphere available to absorb ultraviolet radiation. (This explanation assumes that the cycle is not disrupted by outside agents such as CFCs.)

18.45 (a) The production of Cl atoms in the stratosphere is the result of the photodissociation of a C-Cl bond in the chlorofluorocarbon molecule.

$$CF_2Cl_2(g) \xrightarrow{h\nu} CF_2Cl(g) + Cl(g)$$

According to Table 8.4, the bond dissociation energy of a C-Br bond is 276 kJ/mol, while the value for a C-Cl bond is 328 kJ/mol. Photodissociation of $CBrF_3$ to form Br atoms requires less energy than the production of Cl atoms and should occur readily in the stratosphere.

(b) $$CBrF_3(g) \xrightarrow{h\nu} CF_3(g) + Br(g)$$

$$Br(g) + O_3(g) \longrightarrow BrO(g) + O_2(g)$$

Also, under certain conditions

$$BrO(g) + BrO(g) \longrightarrow Br_2O_2(g)$$

$$Br_2O_2(g) + h\nu \longrightarrow O_2(g) + 2Br(g)$$

18.48 From section 18.4:

$$N_2(g) + O_2(g) \rightleftharpoons 2NO(g) \quad \Delta H = +180.8 \text{ kJ} \quad (1)$$

$$2NO(g) + O_2(g) \rightleftharpoons 2NO_2(g) \quad \Delta H = -113.1 \text{ kJ} \quad (2)$$

In an endothermic reaction, heat is a reactant. As the temperature of the reaction increases, the addition of heat favors formation of products and the value of K increases. The reverse is true for exothermic reactions; as temperature increases, the value of K decreases. Thus, K for reaction (1), which is endothermic, increases with increasing temperature and K for reaction (2), which is exothermic, decreases with increasing temperature.

18.51 (a) According to Section 13.3, the solubility of gases in water decreases with increasing temperature. Thus, the solubility of $CO_2(g)$ in the ocean would decrease if the temperature of the ocean increased.

    (b) If the solubility of $CO_2(g)$ in the ocean decreased because of global warming, more $CO_2(g)$ would be released into the atmosphere, perpetuating a cycle of increasing temperature and concomitant release of $CO_2(g)$ from the ocean.

18.54 (a) CO_3^{2-} is a relatively strong Brønsted base and produces OH^- in aqueous solution according to the hydrolysis reaction:

$$CO_3^{2-}(aq) + H_2O(l) \rightleftharpoons HCO_3^-(aq) + OH^-(aq), \quad K_b = 1.8 \times 10^{-4}$$

If $[OH^-(aq)]$ is sufficient to exceed K_{sp} for $Mg(OH)_2$, the solid will precipitate.

    (b) $$\frac{125 \text{ mg Mg}^{2+}}{1 \text{ kg soln}} \times \frac{1 \text{ g Mg}^{2+}}{1000 \text{ mg Mg}^{2+}} \times \frac{1.00 \text{ kg soln}}{1.00 \text{ L soln}} \times \frac{1 \text{ mol Mg}^{2+}}{24.305 \text{ g Mg}^{2+}} = 5.143 \times 10^{-3}$$

$$= 5.14 \times 10^{-3} \ M \ Mg^{2+}$$

$$\frac{4.0 \text{ g Na}_2CO_3}{1.0 \text{ L soln}} \times \frac{1 \text{ mol CO}_3^{2-}}{106.0 \text{ g Na}_2CO_3} = 0.03774 = 0.038 \ M \ CO_3^{2-}$$

$$K_b = 1.8 \times 10^{-4} = \frac{[HCO_3^-][OH^-]}{[CO_3^{2-}]} \approx \frac{x^2}{0.03774}; \quad x = [OH^-] = 2.606 \times 10^{-3}$$

$$= 2.6 \times 10^{-3} \ M$$

(This represents 6.9% hydrolysis, but the result will not be significantly different using the quadratic formula.)

$$Q = [Mg^{2+}][OH^-]^2 = (5.143 \times 10^{-3})(2.606 \times 10^{-3})^2 = 3.5 \times 10^{-8}$$

K_{sp} for $Mg(OH)_2 = 1.6 \times 10^{-12}$; $Q > K_{sp}$, so $Mg(OH)_2$ will precipitate.

Integrative Exercises

18.57 (a) $$0.021 \text{ ppm NO}_2 = \frac{0.021 \text{ mol NO}_2}{1 \times 10^6 \text{ mol air}} = 2.1 \times 10^{-8} = \chi_{NO_2}$$

$$P_{NO_2} = \chi_{NO_2} \cdot P_{atm} = 2.1 \times 10^{-8} (745 \text{ torr}) = 1.565 \times 10^{-5} = 1.6 \times 10^{-5} \text{ torr}$$

    (b) $$n = \frac{PV}{RT}; \text{ molecules} = n \times \frac{6.022 \times 10^{23} \text{ molecules}}{\text{mol}} = \frac{PV}{RT} \times \frac{6.022 \times 10^{23} \text{ molecules}}{\text{mol}}$$

$$V = 15 \text{ ft} \times 14 \text{ ft} \times 8 \text{ ft} \times \frac{12^3 \text{ in}^3}{\text{ft}^3} \times \frac{2.54^3 \text{ cm}^3}{\text{in}^3} \times \frac{1 \text{ L}}{1000 \text{ cm}^3} = 4.757 \times 10^4 = 5 \times 10^4 \text{ L}$$

$$1.565 \times 10^{-5} \text{ torr} \times \frac{1 \text{ atm}}{760 \text{ torr}} \times \frac{4.757 \times 10^4 \text{ L}}{293 \text{ K}} \times \frac{\text{K} \cdot \text{mol}}{0.08206 \text{ L} \cdot \text{atm}}$$

$$\times \frac{6.022 \times 10^{23} \text{ molecules}}{\text{mol}} = 2.453 \times 10^{19} = 2 \times 10^{19} \text{ molecules}$$

18.59   (a) $8{,}376{,}726 \text{ tons coal} \times \dfrac{83 \text{ ton C}}{100 \text{ ton coal}} \times \dfrac{44.01 \text{ ton CO}_2}{12.01 \text{ ton C}} = 2.5 \times 10^7 \text{ ton CO}_2$

        $8{,}376{,}726 \text{ tons coal} \times \dfrac{2.5 \text{ ton S}}{100 \text{ ton coal}} \times \dfrac{64.07 \text{ ton SO}_2}{32.07 \text{ ton S}} = 4.18 \times 10^5$

                                                                                       $= 4.2 \times 10^5 \text{ ton SO}_2$

  (b) $\text{CaO(s)} + \text{SO}_2\text{(g)} \rightarrow \text{CaSO}_3\text{(s)}$

        $4.18 \times 10^5 \text{ ton SO}_2 \times \dfrac{55 \text{ ton SO}_2 \text{ removed}}{100 \text{ ton SO}_2 \text{ produced}} \times \dfrac{120.15 \text{ ton CaSO}_3}{64.07 \text{ ton SO}_2}$

                                                                   $= 4.3 \times 10^5 \text{ ton CaSO}_3$

18.63   Osmotic pressure is determined by total concentration of dissolved particles. From Table 18.6, $M_T = 1.13$. The minimum pressure needed to initiate reverse osmosis is $\pi = MRT$, Equation [13.13]. Assuming 298 K,

$$\pi = MRT = \frac{1.13 \text{ mol}}{1 \text{ L}} \times 298 \text{ K} \times \frac{0.08206 \text{ L} \cdot \text{atm}}{\text{K} \cdot \text{mol}} = 27.6 \text{ atm}$$

18.66   Initial pressures: $P_{N_2} = 0.78 (1.5 \text{ atm}) = 1.17 = 1.2 \text{ atm}; \quad P_{O_2} = 0.21 (1.5 \text{ atm}) = 0.315$

                                                                                       $= 0.32 \text{ atm}$

$$P_{NO} = \frac{3200 \text{ atm}}{1 \times 10^6 \text{ atm}} \times 1.5 \text{ atm} = 4.8 \times 10^{-3} \text{ atm}$$

Calculate Q to determine which direction the reaction will proceed.

$$Q = \frac{P_{NO}^2}{P_{N_2} \times P_{O_2}} = \frac{(4.8 \times 10^{-3})^2}{(1.17)(0.315)} = 6.3 \times 10^{-5}, \quad K_p = 1.0 \times 10^{-5}$$

$Q > K_p$, the reaction proceeds to the left.

	N_2(g)	+	O_2(g)	$\rightleftharpoons$	2NO(g)
initial	1.17 atm		0.315 atm		4.8×10^{-3} atm
change	+x		+x		-2x
equil	(1.17 + x)atm		(0.315 + x)atm		$(4.8 \times 10^{-3} - 2x)$ atm

$$K_p = 1.0 \times 10^{-5} = \frac{(4.8 \times 10^{-3} - 2x)^2}{(1.17 + x)(0.315 + x)}$$

Assume x is small compared to 1.17 and 0.315 (but not 4.8×10^{-3}).

P_{NO} at equilibrium $= (4.8 \times 10^{-3} - 2x) = y$

$$K_p = 1.0 \times 10^{-5} = \frac{y^2}{(1.17)(0.315)}; \quad y^2 = 3.686 \times 10^{-6}; \quad y = 1.92 \times 10^{-3} = 1.9 \times 10^{-3} \text{ atm}$$

Concentration, $M = \text{mol/L} = n/V = p/RT$;

$$[N_2] = \frac{1.17 \text{ atm}}{1173 \text{ K}} \times \frac{K \cdot mol}{0.08206 \text{ L} \cdot atm} = 1.2 \times 10^{-2} \ M$$

$$[O_2] = \frac{0.315 \text{ atm}}{1173 \text{ K}} \times \frac{K \cdot mol}{0.08206 \text{ L} \cdot atm} = 3.3 \times 10^{-3} \ M$$

$$[NO] = \frac{1.92 \times 10^{-3} \text{ atm}}{1173 \text{ K}} \times \frac{K \cdot mol}{0.0821 \text{ L} \cdot atm} = 2.0 \times 10^{-5} \ M \ (\text{or } 1300 \text{ ppm})$$

Note that the effect of attaining equilibrium is to reduce the concentration of NO, without significantly changing the concentrations of N_2 and O_2.

18.68   (a)   According to Table 18.1, the mole fraction of CO_2 in air is 0.000355.

$$P_{CO_2} = \chi_{CO_2} \cdot P_{atm} = 0.000355 \ (1.00 \text{ atm}) = 3.55 \times 10^{-4} \text{ atm}$$

$$C_{CO_2} = kP_{CO_2} = 3.1 \times 10^{-2} \ M/atm \times 3.55 \times 10^{-4} \text{ atm} = 1.10 \times 10^{-5} = 1.1 \times 10^{-5} \ M$$

(b) H_2CO_3 is a weak acid, so the $[H^+]$ is regulated by the equilibria:

$$H_2CO_3(aq) \rightleftharpoons H^+(aq) + HCO_3^-(aq) \qquad K_{a1} = 4.3 \times 10^{-7}$$

$$HCO_3^-(aq) \rightleftharpoons H^+(aq) + CO_3^{2-}(aq) \qquad K_{a2} = 5.6 \times 10^{-11}$$

Since the value of K_{a2} is small compared to K_{a1}, we will assume that most of the $H^+(aq)$ is produced by the first dissociation.

$$K_{a1} = 4.3 \times 10^{-7} = \frac{[H^+][HCO_3^-]}{[H_2CO_3]}; \ [H^+] = [HCO_3^-] = x, [H_2CO_3] = 1.1 \times 10^{-5} - x$$

Since K_{a1} and $[H_2CO_3]$ have similar values, we cannot assume x is small compared to 1.1×10^{-5}.

$$4.3 \times 10^{-7} = \frac{x^2}{(1.1 \times 10^{-5} - x)}; \ 4.73 \times 10^{-12} - 4.3 \times 10^{-7} x = x^2$$

$$0 = x^2 + 4.3 \times 10^{-7} - 4.73 \times 10^{-12}$$

$$x = \frac{-4.3 \times 10^{-7} \pm \sqrt{(4.3 \times 10^{-7})^2 - 4(1)(-4.73 \times 10^{-12})}}{2(1)}$$

$$x = \frac{-4.3 \times 10^{-7} \pm \sqrt{1.85 \times 10^{-13} + 1.89 \times 10^{-11}}}{2} = \frac{-4.3 \times 10^{-7} \pm 4.37 \times 10^{-6}}{2}$$

The negative result is meaningless; $x = 1.97 \times 10^{-6} = 2.0 \times 10^{-6} \ M \ H^+$; pH = 5.71

Since this $[H^+]$ is quite small, the $[H^+]$ from the autoionization of water might be significant. Calculation shows that for $[H^+] = 2.0 \times 10^{-6} \ M$ from H_2CO_3, $[H^+]$ from $H_2O = 5.2 \times 10^{-9} \ M$, which we can ignore.

19 Chemical Thermodynamics

Spontaneous Processes

19.1   Spontaneous: b, c, d; nonspontaneous: a, e

19.3   (a) $NH_4NO_3(s)$ dissolves in water, as in a chemical cold pack. Naphthalene (moth balls) sublimes at room temperature.

(b)   Melting of a solid is spontaneous above its melting point but nonspontaneous below its melting point.

19.5   (a)   Endothermic

(b)   Above 100°C or 373 K, the process is spontaneous.

(c)   Below 100°C or 373 K, the process is nonspontaneous.

(d)   At 100°C or 373 K, the two phases are in equilibrium.

19.7   (a)   For a *reversible* process, the forward and reverse changes occur by the same path. There is only one reversible pathway for a specified set of conditions.

(b)   If a system is returned to its original state via a reversible path, the surroundings are also returned to their original state. That is, there is no net change in the surroundings.

(c)   The vaporization of water to steam is reversible if it occurs at the boiling temperature of water for a specified external (atmospheric) pressure. This is the temperature and pressure at which the two phases are in equilibrium.

19.9   (a)   E is a state function.

(b)   The quantities q and w depend on path.

(c)   There is only **one** reversible pathway by which a system can change from one state to another, at a specified set of conditions.

Entropy and the Second Law

19.11   (a)   Yes, the process is spontaneous.

(b) $w = -P_{ext}\Delta V$. Since the gas expands into a vacuum, $P_{ext} = 0$ and $w = 0$.

(c)   The driving force for this expansion is the increase in the possible arrangements of the molecules, the increase in disorder of the system.

19.13   (a)   *Entropy* is the disorder or randomness of a system.

(b) ΔS is positive if disorder increases.

(c)   No. ΔS is a state function, so it is independent of path.

183

19.15 (a)   More gaseous particles means more possible arrangements and greater disorder; ΔS is positive.

       (b) ΔS is positive for Exercise 19.2 (a) and (c). (In (e), even though HCl(aq) is a mixture, there are fewer moles of gas in the product, so ΔS is not positive.)

19.17 S increases in (a), (b) and (c); S decreases in (d).

19.19 (a) $Br_2(l) \rightarrow Br_2(g)$, ΔS is positive

       (b) $\Delta S = \dfrac{\Delta H}{T} = \dfrac{29.6\ kJ}{mol\ Br_2(l)} \times 1.00\ mol\ Br_2(l) \times \dfrac{1}{(273.15 + 58.8)\,K} \times \dfrac{1000\ J}{1\ kJ} = 89.2\ J/K$

19.21 (a)   For a spontaneous process, the entropy of the universe increases; for a reversible process, the entropy of the universe does not change.

       (b)   In a reversible process, $\Delta S_{system} + \Delta S_{surroundings} = 0$. If ΔS_{system} is positive, $\Delta S_{surroundings}$ must be negative.

       (c)   Since $\Delta S_{universe}$ must be positive for a spontaneous process, $\Delta S_{surroundings}$ must be positive and greater than 75 J/K.

19.23 (a)   The entropy of a pure crystalline substance at absolute zero is zero.

       (b)   In *translational* motion, the entire molecule moves in a single direction; in *rotational* motion, the molecule rotates or spins around a fixed axis. *Vibrational* motion is reciprocating motion. The bonds within a molecule stretch and bend, but the average position of the atoms does not change.

       (c)   H—Cl $\longleftrightarrow$ H———Cl $\longleftrightarrow$ H–Cl

19.25 (a)   Ar(g) (gases have higher entropy due primarily to much larger volume)

       (b)   He(g) at 1.5 atm (larger volume and more motional freedom)

       (c)   1 mol of Ne(g) in 15.0 L (larger volume provides more motional freedom)

       (d) $CO_2(g)$ (more motional freedom)

19.27 (a) ΔS negative (moles of gas decrease)

       (b) ΔS positive (gas produced, increased disorder)

       (c) ΔS negative (moles of gas decrease)

       (d) ΔS positive (moles of gas increase)

19.29 (a)   Sc(s), 34.6 J/mol•K; Sc(g), 174.7 J/mol•K. In general, the gas phase of a substance has a larger $S°$ than the solid phase because of the greater volume and motional freedom of the molecules.

       (b) $NH_3(g)$, 192.5 J/mol•K; $NH_3(aq)$, 111.3 J/mol•K. Molecules in the gas phase have more motional freedom than molecules in solution.

       (c)   1 mol of $P_4(g)$, 280 J/K; 2 mol of $P_2(g)$, 2(218.1) = 436.2 J/K. More particles have a greater number of arrangements.

(d)   C(diamond), 2.43 J/mol·K ; C(graphite) 5.69 J/mol·K . Diamond is a network covalent solid with each C atom tetrahedrally bound to four other C atoms. Graphite consists of sheets of fused planar 6-membered rings with each C atom bound in a trigonal planar arrangement to three other C atoms. The internal entropy in graphite is greater because there is translational freedom among the planar sheets of C atoms while there is very little vibrational freedom within the network covalent diamond lattice.

19.31   Hydrocarbon $S°$ (J/mol·K)

Hydrocarbon	$S°$ (J/mol·K)
$CH_4(g)$	186.3
$C_2H_6(g)$	229.5
$C_3H_8(g)$	269.9
$C_4H_{10}(g)$	310.0

As the number of C atoms increases, the $S°$ of the hydrocarbon increases. The increased structural complexity means more motional degrees of freedom for each molecule.

19.33   (a) $\Delta S° = S° \; C_2H_6(g) - S° \; C_2H_4(g) - S° \; H_2(g)$

= 229.5 - 219.4 - 130.58 = -120.5 J/K

$\Delta S°$ is negative because there are fewer moles of gas in the products.

(b) $\Delta S° = 2S° \; NO_2(g) - \Delta S° \; N_2O_4(g) = 2(240.45) - 304.3 = +176.6$ J/K

$\Delta S°$ is positive because there are more moles of gas in the products.

(c) $\Delta S° = \Delta S° \; BeO(s) + \Delta S° \; H_2O(g) - \Delta S° \; Be(OH)_2(s)$

= 13.77 + 188.83 - 50.21 = +152.39 J/K

$\Delta S°$ is positive because the product contains more total particles and more moles of gas.

(d) $\Delta S° = 2S° \; CO_2(g) + 4S° \; H_2O(g) - 2S° \; CH_3OH(g) - 3S° \; O_2(g)$

= 2(213.6) + 4(188.83) - 2(237.6) - 3(205.0) = +92.3 J/K

$\Delta S°$ is positive because the product contains more total particles and more moles of gas.

Gibbs Free Energy

19.35   (a) $\Delta G = \Delta H - T\Delta S$

(b)   If ΔG is positive, the process is nonspontaneous, but the reverse process is spontaneous.

(c)   There is no relationship between ΔG and rate of reaction. A spontaneous reaction, one with a $-\Delta G$, may occur at a very slow rate. For example: $2H_2(g) + O_2(g) \rightarrow 2H_2O(g)$, $\Delta G = -457$ kJ is very slow if not initiated by a spark.

19.37   (a) $\Delta H°$ is negative; the reaction is exothermic.

(b) $\Delta S°$ is negative; the reaction leads to decrease in disorder (increase in order) of the system.

(c) $\Delta G° = \Delta H° - T\Delta S° = -35.4$ kJ $- 298$ K $(-0.0855$ kJ/K$) = -9.921 = -9.9$ kJ

(d)   At 298 K, $\Delta G°$ is negative. If all reactants and products are present in their standard states, the reaction is spontaneous at this temperature.

19.39   (a) $\Delta H° = 2(-268.61) - [0 + 0] = -537.22$ kJ

$\Delta S° = 2(173.51) - [130.58 + 202.7] = 13.74 = 13.7$ J/K

$\Delta G° = 2(-270.70) - [0 + 0] = -541.40$ kJ

$\Delta G° = -537.22$ kJ $- 298(0.01374)$ kJ $= -541.31$ kJ

(b) $\Delta H° = -106.7 - [0 + 2(0)] = -106.7$ kJ

$\Delta S° = 309.4 - [5.69 + 2(222.96)] = -142.21 = -142.2$ J/K

$\Delta G° = -64.0 - [0 + 2(0)] = -64.0$ kJ

$\Delta G° = -106.7$ kJ $- 298(-0.14221)$ kJ $= -64.3$ kJ

(c) $\Delta H° = 2(-542.2) - [2(-288.07) + 0] = -508.26 = -508.3$ kJ

$\Delta S° = 2(325) - [2(311.7) + 205.0] = -178.4 = -178$ J/K

$\Delta G° = 2(-502.5) - [2(-269.6) + 0] = -465.8$ kJ

$\Delta G° = -508.26$ kJ $- 298(-0.1784)$ kJ $= -455.097 = -455.1$ kJ

(The discrepancy in $\Delta G°$ values is due to experimental uncertainties in the tabulated thermodynamic data.)

(d) $\Delta H° = -84.68 + 2(-241.82) - [2(-201.2) + 0] = -165.92 = -165.9$ kJ

$\Delta S° = 229.5 + 2(188.83) - [2(237.6) + 130.58] = 1.38 = 1.4$ J/K

$\Delta G° = -32.89 + 2(-228.57) - [2(-161.9) + 0] = -166.23 = -166.2$ kJ

19.41   (a) $\Delta G° = 2\Delta G° \, SO_3(g) - [2\Delta G° \, SO_2(g) + \Delta G° \, O_2(g)]$

        $= 2(-370.4) - [2(-300.4) + 0] = -140.0$ kJ, spontaneous

(b) $\Delta G° = 3\Delta G° \, NO(g) - [\Delta G° \, NO_2(g) + \Delta G° \, N_2O(g)]$

        $= 3(86.71) - [51.84 + 103.59] = +104.70$ kJ, nonspontaneous

(c) $\Delta G° = 4\Delta G° \, FeCl_3(s) + 3\Delta G° \, O_2(g) - [6\Delta G° \, Cl_2(g) + 2\Delta G° \, Fe_2O_3(s)]$

        $= 4(-334) + 3(0) - [6(0) + 2(-740.98)] = +146$ kJ, nonspontaneous

(d) $\Delta G° = \Delta G° \, S(s) + 2\Delta G° \, H_2O(g) - [\Delta G° \, SO_2(g) + 2\Delta G° \, H_2(g)]$

        $= 0 + 2(-228.57) - [(-300.4) + 2(0)] = -156.7$ kJ, spontaneous

19.43   (a) $C_6H_{12}(l) + 9O_2(g) \rightarrow 6CO_2(g) + 6H_2O(l)$

(b)   Because there are fewer moles of gas in the products, $\Delta S°$ is negative, which makes $-T\Delta S$ positive. $\Delta G°$ is less negative (more positive) than $\Delta H°$.

19.45   (a) ΔG is negative at low temperatures, positive at high temperatures. That is, the reaction proceeds in the forward direction spontaneously at lower temperatures but spontaneously reverses at higher temperatures.

(b) ΔG is positive at all temperatures. The reaction is nonspontaneous in the forward direction at all temperatures.

(c) ΔG is positive at low temperatures, negative at high temperatures. That is, the reaction will proceed spontaneously in the forward direction at high temperature.

19.47   At 450 K, $\Delta G < 0$; $\Delta G = \Delta H - T\Delta S < 0$

34.5 kJ - 450 K $(\Delta S) < 0$; 34.5 kJ < 450 K (ΔS); $\Delta S > 34.5$ kJ/450 K

$\Delta S > 0.0767$ kJ/K or $\Delta S > +76.7$ J/K

19.49   (a) $\Delta G = \Delta H - T\Delta S$; $0 = -32$ kJ - T(-98 J/K); 32×10^3 J = T(98 J/K)

T = 32×10^3 J/(98 J/K) = 326.5 = 330 K

(b)   nonspontaneous

19.51   (a)   Calculate $\Delta H°$ and $\Delta S°$ to determine the sign of $T\Delta S°$.

$\Delta H° = 3\Delta H°$ NO(g) - $\Delta H°$ NO$_2$(g) + $\Delta H°$ N$_2$O(g)

       = 3(90.37) - 33.84 - 81.6 = 155.7 kJ

$\Delta S° = 3S°$ NO(g) - S° NO$_2$(g) - S° N$_2$O(g)

       = 3(210.62) - 240.45 - 220.0 = 171.4 J/K

$\Delta G° = \Delta H° - T\Delta S°$. Since $\Delta S°$ is positive, $-T\Delta S°$ becomes more negative as T increases and $\Delta G°$ becomes more negative.

(b) $\Delta G° = \Delta H° - T\Delta S° = 155.7$kJ - (800 K)(0.1714 kJ/K)

$\Delta G° = 155.7$ kJ - 137 kJ = 19 kJ

Since $\Delta G°$ is positive at 800 K, the reaction is not spontaneous at this temperature.

(c) $\Delta G° = 155.7$ kJ - (1000 K)(0.1714 kJ/K) = 155.7 kJ - 171.4 kJ = -15.7 kJ

$\Delta G°$ is negative at 1000 K and the reaction is spontaneous at this temperature.

19.53   (a) $\Delta S_{vap} = \Delta H_{vap}/T_b$; $T_b = \Delta H_{vap}/\Delta S_{vap}$

$\Delta H_{vap} = \Delta H°$ C$_6$H$_6$(g) - $\Delta H°$ C$_6$H$_6$(l) = 82.9 - 49.0 = 33.9 kJ

$\Delta S_{vap} = S°$ C$_6$H$_6$(g) - S° C$_6$H$_6$(l) = 269.2 - 172.8 = 96.4 J/K

$T_b = 33.9 \times 10^3$ J/96.4 J/K = 351.66 = 352 K = 79°C

(b)   From the *Handbook of Chemistry and Physics*, 74th Edition, $T_b = 80.1$°C. The values are remarkably close; the small difference is due to deviation from ideal behavior by C$_6$H$_6$(g) and experimental uncertainty in the boiling point measurement and the thermodynamic data.

19.55   (a)   C$_2$H$_2$(g) + 5/2 O$_2$(g) $\rightarrow$ 2CO$_2$(g) + H$_2$O(l)

(b) $\Delta H° = 2\Delta H°$ CO$_2$(g) + $\Delta H°$ H$_2$O(l) - $\Delta H°$ C$_2$H$_2$(g) - 5/2$\Delta H°$ O$_2$(g)

       = 2(-393.5) - 285.83 - 226.7- 5/2(0) = -1299.5 kJ produced/mol C$_2$H$_2$ burned

(c) $w_{max} = \Delta G° = 2\Delta G°$ CO$_2$(g) + $\Delta G°$ H$_2$O(l) - $\Delta G°$ C$_2$H$_2$(g) - 5/2 $\Delta G°$ O$_2$(g)

       = 2(-394.4) - 237.13 - 209.2 - 5/2(0) = -1235.1 kJ

The negative sign indicates that the system does work on the surroundings; the system can accomplish a maximum of 1235.1 kJ of work on its surroundings.

Free Energy and Equilibrium

19.57   Consider the relationship $\Delta G = \Delta G° + RT \ln Q$ where Q is the reaction quotient.

      (a) $O_2(g)$ appears in the denominator of Q for this reaction. An increase in pressure of O_2 decreases Q and ΔG becomes smaller or more negative. Increasing the concentration of a reactant increases the tendency for a reaction to occur.

      (b) $O_2(g)$ appears in the numerator of Q for this reaction. Increasing the pressure of O_2 increases Q and ΔG becomes more positive. Increasing the concentration of a product decreases the tendency for the reaction to occur.

      (c) $O_2(g)$ appears in the numerator of Q for this reaction. An increase in pressure of O_2 increases Q and ΔG becomes more positive. Since pressure of O_2 is raised to the third power in Q, an increase in pressure of O_2 will have the largest effect on ΔG for this reaction.

19.59   (a) $\Delta G° = \Delta G° \ N_2O_4(g) - 2\Delta G° \ NO_2(g) = 98.28 - 2(51.84) = -5.40$ kJ

      (b) $\Delta G = \Delta G° + RT \ln P_{N_2O_4} / P_{NO_2}^2$

$$= -5.40 \text{ kJ} + \frac{8.314 \text{ J}}{\text{K} \cdot \text{mol}} \times 298 \text{ K} \times \ln[1.60/(0.40)^2] = 0.3048 = 0.30 \text{ kJ}$$

19.61 $\Delta G° = -RT \ln K_p$, Equation 19.20; $\ln K_p = -\Delta G°/RT$

      (a) $\Delta G° = 2\Delta G° \ HI(g) - \Delta G° \ H_2(g) - \Delta G° \ I_2(g)$
              $= 2(1.30) - 0 - 19.37 = -16.77$ kJ

$$\ln K_p = \frac{-(-16.77 \text{ kJ}) \times 10^3 \text{ J/kJ}}{8.314 \text{ J/K} \times 298 \text{ K}} = 6.76876 = 6.769; \ K_p = 870$$

      (b) $\Delta G° = \Delta G° \ C_2H_4(g) + \Delta G° \ H_2O(g) - \Delta G° \ C_2H_5OH(g)$
              $= 68.11 - 228.57 - (-168.5) = 8.04 = 8.0$ kJ

$$\ln K_p = \frac{-8.04 \text{ kJ} \times 10^3 \text{ J/kJ}}{8.314 \text{ J/K} \times 298 \text{ K}} = -3.24511 = -3.2; \ K_p = 0.04$$

      (c) $\Delta G° = \Delta G° \ C_6H_6(g) - 3\Delta G° \ C_2H_2(g) = 129.7 - 3(209.2) = -497.9$ kJ

$$\ln K_p = \frac{-\Delta G°}{RT} = \frac{-(-497.9 \text{ kJ}) \times 10^3 \text{ J/kJ}}{8.314 \text{ J/K} \times 298 \text{ K}} = 200.963 = 201.0; \ K_p = 2 \times 10^{87}$$

19.63 $K_p = P_{CO_2}$. Calculate $\Delta G°$ at the two temperatures using $\Delta G° = \Delta H° - T\Delta S°$ and then calculate K_p and P_{CO_2}.

$\Delta H° = \Delta H° \ BaO(s) + \Delta H° \ CO_2(g) - \Delta H° \ BaCO_3(s)$
        $= -553.5 + -393.5 - (-1216.3) = +269.3$ kJ

$\Delta S° = S° \ BaO(s) + S° \ CO_2(g) - S° \ BaCO_3(s)$
        $= 70.42 + 213.6 - 112.1 = 171.92$ J/K $= 0.1719$ kJ/K

(a) ΔG at 298 K = 269.3 kJ - 298 K (0.17192 kJ/K) = 218.07 = 218.1 kJ

$$\ln K_p = \frac{-\Delta G°}{RT} = \frac{-218.07 \times 10^3 \, J}{8.314 \, J/K \times 298 \, K} = -88.017 = -88.02$$

$K_p = 6.0 \times 10^{-39};\quad P_{CO_2} = 6.0 \times 10^{-39}$ atm

(b) ΔG at 1100 K = 269.3 kJ - 1100 K (0.17192 kJ) = 80.19 = +80.2 kJ

$$\ln K_p = \frac{-\Delta G°}{RT} = \frac{-80.19 \times 10^3 \, J}{8.314 \, J/K \times 1100 \, K} = -8.768 = -8.77$$

$K_p = 1.6 \times 10^{-4};\quad P_{CO_2} = 1.6 \times 10^{-4}$ atm

19.65   (a) $HNO_2(aq) \rightleftharpoons H^+(aq) + NO_2^-(aq)$

        (b) $\Delta G° = -RT \ln K_a = -(8.314 \times 10^{-3})(298) \ln (4.5 \times 10^{-4}) = 19.0928 = 19.1$ kJ

        (c) $\Delta G = 0$ at equilibrium

        (d) $\Delta G = \Delta G° + RT \ln Q$

$$= 19.09 \, kJ + (8.314 \times 10^{-3})(298) \ln \frac{(5.0 \times 10^{-2})(6.0 \times 10^{-4})}{0.20} = -2.72 \, kJ$$

Additional Exercises

19.68

Process	ΔH	ΔS
(a)	+	+
(b)	-	-
(c)	+	+
(d)	+	+
(e)	-	+

19.73   Propylene will have a higher $S°$ at 25°C. At this temperature, both are gases, so there are no lattice effects as in Exercise 19.72. Since they have the same molecular formula, only the details of their structures are different. In propylene, there is free rotation around the C-C single bond, while in cyclopropane the 3-membered ring severely limits rotation. The greater motional freedom of the propylene molecule leads to a higher absolute entropy.

19.76 $\Delta G = \Delta G° + RT \ln Q$

        (a) $Q = \dfrac{P_{NH_3}^2}{P_{N_2} \times P_{H_2}^3} = \dfrac{(1.2)^2}{(2.6)(5.9)^3} = 2.697 \times 10^{-3} = 2.7 \times 10^{-3}$

$\Delta G° = 2\Delta G° \, NH_3(g) - \Delta G° \, N_2(g) - 3\Delta G° \, H_2(g)$

$= 2(-16.66) - 0 - 3(0) = -33.32$ kJ

$\Delta G = -33.32 \, kJ + \dfrac{8.314 \times 10^{-3} \, kJ}{K \bullet mol} \times 298 \, K \times \ln(2.69 \times 10^{-3})$

$\Delta G = -33.32 - 14.66 = -47.98$ kJ

(b) $Q = \dfrac{P_{N_2}^3 \times P_{H_2O}^4}{P_{N_2H_4}^2 \times P_{NO_2}^2} = \dfrac{(0.5)^3(0.3)^4}{(5.0 \times 10^{-2})^2(5.0 \times 10^{-2})^2} = 162 = 2 \times 10^2$

$\Delta G° = 3\Delta G° \ N_2(g) + 4\Delta G° \ H_2O(g) - 2\Delta G° \ N_2H_4(g) - 2\Delta G° \ NO_2(g)$

$= 3(0) + 4(-228.57) - 2(159.4) - 2(51.84) = -1336.8 \ kJ$

$\Delta G = -1336.8 \ kJ + 2.478 \ln 162 = -1324.2 \ kJ$

(c) $Q = \dfrac{P_{N_2} \times P_{H_2}^2}{P_{N_2H_4}} = \dfrac{(1.5)(2.5)^2}{0.5} = 18.75 = 2 \times 10^1$

$\Delta G° = \Delta G° \ N_2(g) + 2\Delta G° \ H_2(g) - \Delta G° \ N_2H_4(g)$

$= 0 + 2(0) - 159.4 = -159.4 \ kJ$

$\Delta G = -159.4 \ kJ + 2.478 \ln 18.75 = -152.1 \ kJ$

19.79   (a) $K = \dfrac{\chi_{CH_3COOH}}{\chi_{CH_3OH} \ P_{CO}}$

$\Delta G° = -RT \ln K; \ \ln K_p = -\Delta G / RT$

$\Delta G° = \Delta G° \ CH_3COOH(l) - \Delta G° \ CH_3OH(l) - \Delta G° \ CO(g)$

$= -392.4 - (-166.23) - (-137.2) = -89.0 \ kJ$

$\ln K_p = \dfrac{-(-89.0 \ kJ)}{(8.314 \times 10^{-3} \ kJ/K)(298 \ K)} = 35.922 = 35.9; \ K_p = 4 \times 10^{15}$

(b) $\Delta H° = \Delta H° \ CH_3COOH(l) - \Delta H° \ CH_3OH(l) - \Delta H° \ CO(g)$

$= -487.0 - (-238.6) - (-110.5) = -137.9 \ kJ$

The reaction is exothermic, so the value of K will decrease with increasing temperature, and the mole fraction of CH_3COOH will also decrease. Elevated temperatures must be used to increase the speed of the reaction. Thermodynamics cannot predict the rate at which a reaction reaches equilibrium.

(c) $\Delta G° = -RT \ln K; \ K = 1, \ln K = 0, \Delta G° = 0$

$\Delta G° = \Delta H° - T\Delta S°; \ when \ \Delta G° = 0, \Delta H° = T\Delta S°$

$\Delta S° = S° \ CH_3COOH(l) - S° \ CH_3OH(l) - S° \ CO(g)$

$= 159.8 - 126.8 - 197.9 = -164.9 \ J/K = -0.1649 \ kJ/K$

$-137.9 \ kJ = T(-0.1649 \ kJ/K), \ T = 836.3 \ K$

The equilibrium favors products up to 836 K or 563 °C, so the elevated temperatures to increase the rate of reaction can be safely employed.

19.82 $\Delta G°$ for the metabolism of glucose is:

$6\Delta G° \ CO_2(g) + 6\Delta G° \ H_2O(l) - \Delta G° \ C_6H_{12}O_6(s) - 6\Delta G° \ O_2(g)$

$\Delta G° = 6(-394.4) + 6(-237.13) - (-910.4) + 6(0) = -2878.8 \ kJ$

moles ATP $= -2878.8 \ kJ \times 1 \ mol \ ATP \ / \ (-30.5 \ kJ) = 94.4 \ mol \ ATP \ / \ mol \ glucose$

19.85   (a)   Both equations describe the entropy change of the system when a gas expands at constant temperature.

$\Delta S = nR \ln(V_2/V_1)$; $\Delta S = q_{rev}/T$ (Equation 19.1)

$q_{rev}/T = nR \ln(V_2/V_1)$; $q_{rev} = nRT \ln(V_2/V_1)$

(b) $n = 0.50$ mol, $V_1 = 10.0$ L, $V_2 = 75.0$ L

$\Delta S = 0.50$ mol $(8.314$ J/mol•K$)$ $\ln(75.0$ L$/10.0$ L$) = 8.376 = 8.4$ J/K

(c)   When a gas expands, there are more possible arrangements for the particles, and entropy increases. The positive sign for ΔS in part (b) is consistent with this prediction.

(d) $n = 8.5$; $V_2 = 1/8\ V_1$; $V_2/V_1 = 1/8$

$\Delta S = 8.5$ mol $(8.314$ J/mol•K$)$ $\ln(1/8) = -146.95 = -1.5 \times 10^2$ J/K

Integrative Exercises

19.89   (a)   Polymerization is the process of joining many small molecules (monomers) into a few very large molecules (polymers). Polyethylene in particular can have extremely high molecular weights. In general, reducing the number of particles in a system reduces entropy, so ΔS_{poly} is expected to be negative.

(b) $\Delta G_{poly} = \Delta H_{poly} - T\Delta S_{poly}$. If the polymerization of ethylene is spontaneous, ΔG_{poly} is negative. If ΔS_{poly} is negative, $-T\Delta S_{poly}$ is positive, so ΔH_{poly} must be negative for ΔG_{poly} to be negative. The enthalpy of polymerization must be exothermic.

(c)   According to Equation 12.1, polymerization of ethylene requires breaking one C=C and forming 2C-C per monomer (1C-C between the C-atoms of the monomer and 2 × 1/2 C-C to two other monomers).

$\Delta H = D(C=C) - 2D(C-C) = 614 - 2(348) = -82$ kJ/mol C_2H_4

$$\frac{-82\ kJ}{mol\ C_2H_4} \times \frac{1\ mol}{6.022 \times 10^{23}\ molecules} \times \frac{1000\ J}{1\ kJ} = 1.36 \times 10^{-19}\ J/C_2H_4\ monomer$$

(d)   The products of a condensation polymerization are the polymer and a small molecule, typically H_2O; there is usually one small molecule formed per monomer unit. Unlike addition polymerization, the total number of particles is not reduced. A condensation polymer does impose more order on the monomer or monomers than an addition polymer. If there is a single monomer, it has different functional groups at the two ends and only one end can react to join the polymer, so orientation is required. If there are two different monomers, as in nylon, the monomers alternate in the polymer, so only the correct monomer can react to join the polymer. In terms of structure, the condensation polymer imposes more order on the monomer(s) than an addition polymer. But, condensation polymerization does not lead to a reduction in the number of particles in the system, so ΔS_{poly} will be less negative than for addition polymerization.

19.92　(a)　Yes, mixing of gases is a spontaneous process. When gases mix, many new positions become available to the gas particles. The number of possible states (W) for a random mixture of gases is much larger than the number of states for the separated gases and ΔS for mixing is positive. Assuming no significant change in enthalpy, the increase in entropy results in a spontaneous process.

(b)　Consider the expansion of the two gases separately. Then, $P_T = P_{He} + P_{Ar}$.

He: $P_1V_1 = P_2V_2$; 1.30 atm × 1.75 L = P_2 × 5.75 L; $P_2 = 0.3957 = 0.396$ atm

Ar: $P_1V_1 = P_2V_2$; 735 torr × 4.00 L = P_2 × 5.75 L; $P_2 = 511.3 = 511$ torr

$P_T = P_{He} + P_{Ar} = 0.3957$ atm + 511.3 torr × $\dfrac{1 \text{ atm}}{760 \text{ torr}}$ = 1.0684 = 1.068 atm

(c)　$P_{He} = 0.396$ atm

(d)　When the two gases are separated, the entropy of the system decreases but the entropy of surroundings increases as heat is removed from the system to effect condensation. The second law requires only that $\Delta S_{universe}$ is ≥ 0.

19.96　(a)　$\Delta G° = 3\Delta G°_f$ S(s) + $2\Delta G°_f$ H_2O(g) - $\Delta G°_f$ SO_2(g) - $2\Delta G°_f$ H_2S(g)

$= 3(0) + 2(-228.57) - (-300.4) - 2(-33.01) = -90.72 = -90.7$ kJ

$\ln K = \dfrac{-\Delta G°}{RT} = \dfrac{-(-90.72 \text{ kJ})}{(8.314 \times 10^{-3} \text{ kJ/K})(298 \text{ K})}$ = 36.6165 = 36.6;　K = 7.99 × 10^{15}

$= 8 \times 10^{15}$

(b)　The reaction is highly spontaneous at 298 K and feasible in principle. However, use of H_2S(g) produces a severe safety hazard for workers and the surrounding community.

(c)　$P_{H_2O} = \dfrac{25 \text{ torr}}{760 \text{ torr/atm}} = 0.033$ atm

$K = \dfrac{P^2_{H_2O}}{P_{SO_2} \times P^2_{H_2S}}$;　$P_{SO_2} = P_{H_2S} = x$ atm

$K = 7.99 \times 10^{15} = \dfrac{(0.033)^2}{x(x)^2}$;　$x^3 = \dfrac{(0.033)^2}{7.99 \times 10^{15}}$

$x = 5 \times 10^{-7}$ atm

(d)　$\Delta H° = 3\Delta H°_f$ S(s) + $2\Delta H°_f$ H_2O(g) - $\Delta H°_f$ SO_2(g) - $2\Delta H°_f$ H_2S(g)

$= 3(0) + 2(-241.82) - (-296.9) - 2(-20.17) = -146.4$ kJ

$\Delta S° = 3S°$ S(s) + $2S°$ H_2O(g) - $S°$ SO_2(g) - $2S°$ H_2S(g)

$= 3(31.88) + 2(188.83) - 248.5 - 2(205.6) = -186.4$ J/K

The reaction is exothermic (-ΔH), so the value of K will decrease with increasing temperature. The negative $\Delta S°$ value means that the reaction will become nonspontaneous at some higher temperature. The process will be less effective at elevated temperatures.

20 Electrochemistry

Oxidation-Reduction Reactions

20.1 (a) *Oxidation* is the loss of electrons.

(b) The electrons appear on the products side (right side) of an oxidation half-reaction.

(c) The *oxidant* is the reactant that is reduced; it gains the electrons that are lost by the substance being oxidized.

20.3 (a) I is reduced from +5 to 0; C is oxidized from +2 to +4.

(b) Hg is reduced from +2 to 0; N is oxidized from -2 to 0.

(c) N is reduced from +5 to +2; S is oxidized from -2 to 0.

(d) Cl is reduced from +4 to +3; O is oxidized from -1 to 0.

20.5 (a) $TiCl_4(g) + 2Mg(l) \rightarrow Ti(s) + 2MgCl_2(l)$

(b) $Mg(l)$ is the reductant; $TiCl_4(g)$ is the oxidant.

20.7 (a) $Sn^{2+}(aq) \rightarrow Sn^{4+}(aq) + 2e^-$, oxidation

(b) $TiO_2(s) + 4H^+(aq) + 2e^- \rightarrow Ti^{2+}(aq) + 2H_2O(l)$, reduction

(c) $2HOCl(aq) + 2H^+(aq) + 2e^- \rightarrow Cl_2(aq) + 2H_2O(l)$, reduction

(d) $La(s) + 3OH^-(aq) \rightarrow La(OH)_3(s) + 3e^-$, oxidation

(e) $NO_3^-(aq) + H_2O(l) + 2e^- \rightarrow NO_2^-(aq) + 2OH^-(aq)$, reduction

20.9 (a) $Cr_2O_7^{2-}(aq) + I^-(aq) + 8H^+ \rightarrow 2Cr^{3+}(aq) + IO_3^-(aq) + 4H_2O(l)$

(b) $4MnO_4^-(aq) + 5CH_3OH(aq) + 12H^+(aq) \rightarrow 4Mn^{2+}(aq) + 5HCO_2H(aq) + 11H_2O(l)$

(c) $4As(s) + 3ClO_3^-(aq) + 3H^+(aq) + 6H_2O(l) \rightarrow 4H_3AsO_3(aq) + 3HClO(aq)$

(d) $As_2O_3(s) + 2NO_3^-(aq) + 2H_2O(l) + 2H^+(aq) \rightarrow 2H_3AsO_4(aq) + N_2O_3(aq)$

(e) $2MnO_4^-(aq) + Br^-(aq) + H_2O(l) \rightarrow 2MnO_2(s) + BrO_3^-(aq) + 2OH^-(aq)$

(f) $4H_2O_2(aq) + Cl_2O_7(aq) + 2OH^-(aq) \rightarrow 2ClO_2^-(aq) + 4O_2(g) + 5H_2O(l)$

Voltaic Cells; Cell Potential

20.11 (a) The reaction $Cu^{2+}(aq) + Zn(s) \rightarrow Cu(s) + Zn^{2+}(aq)$ is occurring in both Figures. In Figure 20.3, the reactants are in contact, and the concentrations of the ions in solution aren't specified. In Figure 20.4, the oxidation half-reaction and reduction half-reaction are occurring in separate compartments, joined by a porous connector. The concentrations of the two solutions are initially 1.0 *M*. In Figure 20.4, electrical current is isolated and flows through the voltmeter. In Figure 20.3, the flow of electrons cannot be isolated or utilized.

(b)   In the cathode compartment of the voltaic cell in Figure 20.5, Cu^{2+} cations are reduced to Cu atoms, decreasing the number of positively charged particles in the compartment. Na^+ cations are drawn into the compartment to maintain charge balance as Cu^{2+} ions are removed.

20.13   (a) $Cd(s) \rightarrow Cd^{2+}(aq) + 2e^-$; $Ni^{2+}(aq) + 2e^- \rightarrow Ni(s)$

        (b)   Cd(s) is the anode;   Ni(s) is the cathode.

        (c)   Cd(s) is negative (-); Ni(s) is positive (+).

        (d)   Electrons flow from the Cd(-) electrode toward the Ni(+) electrode.

        (e)   Cations migrate toward the Ni(s) cathode; anions migrate toward the Cd(s) anode.

20.15

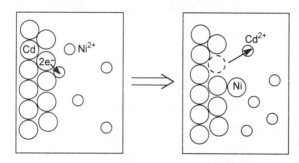

20.17   (a)   *Electromotive force*, emf, is the driving force that causes electrons to flow through the external circuit of a voltaic cell. It is the potential energy difference between an electron at the anode and an electron at the cathode.

        (b)   One *volt* is the potential energy difference required to impart 1 J of energy to a charge of 1 coulomb. 1 V = 1 J/C.

        (c)   *Cell potential*, E_{cell}, is the emf of an electrochemical cell.

20.19   (a) $2H^+(aq) + 2e^- \rightarrow H_2(g)$

        (b)   A *standard* hydrogen electrode is a hydrogen electrode where the components are at standard conditions, 1 M $H^+(aq)$ and $H_2(g)$ at 1 atm.

        (c)   The platinum foil in an SHE serves as an inert electron carrier and a solid reaction surface.

20.21   (a)   A *standard reduction potential* is the relative potential of a reduction half-reaction measured at standard conditions, 1 M aqueous solutions and 1 atm gas pressure.

        (b) $E^{\circ}_{red} = 0$ V for a standard hydrogen electrode.

        (c)   The reduction of $Ag^+(aq)$ to Ag(s) is much more energetically favorable, because it has a substantially more positive E°_{red} (0.799 V) than the reduction of $Sn^{2+}(aq)$ to Sn(s) (-0.136 V).

20.23 (a) The two half-reactions are:

$Tl^{3+}(aq) + 2e^- \rightarrow Tl^+(aq)$ cathode E°_{red} = ?

$2[Cr^{2+}(aq) \rightarrow Cr^{3+}(aq) + e^-]$ anode E°_{red} = -0.41

(b) $E^{\circ}_{cell} = E^{\circ}_{red}$ (cathode) - E°_{red} (anode); 1.19 V = E°_{red} - (-0.41 V);

E°_{red} = 1.19 V - 0.41 V = 0.78 V

(c)

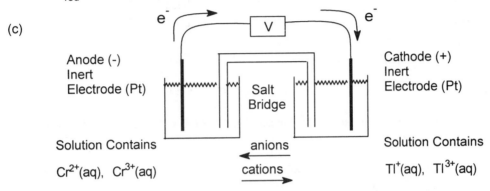

Note that because $Cr^{2+}(aq)$ is readily oxidized, it would be necessary to keep oxygen out of the left-hand cell compartment.

20.25 (a) $H_2(g) \rightarrow 2H^+(aq) + 2e^-$ E°_{red} = 0.000 V

$I_2(s) + 2e^- \rightarrow 2I^-(aq)$ E°_{red} = 0.536 V

E° = 0.536 V - 0.000 V = 0.536 V

(b) $Ni(s) \rightarrow Ni^{2+}(aq) + 2e^-$ E°_{red} = -0.28 V

$2[Ce^{4+}(aq) + 1e^- \rightarrow Ce^{3+}(aq)]$ E°_{red} = 1.61 V

E° = 1.61 V - (-0.28 V) = 1.89 V

(c) $Cr(s) \rightarrow Cr^{3+}(aq) + 3e^-$ E°_{red} = -0.74 V

$3[Cr^{3+}(aq) + 1e^- \rightarrow Cr^{2+}(aq)]$ E°_{red} = -0.41 V

E° = -0.41 V - (-0.74 V) = 0.33 V

(d) $3[Cd(s) \rightarrow Cd^{2+}(aq) + 2e^-]$ E°_{red} = -0.403 V

$2[Al^{3+}(aq) + 3e^- \rightarrow Al(s)]$ E°_{red} = -1.66 V

E° = -1.66 V - (-0.403 V)] = -1.26 V

20.27 (a) $3[Ag^+(aq) + 1e^- \rightarrow Ag(s)]$ E°_{red} = 0.799

$Cr(s) \rightarrow Cr^{3+}(aq) + 3e^-$ E°_{red} = -0.74

$3Ag^+(aq) + Cr(s) \rightarrow 3Ag(s) + Cr^{3+}(aq)$ E° = 0.799 - (-0.74) = 1.54 V

(b)   Two of the combinations have essentially equal E° values.

$$2[Ag^+(aq) + 1e^- \rightarrow Ag(s)] \qquad E^{\circ}_{red} = 0.799 \text{ V}$$
$$Cu(s) \rightarrow Cu^{2+}(aq) + 2e^- \qquad E^{\circ}_{red} = 0.337 \text{ V}$$

$$2Ag^+(aq) + Cu(s) \rightarrow 2Ag(s) + Cu^{2+}(aq) \qquad E^{\circ} = 0.799 \text{ V} - 0.337 \text{ V} = 0.462 \text{ V}$$

$$3[Ni^{2+}(aq) + 2e^- \rightarrow Ni(s)] \qquad E^{\circ}_{red} = -0.28 \text{ V}$$
$$2[Cr(s) \rightarrow Cr^{3+}(aq) + 3e^-] \qquad E^{\circ}_{red} = -0.74 \text{ V}$$

$$3Ni^{2+}(aq) + 2Cr(s) \rightarrow 3Ni(s) + 2Cr^{3+}(aq) \qquad E^{\circ} = -0.28 \text{ V} - (-0.74 \text{ V}) = 0.46 \text{ V}$$

20.29   (a) $MnO_4^-(aq) + 8H^+(aq) + 5e^- \rightarrow Mn^{2+}(aq) + 4H_2O(l) \qquad E^{\circ}_{red} = 1.51 \text{ V}$

        (b)   Because the half-reaction in part (a) is the more favorable reduction, it is the cathode reaction.

        (c) $Sn^{2+}(aq) \rightarrow Sn^{4+}(aq) + 2e^- \qquad\qquad\qquad\qquad E^{\circ}_{red} = 0.154 \text{ V}$

        (d)   Balance electrons by multiplying the cathode reaction by 2 and the anode reaction by 5. $5Sn^{2+}(aq) + 2MnO_4^-(aq) + 16H^+(aq) \rightarrow 5Sn^{4+}(aq) + 2Mn^{2+}(aq) + 8H_2O(l)$

        (e) $E^{\circ} = 1.51 \text{ V} - 0.154 \text{ V} = 1.356 = 1.36 \text{ V}$

20.31   The reduction half-reactions are:

$$Cu^{2+}(aq) + 2e^- \rightarrow Cu(s) \qquad E^{\circ} = 0.337 \text{ V}$$
$$Sn^{2+}(aq) + 2e^- \rightarrow Sn(s) \qquad E^{\circ} = -0.136 \text{ V}$$

        (a)   It is evident that Cu^{2+} is more readily reduced. Therefore, Cu serves as the cathode, Sn as the anode.

        (b)   The copper electrode gains mass as Cu is plated out, the Sn electrode loses mass as Sn is oxidized.

        (c)   The overall cell reaction is $Cu^{2+}(aq) + Sn(s) \rightarrow Cu(s) + Sn^{2+}(aq)$

        (d) $E^{\circ} = 0.337 \text{ V} - (-0.136 \text{ V}) = 0.473 \text{ V}$

Oxidizing and Reducing Agents; Spontaneity

20.33   (a)   Negative. A strong reductant is likely to be oxidized, thus having a negative reduction potential.

        (b)   Right. Reducing agents are likely to be oxidized, and thus to be in a low oxidation state; the products of reduction half-reactions are in lower oxidation states than reactants.

20.35   In each case, choose the half-reaction with the more positive reduction potential and with the given substance on the left.

        (a) $Cl_2(g)$ (1.359 V vs. 1.065 V)   (b) $Ni^{2+}(aq)$ (-0.28V vs. -0.403 V)

        (c) $BrO_3^-(aq)$ (1.52 V vs. 1.195 V)   (d) $O_3(g)$ (2.07 V vs. 1.776 V)

20.37   If the substance is on the left of a reduction half-reaction, it will be an oxidant; if it is on the right, it will be a reductant. The sign and magnitude of the E_{red}° determines whether it is strong or weak.

(a) Cl^-(aq): very weak reductant (on the right, E_{red}° = 1.359 V)

(b) MnO_4^-(aq, acidic): strong oxidant (on the left, E_{red}° = 1.51 V)

(c)   Ba(s): strong reductant (on the right, E_{red}° = -2.90 V)

(d) Zn^{2+}(aq): weak oxidant (on the left, E_{red}° = -0.763 V)

20.39   (a)   Arranged in order of increasing strength as oxidizing agents (and increasing reduction potential):

Cu^{2+}(aq) $<$ O_2(g) $<$ $Cr_2O_7^{2-}$(aq) $<$ Cl_2(g) $<$ H_2O_2(aq)

(b)   Arranged in order of increasing strength as reducing agents (and decreasing reduction potential):

H_2O_2(aq) $<$ I^-(aq) $<$ Sn^{2+}(aq) $<$ Zn(s) $<$ Al(s)

20.41   Any of the **reduced** species in Table 20.1 from a half-reaction with a reduction potential more negative than -0.43 V will reduce Eu^{3+} to Eu^{2+}. These include Zn(s), H_2(g) in basic solution, etc. Fe(s) is questionable.

20.43   (a)   The more positive the emf of a reaction the more spontaneous the reaction.

(b)   Reactions (a), (b) and (c) in Exercise 20.25 have positive E° values and are spontaneous.

(c) $\Delta G^{\circ} = -nFE^{\circ}$; F = 96,500 J/V•mol e^- = 96.5 kJ/V•mol e^-

20.25 (a) ΔG° = -2 mol $e^- \times \dfrac{96.5 \text{ kJ}}{V \cdot mol\ e^-} \times$ 0.536 V = -103.448 = -103 kJ

20.25 (b) ΔG° = -2(96.5)(1.89) = -364.77 = -365 kJ

20.25 (c) ΔG° = -3(96.5)(0.33) = -95.5 kJ

20.25 (d) ΔG° = -6(96.5)(-1.26) = 729.54 = 730 kJ

20.45   (a) $2Fe^{2+}$(aq) + $S_2O_6^{2-}$(aq) + $4H^+$(aq) $\rightarrow$ $2Fe^{3+}$(aq) + $2H_2SO_3$(aq)

E° = 0.60 V - 0.77 V = -0.17 V

$2Fe^{2+}$(aq) + N_2O(aq) + $2H^+$(aq) $\rightarrow$ $2Fe^{3+}$(aq) + N_2(g) + H_2O(l)

E° = -1.77 V - 0.77 V = -2.54 V

Fe^{2+}(aq) + VO_2^+(aq) + $2H^+$(aq) $\rightarrow$ Fe^{3+}(aq) + VO^{2+}(aq) + H_2O(l)

E° = 1.00 V - 0.77 V = +0.23 V

(b) $\Delta G^{\circ} = -nFE^{\circ}$ For the first reaction,

ΔG° = -2 mol $\times \dfrac{96,500 \text{ J}}{1\ V \cdot mol} \times$ (-0.17 V) = 3.3 $\times 10^5$ J or 33 kJ

For the second reaction, ΔG° = -2(96,500)(-2.54) = 4.90 $\times 10^2$ kJ

For the third reaction, ΔG° = -1(96,500)(0.23) = -22 kJ

EMF and Concentration

20.47 (a) The *Nernst equation* is applicable when the components of an electrochemical cell are at nonstandard conditions.

(b) $Q = 1$ if all reactants and products are at standard conditions.

(c) If concentration of reactants increases, Q decreases, and E increases.

20.49 $Zn(s) + 2H^+(aq) \rightarrow Zn^{2+}(aq) + H_2(g); \quad E = E° - \dfrac{0.0592}{n} \log Q; \quad Q = \dfrac{[Zn^{2+}] P_{H_2}}{[H^+]^2}$

(a) P_{H_2} decreases, Q decreases, E increases

(b) No effect (Zn(s) does not appear in Q expression.)

(c) $[H^+]$ increases, Q decreases, E increases

(d) No effect ($NaNO_3$ does not participate in the reaction.)

20.51 (a)

$$Cd^{2+}(aq) + 2e^- \rightarrow Cd(s) \qquad E°_{red} = -0.403 \text{ V}$$
$$Zn(s) \rightarrow Zn^{2+}(aq) + 2e^- \qquad E°_{red} = -0.763 \text{ V}$$

$$Cd^{2+}(aq) + Zn(s) \rightarrow Cd(s) + Zn^{2+}(aq) \qquad E° = -0.403 - (-0.763) = 0.360 \text{ V}$$

(b) $E = E° - \dfrac{0.0592}{n} \log \dfrac{[Zn^{2+}]}{[Cd^{2+}]}; \quad n = 2$

$E = 0.360 - \dfrac{0.0592}{2} \log \dfrac{(0.150)}{(1.50)} = 0.360 - \dfrac{0.0592}{2} \log (0.100)$

$E = 0.360 - \dfrac{0.0592 (-1.000)}{2} = 0.360 + 0.0296 = 0.390 \text{ V}$

(c) $E = 0.360 - \dfrac{0.0592}{2} \log \dfrac{(0.950)}{(0.0750)} = 0.360 - 0.0326 = 0.327 \text{ V}$

20.53 (a)

$$4[Fe^{2+}(aq) \rightarrow Fe^{3+}(aq) + 1e^-] \qquad E°_{red} = 0.771 \text{ V}$$
$$O_2(g) + 4H^+(aq) + 4e^- \rightarrow 2H_2O(l) \qquad E°_{red} = 1.23 \text{ V}$$

$$4Fe^{2+}(aq) + O_2(g) + 4H^+(aq) \rightarrow 4Fe^{3+}(aq) + 2H_2O(l) \qquad E° = 1.23 - 0.771 = 0.46 \text{ V}$$

(b) $E = E° - \dfrac{0.0592}{n} \log \dfrac{[Fe^{3+}]^4}{[Fe^{2+}]^4 [H^+]^4 P_{O_2}}; \quad n = 4, \; [H^+] = 1.00 \times 10^{-3} M$

$E = 0.46 \text{ V} - \dfrac{0.0592}{4} \log \dfrac{(1.0 \times 10^{-3})^4}{(2.0)^4 (1.0 \times 10^{-3})^4 (0.50)} = 0.46 - \dfrac{0.0592}{4} \log (0.125)$

$E = 0.46 - \dfrac{0.0592}{4} (-0.903) = 0.46 + 0.0134 = 0.47 \text{ V}$

20.55 $E = E° - \dfrac{0.0592}{2} \log \dfrac{[P_{H_2}][Zn^{2+}]}{[H^+]^2}$; $E° = 0.0\ V - (-0.763\ V) = 0.763\ V$

$0.684 = 0.763 - \dfrac{0.0592}{2} \times (\log[P_{H_2}][Zn^{2+}] - 2 \log[H^+]) = 0.763 - \dfrac{0.0592}{2} \times (-0.5686 - 2 \log[H^+])$

$0.684 = 0.763 + 0.0168 + 0.0592 \log[H^+]$; $\log[H^+] = \dfrac{0.684 - 0.0168 - 0.763}{0.0592}$

$\log[H^+] = -1.6188 = -1.6$; $[H^+] = 0.0241 = 0.02\ M$; $pH = 1.6$

20.57   (a)   The compartment with the more dilute solution will be the anode. That is, the compartment with $[Zn^{2+}] = 1.00 \times 10^{-2}\ M$ is the anode.

(b)   Since the oxidation half-reaction is the opposite of the reduction half-reaction, $E°$ is zero.

(c) $E = E° - \dfrac{0.0592}{n} \log Q$; $Q = [Zn^{2+}, \text{dilute}] / [Zn^{2+}, \text{conc.}]$

$E = 0 - \dfrac{0.0592}{2} \log \dfrac{(1.00 \times 10^{-2})}{(1.00)} = 0.0592\ V$

(d)   In the anode compartment, $Zn(s) \rightarrow Zn^{2+}(aq)$, so $[Zn^{2+}]$ increases from $1.00 \times 10^{-2}\ M$. In the cathode compartment, $Zn^{2+}(aq) \rightarrow Zn(s)$, so $[Zn^{2+}]$ decreases from $1.00\ M$.

20.59 $E° = \dfrac{0.0592\ V}{n} \log K$; $\log K = \dfrac{nE°}{0.0592\ V}$

(a) $E° = -0.136 - (-0.763) = 0.627\ V$; $n = 2$ $(Sn^{+2} + 2e^- \rightarrow Sn)$

$\log K = \dfrac{2(0.627)}{0.0592} = 21.182 = 21.2$; $K = 1.52 \times 10^{21} = 2 \times 10^{21}$

(b) $E° = 0 - (-0.277) = 0.277\ V$; $n = 2$ $(2H^+ + 2e^- \rightarrow H_2)$

$\log K = \dfrac{2(0.277)}{0.0592} = 9.358 = 9.36$; $K = 2.3 \times 10^9$

(c) $E° = 1.51 - 1.065 = 0.445 = 0.45\ V$; $n = 10$ $(2MnO_4^- + 10e^- \rightarrow 2Mn^{+2})$

$\log K = \dfrac{10(0.445)}{0.0592} = 75.169 \approx 75$; $K = 1.5 \times 10^{75} = 10^{75}$

20.61 $E° = \dfrac{0.0592}{n} \log K$; $\log K = \dfrac{nE°}{0.0592\ V}$

(a) $\log K = \dfrac{1(0.217\ V)}{0.0592\ V} = 3.6655 = 3.67$; $K = 4.6 \times 10^3$

(b) $\log K = \dfrac{2(0.217\ V)}{0.0592\ V} = 7.3311 = 7.33$; $K = 2.1 \times 10^7$

(c) $\log K = \dfrac{3(0.217\ V)}{0.0592\ V} = 10.9966 = 11.0;\ K = 9.92 \times 10^{10} = 1 \times 10^{11}$

Batteries; Corrosion

20.63   (a)   A *battery* is a portable, self-contained electrochemical power source composed of one or more voltaic cells.

        (b)   A *primary* battery is not rechargeable, while a *secondary* battery can be recharged.

        (c)   No. No single voltaic cell is capable of producing 7.5 V. If a single voltaic cell could be designed to produce 2.5 V, three of these cells connected in series would produce the desired voltage.

20.65   The overall cell reaction (Equation [20.19]) is:

$Pb(s) + PbO_2(s) + 2H^+(aq) + 2HSO_4^-(aq) \rightarrow 2PbSO_4(s) + 2H_2O(l)$

$435\ g\ Pb \times \dfrac{1\ mol\ Pb}{207.2\ g\ Pb} \times \dfrac{1\ mol\ PbO_2}{1\ mol\ Pb} \times \dfrac{239.2\ g\ PbO_2}{1\ mol\ PbO_2} = 502\ g\ PbO_2$

20.67   (a)   Li(s) is oxidized at the anode.

        (b) $Ag_2CrO_4(s) + 2e^- \rightarrow 2Ag(s) + CrO_4^{2-}(aq)$ $E_{red}^\circ = 0.446\ V$

                     $2[Li(s) \rightarrow Li^+(aq) + 1e^-]$ $E_{red}^\circ = -3.05\ V$

             $Ag_2CrO_4(s) + 2Li(s) \rightarrow 2Ag(s) + CrO_4^-(aq) + 2Li^+(aq)$

             $E^\circ = 0.446\ V - (-3.05\ V) = 3.496 = 3.50\ V$

        (c)   The emf of the battery, 3.5 V, is exactly the cell potential calculated in part (b).

20.69   (a) E_{red}° for Cd (-0.40 V) is less negative than E_{red}° for Zn (-0.76 V), so E_{cell} will have a smaller (less positive) value.

        (b)   NiMH batteries use an alloy such as $ZrNi_2$ as the anode material. This eliminates the use and concomitant disposal problems associated with Cd, a toxic heavy metal.

20.71   (a)   anode: $Fe(s) \rightarrow Fe^{2+}(aq) + 2e^-$

              cathode: $O_2(g) + 4H^+(aq) + 4e^- \rightarrow 2H_2O(l)$

        (b) $2Fe^{2+}(aq) + 6H_2O(l) \rightarrow Fe_2O_3 \cdot 3H_2O(s) + 6H^+(aq) + 2e^-$

             $O_2(g) + 4H^+(aq) + 4e^- \rightarrow 2H_2O(l)$

             (Multiply the oxidation half-reaction by two to balance electrons and obtain the overall balanced reaction.)

20.73   (a) Zn^{2+} has a more negative reduction potential than Fe^{2+}, so Zn(s) is more readily oxidized. If Zn and Fe are both available for oxidation by O_2 (corrosion), Zn will be oxidized and Fe will not; Zn acts as a sacrificial anode.

(b)   During the corrosion of galvanized iron, Zn acts as the anode and Fe acts as the inert cathode at which O_2 is reduced. Zn protects Fe by making it the cathode in the electrochemical process; this is called *cathodic protection*.

Electrolysis; Electrical Work

20.75   (a)   *Electrolysis* is an electrochemical process driven by an outside energy source.

        (b)   Electrolysis reactions are, by definition, nonspontaneous.

        (c) $2Cl^-(l) \rightarrow Cl_2(g) + 2e^-$

20.77   (a)   The products are different because in aqueous electrolysis water is reduced in preference to Mg^{2+}.

        (b) $MgCl_2(l) \rightarrow Mg(l) + Cl_2(g)$

                $2Cl^-(aq) + 2H_2O(l) \rightarrow Cl_2(g) + H_2(g) + 2OH^-(aq)$

                The aqueous solution electrolysis is entirely analogous to that for NaCl(aq), Section 20.9.

        (c)

$$Mg^{2+}(aq) + 2e^- \rightarrow Mg(s) \qquad E^\circ_{red} = -2.37 \text{ V}$$
$$2Cl^-(aq) \rightarrow Cl_2(g) + 2e^- \qquad E^\circ_{red} = 1.359 \text{ V}$$

$$MgCl_2(aq) \rightarrow Mg(s) + Cl_2(g) \qquad E^\circ = -2.37 - 1.359 = -3.73 \text{ V}$$

$$H_2O(l) + 2e^- \rightarrow H_2(g) + 2OH^-(aq) \qquad E^\circ_{red} = -0.83 \text{ V}$$
$$2Cl^-(aq) \rightarrow Cl_2(g) + 2e^- \qquad E^\circ_{red} = 1.359 \text{ V}$$

$$2Cl^-(aq) + 2H_2O(l) \rightarrow Cl_2(g) + H_2(g) + 2OH^-(aq) \quad E^\circ = -0.83 - 1.359 = -2.19 \text{ V}$$

                The minus signs mean that voltage must be applied in order for the reaction to occur.

20.79

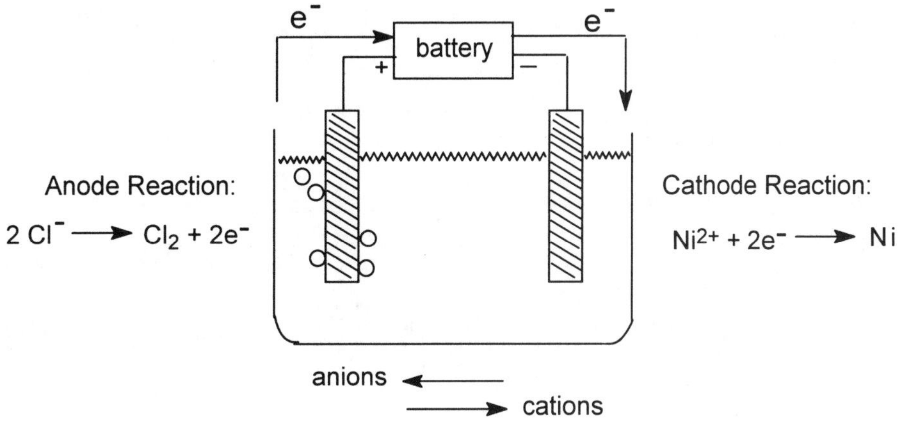

Anode Reaction:

$2\,Cl^- \longrightarrow Cl_2 + 2e^-$

Cathode Reaction:

$Ni^{2+} + 2e^- \longrightarrow Ni$

anions $\longleftarrow$

$\longrightarrow$ cations

Chlorine is produced in preference to oxidation of water because of a large overvoltage for O_2 formation.

20.81 Coulombs = amps•s, since this is a 3e⁻ reduction, each mole of Cr(s) requires 3 Faradays.

(a) $9.75 \text{ A} \times 1.50 \text{ d} \times \dfrac{24 \text{ hr}}{1 \text{ d}} \times \dfrac{60 \text{ min}}{1 \text{ hr}} \times \dfrac{60 \text{ s}}{1 \text{ min}} \times \dfrac{1 \text{ C}}{1 \text{ amp•s}} \times \dfrac{1 \text{ F}}{96,500 \text{ C}}$

$\times \dfrac{1 \text{ mol Cr}}{3 \text{ F}} \times \dfrac{52.00 \text{ g Cr}}{1 \text{ mol Cr}} = 227 \text{ g Cr(s)}$

(b) $0.50 \text{ mol Cr} \times \dfrac{3 \text{ F}}{1 \text{ mol Cr}} \times \dfrac{96,500 \text{ C}}{\text{F}} \times \dfrac{1 \text{ amp•s}}{1 \text{ C}} \times \dfrac{1}{9.0 \text{ hr}} \times \dfrac{1 \text{ hr}}{60 \text{ min}} \times \dfrac{1 \text{ min}}{60 \text{ s}}$

$= 4.5 \text{ A}$

20.83 (a) $16.8 \text{ A} \times 90.0 \text{ min} \times \dfrac{60 \text{ s}}{1 \text{ min}} \times \dfrac{1 \text{ C}}{1 \text{ amp•s}} \times \dfrac{1 \text{ F}}{96,500 \text{ C}} \times \dfrac{1 \text{ mol Cl}_2}{2 \text{ F}}$

$\times \dfrac{22.400 \text{ L Cl}_2}{1 \text{ mol Cl}_2} = 10.5 \text{ L Cl}_2$

(b) From the balanced equation (Section 20.9), we see that 2 mol NaOH are formed per mol Cl_2. Proceeding as in (a), but replacing the last factor by (2 mol NaOH/1 mol Cl_2), we obtain 0.940 mol NaOH.

20.85 For a voltaic cell at standard conditions, $w_{max} = \Delta G° = -nFE°$.

$$I_2(s) + 2e^- \rightarrow 2I^-(aq) \qquad E°_{red} = 0.536 \text{ V}$$

$$Sn(s) \rightarrow Sn^{2+}(aq) + 2e^- \qquad E°_{red} = -0.136 \text{ V}$$

$$I_2(s) + Sn(s) \rightarrow 2I^-(aq) + Sn^{2+}(aq) \qquad E° = 0.536 - (-0.136) = 0.672 \text{ V}$$

$w_{max} = -2(96.5)(0.672) = -129.7 = -130 \text{ kJ/mol Sn}$

$\dfrac{-129.7 \text{ kJ}}{\text{mol Sn(s)}} \times 0.850 \text{ mol Sn} = -110 \text{ kJ}$

20.87 (a) $8.7 \times 10^4 \text{ A} \times 18 \text{ hr} \times \dfrac{3600 \text{ s}}{1 \text{ hr}} \times \dfrac{1 \text{ C}}{1 \text{ amp•s}} \times \dfrac{1 \text{ F}}{96,500 \text{ C}} \times \dfrac{1 \text{ mol Li}}{1 \text{ F}}$

$\times \dfrac{6.94 \text{ g Li}}{1 \text{ mol Li}} \times 0.85 = 3.446 \times 10^5 = 3.4 \times 10^5 \text{ g Li}$

(b) If the cell is 85% efficient, $\dfrac{96,500 \text{ C}}{\text{F}} \times \dfrac{1 \text{ F}}{0.85 \text{ mol}} = 1.135 \times 10^5$

$= 1.1 \times 10^5 \text{ C/mol Li required}$

$\text{Energy} = 7.5 \text{ V} \times \dfrac{1.135 \times 10^5 \text{ C}}{\text{mol Li}} \times \dfrac{1 \text{ J}}{1 \text{ C•V}} \times \dfrac{1 \text{ kWh}}{3.6 \times 10^6 \text{ J}} = 0.24 \text{ kWh/mol Li}$

Additional Exercises

20.89   (a) $MnO_4^{2-}(aq) + 4H^+(aq) + 2e^- \rightarrow MnO_2(s) + 2H_2O(l)$

                         $2\,[MnO_4^{2-}(aq) \rightarrow MnO_4^-(aq) + 1e^-]$

                 $3MnO_4^{2-}(aq) + 4H^+(aq) \rightarrow 2MnO_4^-(aq) + MnO_2(s) + 2H_2O(l)$

  (b) $H_2SO_3(aq) + 4H^+(aq) + 4e^- \rightarrow S(s) + 3H_2O(l)$

                $2[H_2SO_3(aq) + H_2O \rightarrow HSO_4^-(aq) + 3H^+(aq) + 2e^-]$

                      $3H_2SO_3(aq) \rightarrow S(s) + 2HSO_4^-(aq) + 2H^+(aq) + H_2O(l)$

  (c) $Cl_2(aq) + 2H_2O(l) \rightarrow 2ClO^-(aq) + 4H^+(aq) + 2e^-$

        $4OH^-(aq)$ $+ 4OH^-\ aq)$

          $Cl_2(aq) + 4OH^-(aq) \rightarrow 2ClO^-(aq) + 2H_2O(l) + 2e^-$

          $Cl_2(aq) + 2e^- \rightarrow 2Cl^-(aq)$

      $1/2[2Cl_2(aq) + 4OH^-(aq) \rightarrow 2Cl^-(aq) + 2ClO^-(aq) + 2H_2O(l)]$

        $Cl_2(aq) + 2OH^-(aq) \rightarrow Cl^-(aq) + ClO^-(aq) + H_2O(l)$

20.92 $2[Rh^{3+}(aq) + 3e^- \rightarrow Rh(s)]$ $E^{\circ}_{red} = ?$

            $3[Cd(s) \rightarrow Cd^{2+}(aq) + 2e^-]$ $E^{\circ}_{red} = -0.403\ V$

    $2Rh^{3+}(aq) + 3Cd(s) \rightarrow 2Rh(s) + 3Cd^{2+}(aq)$ $E^{\circ} = 1.20\ V$

  (b) $Cd(s)$ is the anode, and $Rh(s)$ is the cathode.

  (c)   The cell is at standard conditions. $E^{\circ}_{cell} = E^{\circ}_{red}$ (cathode) - E°_{red} (anode)

          $E^{\circ}_{red} = E^{\circ}_{cell} + E^{\circ}_{red}$ (anode) $= 1.20\ V - 0.403\ V = 0.80\ V$

  (d) $\Delta G^{\circ} = -nFE^{\circ} = -6(96.5)(1.20) = -695\ kJ$

20.95   (a) $2[Ag^+(aq) + 1e^- \rightarrow Ag(s)]$ $E^{\circ}_{red} = 0.80\ V$

                  $Ni(s) \rightarrow Ni^{2+}(aq) + 2e^-$ $E^{\circ}_{red} = -0.28$

        $2Ag^+(aq) + Ni(s) \rightarrow 2Ag(s) + Ni^{2+}(aq)$ $E^{\circ} = 0.80 - (-0.28) = 1.08\ V$

  (b)   As the reaction proceeds, $Ni^{2+}(aq)$ is produced, so $[Ni^{2+}]$ increases as the cell operates.

  (c) $E = E^{\circ} - \dfrac{0.0592}{n} \log K$; $1.14 = 1.08 - \dfrac{0.0592}{2} \log \dfrac{[Ni^{2+}]}{[Ag^+]^2}$

        $-\dfrac{0.06(2)}{0.0592} = \log(0.0050) - \log[Ag^+]^2$; $\log[Ag^+]^2 = \log(0.0050) + \dfrac{0.06(2)}{0.0592}$

        $\log[Ag^+]^2 = -2.301 + 2.027 = -0.274$; $[Ag^+]^2 = 0.532\ M$; $[Ag^+] = 0.729 = 0.73\ M$

20.97

$$Cu^+(aq) \rightarrow Cu^{2+}(aq) + 1e^- \qquad E^\circ_{red} = +0.153 \text{ V}$$

$$1e^- + Cu^+(aq) \rightarrow Cu^\circ(s) \qquad E^\circ_{red} = +0.521 \text{ V}$$

$$2Cu^+(aq) \rightarrow Cu^\circ(s) + Cu^{2+}(aq) \qquad E^\circ = +0.521 - 0.153 = 0.368 \text{ V}$$

$$E^\circ = \frac{0.0592}{n} \log K; \quad \log K = \frac{nE^\circ}{0.0592} = \frac{1(0.368)}{0.0592} = 6.216 = 6.22$$

$$K = 10^{6.216} = 1.6 \times 10^6$$

20.100 (a) In discharge: $Cd(s) + 2NiO(OH)(s) + 2H_2O(l) \rightarrow Cd(OH)_2(s) + 2Ni(OH)_2(s)$

In charging, the reverse reaction occurs.

(b) $E^\circ = 0.49 \text{ V} - (-0.76 \text{ V}) = 1.25 \text{ V}$

(c) The 1.25 V calculated in part (b) is the standard cell potential, E°. The concentrations of reactants and products inside the battery are adjusted so that the cell output is greater than E°. Note that most of the reactants and products are pure solids or liquids, which do not appear in the Q expression. It must be [OH$^-$] that is other than 1.0 M, producing an emf of 1.30 rather than 1.25.

20.103 It is well established that corrosion occurs most readily when the metal surface is in contact with water. Thus, moisture is a requirement for corrosion. Corrosion also occurs more readily in acid solution, because O_2 has a more positive reduction potential in the presence of $H^+(aq)$. SO_2 and its oxidation products dissolve in water to produce acidic solutions, which encourage corrosion. The anodic and cathodic reactions for the corrosion of Ni are:

$$Ni(s) \rightarrow Ni^{2+}(aq) + 2e^- \qquad E^\circ_{red} = -0.28 \text{ V}$$

$$O_2(g) + 4H^+(aq) + 4e^- \rightarrow 2H_2O(l) \qquad E^\circ_{red} = 1.23 \text{ V}$$

Nickel(II) oxide, NiO(s), can form by the dry air oxidation of Ni. This NiO coating serves to protect against further corrosion. However, NiO dissolves in acidic solutions such as those produced by SO_2 or SO_3, according to the reaction:

$$NiO(s) + 2H^+(aq) \rightarrow Ni^{2+}(aq) + H_2O(l)$$

This exposes Ni(s) to further wet corrosion.

20.106 (a) The work obtainable is given by the product of the voltage, which has units of J/C, times the number of Coulombs of electricity produced:

$$w_{max} = 300 \text{ amp} \cdot \text{hr} \times \frac{3600 \text{ s}}{1 \text{ hr}} \times \frac{1 \text{ C}}{1 \text{ amp} \cdot \text{s}} \times \frac{6 \text{ J}}{1 \text{ C}} \times \frac{1 \text{ kWh}}{3.6 \times 10^6 \text{ J}} = 1.8 \text{ kWh} \approx 2 \text{ kWh}$$

(b) This maximum amount of work is never realized because some of the electrical energy is dissipated in overcoming the internal resistance of the battery; because the cell voltage does not remain constant as the reaction proceeds; because the systems to which the electrical energy is delivered are not capable of completely converting electrical energy into work.

Integrative Exercises

20.109 In an electrode process where a gas is involved, the electrode is usually inert; it does not participate directly in the reaction. The electrode does act as an electron carrier, a heterogeneous catalyst for the reaction. The reactant is adsorbed onto the surface of the electrode at an active site. For all heterogeneous catalysts, the preparation of the catalyst determines the number of active sites and the effectiveness of the catalyst. In this case, it determines the rate of the redox and other processes at the electrode.

20.112 (a)

$$Ag^+(aq) + e^- \rightarrow Ag(s) \qquad E^\circ_{red} = 0.799 \text{ V}$$

$$Fe^{2+}(aq) \rightarrow Fe^{3+}(aq) + 1e^- \qquad E^\circ_{red} = 0.771 \text{ V}$$

$$Ag^+(aq) + Fe^{2+}(aq) \rightarrow Ag(s) + Fe^{3+}(aq) \quad E^\circ = 0.799 \text{ V} - 0.771 \text{ V} = 0.028 \text{ V}$$

(b) $Ag^+(aq)$ is reduced at the cathode and $Fe^{2+}(aq)$ is oxidized at the anode.

(c) $\Delta G^\circ = -nFE^\circ = -(1)(96.5)(0.028) = -2.7 \text{ kJ}$

$\Delta S^\circ = S^\circ Ag(s) + S^\circ Fe^{3+}(aq) - S^\circ Ag^+(aq) - S^\circ Fe^{2+}(aq)$

$= 42.55 \text{ J} + 293.3 \text{ J} - 73.93 \text{ J} - 113.4 \text{ J} = 148.5 \text{ J}$

$\Delta G^\circ = \Delta H^\circ - T\Delta S^\circ$ Since ΔS° is positive, ΔG° will become more negative and E° will become more positive as temperature is increased.

20.115

$$AgSCN(s) + e^- \rightarrow Ag(s) + SCN^-(aq) \qquad E^\circ_{red} = 0.0895 \text{ V}$$

$$Ag(s) \rightarrow Ag^+(aq) + e^- \qquad E^\circ_{red} = 0.799 \text{ V}$$

$$AgSCN(s) \rightarrow Ag^+(aq) + SCN^-(aq) \quad E^\circ = 0.0895 - 0.799 = -0.710 \text{ V}$$

$$E^\circ = \frac{0.0592}{n} \log K_{sp}; \quad \log K_{sp} = \frac{(-0.710)(1)}{0.0592} = -11.993 = -12.0$$

$$K_{sp} = 10^{-11.993} = 1.02 \times 10^{-12} = 1 \times 10^{-12}$$

21 Nuclear Chemistry

Radioactivity

21.1 p = protons, n = neutrons, e = electrons; number of protons = atomic number; number of neutrons = mass number - atomic number

    (a) $^{55}_{25}$Mn: 25p, 30n   (b) ^{201}Hg: 80p, 121n   (c) ^{39}K: 19p, 20n

21.3 (a) $^{1}_{1}$p or $^{1}_{1}$H   (b) $^{0}_{1}$e   (c) $^{0}_{-1}\beta$ or $^{0}_{-1}$e

21.5 (a) $^{214}_{83}$Bi $\rightarrow$ $^{214}_{84}$Po + $^{0}_{-1}$e   (b) $^{195}_{79}$Au + $^{0}_{-1}$e (orbital electron) $\rightarrow$ $^{195}_{78}$Pt

    (c) $^{38}_{19}$K $\rightarrow$ $^{38}_{18}$Ar + $^{0}_{1}$e   (d) $^{242}_{94}$Pu $\rightarrow$ $^{238}_{92}$U + $^{4}_{2}$He

21.7 (a) $^{211}_{82}$Pb $\rightarrow$ $^{211}_{83}$Bi + $^{0}_{-1}\beta$ (b) $^{50}_{25}$Mn $\rightarrow$ $^{50}_{24}$Cr + $^{0}_{1}$e

    (c) $^{179}_{74}$W + $^{0}_{-1}$e $\rightarrow$ $^{179}_{73}$Ta   (d) $^{230}_{90}$Th $\rightarrow$ $^{226}_{88}$Ra + $^{4}_{2}$He

21.9 The total mass number change is (235-207) = 28. Since each α particle emission decreases the mass number by four, whereas emission of a β particle does not correspond to a mass change, there are 7 α particle emissions. The change in atomic number in the series is 10. Each α particle results in an atomic number lower by two. The 7 α particle emissions alone would cause a decrease of 14 in atomic number. Each β particle emission raises the atomic number by one. To obtain the observed lowering of 10 in the series, there must be 4 β emissions.

Nuclear Stability

21.11 (a) $^{8}_{5}$B - low neutron/proton ratio, positron emission (for low atomic numbers, positron emission is more common than orbital electron capture)

    (b) $^{68}_{29}$Cu - high neutron/proton ratio, beta emission

    (c) $^{241}_{93}$Np - high neutron/proton ratio, beta emission
(Even though ^{241}Np has an atomic number ≥ 84, the most common decay pathway for nuclides with neutron/proton ratios higher than the isotope listed on the periodic chart is beta decay.)

    (d) $^{39}_{17}$Cl - high neutron/proton ratio, beta emission

21.13 (a)   No - low neutron/proton ratio; probably a positron emitter (for low atomic numbers, positron emission is more common than orbital electron capture)

    (b)   No - high atomic number; alpha emitter.

(c)   No - somewhat high neutron/proton ratio; beta emitter.

(d)   No - low neutron/proton ratio; could be a positron emitter or undergo orbital electron capture.

21.15   Use the criteria listed in Table 21.3.

(a)   Stable: $^{39}_{19}$K   odd proton, even neutron more abundant than odd proton, odd neutron; 20 neutrons is a magic number.

(b)   Stable: $^{209}_{83}$Bi   odd proton, even neutron more abundant than odd proton, odd neutron; 126 neutrons is a magic number.

(c)   Stable: $^{25}_{12}$Mg   even though $^{24}_{10}$Ne is an even proton, even neutron nuclide, it has a very high neutron/proton ratio and lies outside the band of stability.

21.17   (a) $^{4}_{2}$He   (c) $^{40}_{20}$Ca   (e) $^{208}_{82}$Pb

(d) $^{58}_{28}$Ni has a magic number of protons, but not neutrons.

21.19   Radioactive: $^{14}_{8}$O, $^{115}_{52}$Te – low neutron/proton ratio; $^{208}_{84}$Po – atomic number $\geq$ 84

Stable: $^{32}_{16}$S, $^{78}_{34}$Se – even proton, even neutron, stable neutron/proton ratio

Nuclear Transmutations

21.21   Protons and alpha particles are positively charged and must be moving very fast to overcome electrostatic forces which would repel them from the target nucleus. Neutrons are electrically neutral and not repelled by the nucleus.

21.23   (a) $^{32}_{16}$S + $^{1}_{0}$n $\rightarrow$ $^{1}_{1}$p + $^{32}_{15}$P   (b) $^{7}_{4}$Be + $^{0}_{-1}$e (orbital electron) $\rightarrow$ $^{7}_{3}$Li

(c) $^{187}_{75}$Re $\rightarrow$ $^{187}_{76}$Os + $^{0}_{-1}$e   (d) $^{98}_{42}$Mo + $^{2}_{1}$H $\rightarrow$ $^{1}_{0}$n + $^{99}_{43}$Tc

(e) $^{235}_{92}$U + $^{1}_{0}$n $\rightarrow$ $^{135}_{54}$Xe + $^{99}_{38}$Sr + 2 $^{1}_{0}$n

21.25   (a) $^{238}_{92}$U + $^{1}_{0}$n $\rightarrow$ $^{239}_{92}$U + $^{0}_{0}\gamma$ (b) $^{14}_{7}$N + $^{1}_{1}$H $\rightarrow$ $^{11}_{6}$C + $^{4}_{2}$He

(c) $^{18}_{8}$O + $^{1}_{0}$n $\rightarrow$ $^{19}_{9}$F + $^{0}_{-1}$e

Rates of Radioactive Decay

21.27   Chemical reactions do not affect the character of atomic nuclei. The energy changes involved in chemical reactions are much too small to allow us to alter nuclear properties via chemical processes. Therefore, the nuclei that are formed in a nuclear reaction will continue to emit radioactivity regardless of any chemical changes we bring to bear. However, we can hope to use chemical means to separate radioactive substances, or remove them from foods or a portion of the environment.

21.29 After 12.3 yr, one half-life, there are (1/2)48.0 = 24.0 mg. 49.2 yr is exactly four half-lives. There are then $(48.0)(1/2)^4$ = 3.0 mg tritium remaining.

21.31 Using Equation [21.19],

$$k = \frac{-1}{t} \ln \frac{N_t}{N_o} = \frac{-1}{1.00\,yr} \times \ln \frac{2921}{3012} = 0.03068 = 0.0307\ yr^{-1}$$

Using Equation [21.20],

$$t_{1/2} = 0.693/k = 0.693/(0.03068\ yr^{-1}) = 22.6\ yr$$

21.33 $k = 0.693 / t_{1/2} = 0.693/27.8\ d = 0.02493 = 0.0249\ d^{-1}$

$$t = \frac{-1}{k} \ln \frac{N_t}{N_o} = \frac{-1}{0.02493\ d^{-1}} \ln \frac{1.50}{5.75} = 53.9\ d$$

21.35 $^{226}_{88}Ra \rightarrow\ ^{222}_{86}Rn +\ ^{4}_{2}He$

1 α particle is produced for each ^{226}Ra that decays. Calculate the mass of ^{226}Ra remaining after 1.0 min, calculate by subtraction the mass that has decayed, and use Avogadro's number to get the number of $^{4}_{2}He$ particles.

Calculate k in min^{-1}. $1622\ yr \times \dfrac{365\,d}{1\,yr} \times \dfrac{24\,hr}{1\,d} \times \dfrac{60\,min}{1\,hr} = 8.525 \times 10^8\ min$

$$k = \frac{0.693}{t_{1/2}} = \frac{0.693}{8.525 \times 10^8\ min} = 8.129 \times 10^{-10}\ min^{-1}$$

$$\ln \frac{N_t}{N_o} = -kt = (-8.129 \times 10^{-10}\ min^{-1})(1.0\ min) = -8.129 \times 10^{-10}$$

$$\frac{N_t}{N_o} = (1.000 - 8.129 \times 10^{-10});\ \ (don't\ round\ here!)$$

$N_t = 5.0 \times 10^{-3}\ g\ (1.00 - 8.129 \times 10^{-10})$ The amount that decays is $N_o - N_t$:

$$5.0 \times 10^{-3}\ g - [5.0 \times 10^{-3}\ (1.00 - 8.129 \times 10^{-10})] = 5.0 \times 10^{-3}\ g\ (8.129 \times 10^{-10})$$

$$= 4.065 \times 10^{-12} = 4.1 \times 10^{-12}\ g\ Ra$$

$$[N_o - N_t] = 4.065 \times 10^{-12}\ g\ Ra \times \frac{1\ mol\ Ra}{226.0\ g\ Ra} \times \frac{6.022 \times 10^{23}\ Ra\ atoms}{1\ mol\ Ra} \times \frac{1\ ^{4}_{2}He}{1\ Ra\ atom}$$

$$= 1.1 \times 10^{10}\ \alpha\ particles\ emitted\ in\ 1\ min$$

21.37 $t = \dfrac{-1}{k} \ln \dfrac{N_t}{N_o}$; $k = 0.693/5715\ yr = 1.213 \times 10^{-4} = 1.21 \times 10^{-4}\ yr^{-1}$

$$t = \frac{-1}{1.213 \times 10^{-4}\ yr^{-1}} \ln \frac{24.9}{32.5} = 2.20 \times 10^3\ yr$$

21.39   Follow the procedure outlined in Sample Exercise 21.7. The original quantity of ^{238}U is 50.0 mg plus the amount that gave rise to 14.0 mg of ^{206}Pb. This amount is 14.0(238/206) = 16.2 mg.

$k = 0.693/4.5 \times 10^9$ yr $= 1.54 \times 10^{-10} = 1.5 \times 10^{-10}$ yr^{-1}

$t = \dfrac{-1}{k} \ln \dfrac{N_t}{N_o} = \dfrac{-1}{1.54 \times 10^{-10} \text{ yr}^{-1}} \ln \dfrac{50.0}{66.2} = 1.8 \times 10^9$ yr

Energy Changes

21.41 $\Delta E = c^2 \Delta m$; $\Delta m = \Delta E/c^2$; 1 J $=$ kg$\bullet$m^2/s^2

$\Delta m = \dfrac{393.5 \times 10^3 \text{ kg} \bullet \text{m}^2/\text{s}^2}{(2.9979 \times 10^8 \text{ m/s})^2} \times \dfrac{1000 \text{ g}}{1 \text{ kg}} = 4.378 \times 10^{-9}$ g

21.43 $\Delta m =$ mass of individual protons and neutrons - mass of nucleus

$\Delta m = 11(1.0072765 \text{ amu}) + 12(1.0086649 \text{ amu}) - 22.983733 \text{ amu} = 0.2002873$
$= 0.200287$ amu

$\Delta E = (2.9979246 \times 10^8 \text{ m/s})^2 \times 0.2002873 \text{ amu} \times \dfrac{1 \text{ g}}{6.0221421 \times 10^{23} \text{ amu}} \times \dfrac{1 \text{ kg}}{1 \times 10^3 \text{ g}}$

$= 2.989123 \times 10^{-11} = 2.98912 \times 10^{-11}$ J / ^{23}Na nucleus required

$2.989123 \times 10^{-11} \dfrac{\text{J}}{\text{nucleus}} \times \dfrac{6.0221421 \times 10^{23} \text{ atoms}}{\text{mol}} = 1.80009 \times 10^{13}$ J/mol ^{23}Na

21.45   In each case, calculate the mass defect (Δm), total nuclear binding energy and then binding energy per nucleon.

(a) $\Delta m = 6(1.0072765) + 6(1.0086649) - 11.996708 = 0.0989404 = 0.098940$ amu

$\Delta E = 0.0989404 \text{ amu} \times \dfrac{1 \text{ g}}{6.0221421 \times 10^{23} \text{ amu}} \times \dfrac{1 \text{ kg}}{1000 \text{ g}} \times \dfrac{8.987551 \times 10^{16} \text{ m}^2}{\text{s}^2}$

$= 1.476604 \times 10^{-11} = 1.4766 \times 10^{-11}$ J

binding energy/nucleon $= 1.476604 \times 10^{-11}$ J /12 $= 1.2305 \times 10^{-12}$ J/nucleon

(b) $\Delta m = 17(1.0072765) + 20(1.0086649) - 36.956576 = 0.3404225 = 0.340423$ amu

$\Delta E = 0.3404225 \text{ amu} \times \dfrac{1 \text{ g}}{6.0221421 \times 10^{23} \text{ amu}} \times \dfrac{1 \text{ kg}}{1000 \text{ g}} \times \dfrac{8.987551 \times 10^{16} \text{ m}^2}{\text{s}^2}$

$= 5.080525 \times 10^{-11} = 5.08053 \times 10^{-11}$ J

binding energy/ nucleon $= 5.080525 \times 10^{-11}$ J / 37 $= 1.37312 \times 10^{-12}$ J/nucleon

(c)   Calculate the nuclear mass by subtracting the electron mass from the atomic mass.

$$136.905812 \text{ amu} - 56(5.485799 \times 10^{-4} \text{ amu}) = 136.875092 \text{ amu}$$

$$\Delta m = 56(1.0072765) + 81(1.0086649) - 136.875092 = 1.2342489 = 1.234249 \text{ amu}$$

$$\Delta E = 1.2342489 \text{ amu} \times \frac{1 \text{ g}}{6.0221421 \times 10^{23} \text{ amu}} \times \frac{1 \text{ kg}}{1000 \text{ g}} \times \frac{8.987551 \times 10^{16} \text{ m}^2}{\text{s}^2}$$

$$= 1.842014 \times 10^{-10} \text{ J}$$

binding energy/nucleon = 1.842014×10^{-10} J / 137 = 1.344536×10^{-12} J/nucleon

21.47   (a)

$$\frac{1.07 \times 10^{16} \text{ kJ}}{1 \text{ min}} \times \frac{60 \text{ min}}{1 \text{ hr}} \times \frac{24 \text{ hr}}{1 \text{ day}} = 1.541 \times 10^{19} \frac{\text{kJ}}{\text{day}} = 1.54 \times 10^{22} \text{ J/day}$$

$$\Delta m = \frac{1.541 \times 10^{22} \text{ kg} \cdot \text{m}^2/\text{s}^2/\text{d}}{(2.998 \times 10^8 \text{ m/s})^2} = 1.714 \times 10^5 = 1.71 \times 10^5 \text{ kg/d}$$

(b)   Calculate the mass change in the given nuclear reaction:

$$\Delta m = 140.8833 + 91.9021 + 2(1.0086649) - 234.9935 = -0.19077 = -0.1908 \text{ amu}$$

Converting from atoms to moles and amu to grams, it requires 1.000 mol or 235.0 g ^{235}U to produce energy equivalent to a change in mass of 0.1908 g.

0.10% of 1.714×10^5 kg is 1.714×10^2 kg = 1.714×10^5 g

$$1.714 \times 10^5 \text{ g} \times \frac{235.0 \text{ g }^{235}\text{U}}{0.1908 \text{ g}} = 2.111 \times 10^8 = 2.1 \times 10^8 \text{ g }^{235}\text{U}$$

(This is about 230 tons of ^{235}U **per day**.)

21.49   We can use Figure 21.13 to see that the binding energy per nucleon (which gives rise to the mass defect) is greatest for nuclei of mass numbers around 50. Thus (a) $^{59}_{27}$Co should possess the greatest mass defect per nucleon.

Effects and Uses of Radioisotopes

21.51   The ^{59}Fe would be incorporated into the diet component, which in turn is fed to the rabbits. After a time blood samples could be removed from the animals, the red blood cells separated, and the radioactivity of the sample measured. If the iron in the dietary compound has been incorporated into blood hemoglobin, the blood cell sample should show beta emission. Samples could be taken at various times to determine the rate of iron uptake, rate of loss of the iron from the blood, and so forth.

21.53   (a)   *Control rods* control neutron flux so that there are enough neutrons to sustain the chain reaction but not so many that the core overheats.

(b)   A *moderator* slows neutrons so that they are more easily captured by fissioning nuclei.

21.55 (a) $^{235}_{92}U + ^1_0n \rightarrow ^{160}_{62}Sm + ^{72}_{30}Zn + 4\,^1_0n$ (b) $^{239}_{94}Pu + ^1_0n \rightarrow ^{144}_{58}Ce + ^{94}_{36}Kr + 2\,^1_0n$

21.57 The extremely high temperature is required to overcome the electrostatic charge repulsions between the nuclei so that they come together to react.

21.59 •OH is a free radical; it contains an unpaired (free) electron, which makes it an extremely reactive species. (As an odd electron molecule, it violates the octet rule.) It can react with almost any particle (atom, molecule, ion) to acquire an electron and become OH^-. This often starts a disruptive chain of reactions, each producing a different free radical.

Hydroxide ion, OH^-, on the other hand, will be attracted to cations or the positive end of a polar molecule. Its most common reaction is ubiquitous and innocuous: $H^+ + OH^- \rightarrow H_2O$. The acid-base reactions of OH^- are usually much less disruptive to the organism than the chain of redox reactions initiated by •OH radical.

21.61 (a) $1\,Ci = 3.7 \times 10^{10}$ disintegrations(dis)/s; $1\,Bq = 1\,dis/s$

$$8.7\,mCi \times \frac{1\,Ci}{1000\,mCi} \times \frac{3.7 \times 10^{10}\,dis/s}{Ci} = 3.22 \times 10^8 = 3.2 \times 10^8\,dis/s = 3.2 \times 10^8\,Bq$$

(b) $1\,rad = 1 \times 10^{-2}\,J/kg$; $1\,Gy = 1\,J/kg = 100\,rad$. From part (a), the activity of the source is $3.2 \times 10^8\,dis/s$.

$$3.22 \times 10^8\,dis/s \times 2.0\,s \times 0.65 \times \frac{9.12 \times 10^{-13}\,J}{dis} \times \frac{1}{0.250\,kg} = 1.53 \times 10^{-3}$$

$$= 1.5 \times 10^{-3}\,J/kg$$

$$1.5 \times 10^{-3}\,J/kg \times \frac{1\,rad}{1 \times 10^{-2}\,J/kg} \times \frac{1000\,mrad}{rad} = 1.5 \times 10^2\,mrad$$

$$1.5 \times 10^{-3}\,J/kg \times \frac{1\,Gy}{1\,J/kg} = 1.5 \times 10^{-3}\,Gy$$

(c) $rem = rad\,(RBE)$; $Sv = Gy\,(RBE) = 100\,rem$

$mrem = 1.53 \times 10^2\,mrad\,(9.5) = 1.45 \times 10^3 = 1.5 \times 10^3\,mrem$ (or 1.5 rem)

$Sv = 1.53 \times 10^{-3}\,Gy\,(9.5) = 1.45 \times 10^{-2} = 1.5 \times 10^{-2}\,Sv$

Additional Exercises

21.63 $^{222}_{86}Rn \rightarrow X + 3\,^4_2He + 2\,^0_{-1}\beta$

This corresponds to a reduction in mass number of $(3 \times 4 =)$ 12 and a reduction in atomic number of $(3 \times 2 - 2) = 4$. The stable nucleus is $^{210}_{82}Pb$. [This is part of the sequence in Figure 21.4.]

21.65 The most massive radionuclides will have the highest neutron/proton ratios. Thus, they are most likely to decay by a process that lowers this ratio, beta emission. The least massive nuclides, on the other hand, will decay by a process that increases the neutron/proton ratio, positron emission or orbital electron capture.

21.68   This is similar to Exercises 21.35 and 21.36.

$$^{212}_{86}\text{Rn} \rightarrow {}^{208}_{84}\text{Po} + {}^{4}_{2}\text{He}$$

Each ^{212}Rn nucleus that decays is 1 disintegration. Calculate the mass of ^{212}Rn remaining after 1.0 s, calculate by subtraction the mass that has decayed, and use Avogadro's number to get the number of nuclei that have decayed.

Calculate k in s^{-1}. $25 \text{ min} \times \dfrac{60\text{ s}}{1\text{ min}} = 1.5 \times 10^3 \text{ s}$

$k = 0.693 / t_{1/2} = 0.693/1.5 \times 10^3 \text{ s} = 4.62 \times 10^{-4} = 4.6 \times 10^{-4} \text{ s}^{-1}$

$\ln(N_t / N_o) - kt = -(4.62 \times 10^{-4} \text{ s}^{-1})(1.0 \text{ s}) = -4.62 \times 10^{-4} = -4.6 \times 10^{-4}$

$N_t / N_o = e^{-4.62 \times 10^{-4}} = (1.00 - 4.62 \times 10^{-4})$; $N_t = 1.0 \times 10^{-12} \text{ g } (1.000 - 4.62 \times 10^{-4})$

The amount that decays is $N_o - N_t$:

$1.0 \times 10^{-12} \text{ g} - [1.0 \times 10^{-12} \text{ g } (1.000 - 4.62 \times 10^{-4})] = 1.0 \times 10^{-12} \text{ g } (4.62 \times 10^{-4})$

$$= 4.62 \times 10^{-16} = 4.6 \times 10^{-16} \text{ g } {}^{212}\text{Rn}$$

$N_o - N_t = 4.62 \times 10^{-16} \text{ g Rn} \times \dfrac{1 \text{ mol Rn}}{212 \text{ g Rn}} \times \dfrac{6.022 \times 10^{23} \text{ Rn atoms}}{1 \text{ mol Rn}} = 1.31 \times 10^6 = 1.3 \times 10^6 \text{ dis}$

This is 1.3×10^6 disintegrations in 1.0 s, or approximately 1.3×10^6 α particles/s

$1.31 \times 10^6 \text{ dis/s} \times \dfrac{1 \text{ Ci}}{3.7 \times 10^{10} \text{ dis/s}} = 3.547 \times 10^{-5} = 3.5 \times 10^{-5} \text{ Ci}$

21.70 $1 \times 10^{-6} \text{ curie} \times \dfrac{3.7 \times 10^{10} \text{ dis/s}}{\text{curie}} = 3.7 \times 10^4 \text{ dis/s}$

rate = 3.7×10^4 nuclei/s = kN

$k = \dfrac{0.693}{t_{1/2}} = \dfrac{0.693}{28.8 \text{ yr}} \times \dfrac{1 \text{ yr}}{365 \times 24 \times 3600 \text{ sec}} = 7.630 \times 10^{-10} = 7.63 \times 10^{-10} \text{ s}^{-1}$

3.7×10^4 nuclei/s = $(7.63 \times 10^{-10}/\text{s})$ N;   N = $4.849 \times 10^{13} = 4.8 \times 10^{13}$ nuclei

mass ^{90}Sr = 4.849×10^{13} nuclei $\times \dfrac{90 \text{ g Sr}}{6.022 \times 10^{23} \text{ nuclei}} = 7.2 \times 10^{-9}$ g Sr

21.72   Assume that no depletion of iodide from the water due to plant uptake has occurred. Then the activity after 32 days would be:

$k = 0.693/t_{1/2} = 0.693/8.1 \text{ d} = 0.0856 = 0.086 \text{ d}^{-1}$

$\ln \dfrac{N_t}{N_o} = -(0.0856 \text{ d}^{-1})(32 \text{ d}) = -2.739 = -2.7$; $\dfrac{N_t}{N_o} = 0.0646 = 0.06$

We thus expect N_t = 0.0646(89) = 5.7 counts/min. This is just the **observed** activity; we can assume that the plants did not absorb iodide, because that would have resulted in a lower level of remaining activity.

21.75 Because of the relationship $\Delta E = \Delta m c^2$, the mass defect (Δm) is directly related to the binding energy (ΔE) of the nucleus.

^{7}Be: 4p, 3n; 4(1.0072765) + 3(1.0086649) = 7.05510 amu

Total mass defect = 7.0551 - 7.0147 = 0.0404 amu

0.0404 amu/7 nucleons = 5.77 × 10^{-3} amu/nucleon

$$\Delta E = \Delta m \times c^2 = \frac{5.77 \times 10^{-3} \text{ amu}}{\text{nucleon}} \times \frac{1 \text{ g}}{6.022 \times 10^{23} \text{ amu}} \times \frac{1 \text{ kg}}{1 \times 10^3 \text{ g}} \times \frac{8.988 \times 10^{16} \text{ m}^2}{\text{sec}^2}$$

$$= \frac{5.77 \times 10^{-3} \text{ amu}}{\text{nucleon}} \times \frac{1.4925 \times 10^{-10} \text{ J}}{1 \text{ amu}} = 8.612 \times 10^{-13} = 8.61 \times 10^{-13} \text{ J/nucleon}$$

^{9}Be: 4p, 5n; 4(1.0072765) + 5(1.0086649) = 9.07243 amu

Total mass defect = 9.0724 - 9.0100 = 0.06243 = 0.0624 amu

0.0624 amu/9 nucleons = 6.937 × 10^{-3} = 6.94 × 10^{-3} amu/nucleon

6.937 × 10^{-3} amu/nucleon × 1.4925 × 10^{-10} J/amu = 1.035 × 10^{-12} = 1.04 × 10^{-12} J/nucleon

^{10}Be: 4p, 6n; 4(1.0072765) + 6(1.0086649) = 10.0811 amu

Total mass defect = 10.0811 - 10.0113 = 0.0698 amu

0.0698 amu/10 nucleons = 6.98 × 10^{-3} amu/nucleon

6.98 × 10^{-3} amu/nucleon × 1.4925 × 10^{-10} J/amu = 1.042 × 10^{-12} = 1.04 × 10^{-12} J/nucleon

The binding energies/nucleon for ^{9}Be and ^{10}Be are very similar; that for ^{10}Be is slightly higher.

21.77 $\quad$ 1000 Mwatts × $\dfrac{1 \times 10^6 \text{ watts}}{1 \text{ Mwatt}}$ × $\dfrac{1 \text{ J}}{1 \text{ watt} \cdot \text{s}}$ × $\dfrac{1 \ ^{235}\text{U atom}}{3 \times 10^{-11} \text{ J}}$ × $\dfrac{1 \text{ mol U}}{6.02 \times 10^{23} \text{ atoms}}$

$\quad$ × $\dfrac{235 \text{ g U}}{1 \text{ mol}}$ × $\dfrac{3600 \text{ s}}{1 \text{ hr}}$ × $\dfrac{24 \text{ hr}}{1 \text{ d}}$ × $\dfrac{365 \text{ d}}{1 \text{ yr}}$ × $\dfrac{40}{100}$ (efficiency) = 1.64 × 10^5

$\hspace{8cm}$ = 2 × 10^5 g U/ yr = 200 kg U/yr

Integrative Exercises

21.79 Calculate the molar mass of NaClO$_4$ that contains 31% ^{36}Cl. Atomic mass of the enhanced Cl is 0.31(36) + 0.69(35.453) = 35.62. The molar mass of NaClO$_4$ is then (22.99 + 35.62 + 64.00) = 122.61. Calculate N, the number of ^{36}Cl nuclei, the value of k in s^{-1}, and the activity in dis/s.

$$49.5 \text{ mg NaClO}_4 \times \frac{1 \text{ g}}{1000 \text{ mg}} \times \frac{1 \text{ mol NaClO}_4}{122.61 \text{ g NaClO}_4} \times \frac{1 \text{ mol Cl}}{1 \text{ mol NaClO}_4} \times \frac{6.022 \times 10^{23} \text{ Cl atoms}}{\text{mol Cl}}$$

$$\times \frac{31 \;{}^{36}\text{Cl atoms}}{100 \text{ Cl atoms}} = 7.537 \times 10^{19} = 7.54 \times 10^{19} \;{}^{36}\text{Cl atoms}$$

$$k = 0.693/t_{1/2} = \frac{0.693}{3.0 \times 10^5 \text{ yr}} \times \frac{1 \text{ yr}}{365 \times 24 \times 3600 \text{ s}} = 7.32 \times 10^{-14} = 7.3 \times 10^{-14} \text{ s}^{-1}$$

rate $= kN = (7.32 \times 10^{-14} \text{ s}^{-1})(7.547 \times 10^{19} \text{ nuclei}) = 5.52 \times 10^6 = 5.5 \times 10^6$ dis/s

21.81 (a) $\quad 0.18 \text{ Ci} \times \dfrac{3.7 \times 10^{10} \text{ dis/s}}{\text{Ci}} \times \dfrac{3600 \text{ s}}{\text{hr}} \times \dfrac{24 \text{ hr}}{\text{d}} \times 235 \text{ d} = 1.35 \times 10^{17}$

$$= 1.4 \times 10^{17} \; \alpha \text{ particles}$$

(b) $\quad P = nRT/V = 1.35 \times 10^{17} \text{ He atoms} \times \dfrac{1 \text{ mol He}}{6.022 \times 10^{23} \text{ atoms}} \times \dfrac{295 \text{ K}}{0.0150 \text{ L}} \times \dfrac{0.08206 \text{ L} \cdot \text{atm}}{\text{K} \cdot \text{mol}}$

$$= 3.62 \times 10^{-4} = 3.6 \times 10^{-4} \text{ atm} = 0.28 \text{ torr}$$

21.84   Determine the wavelengths of the photons by first calculating the energy equivalent of the mass of an electron or positron. (Since **two** photons are formed by annihilation of **two** particles of equal mass, we need to calculate the energy equivalent of just one particle.) The mass of an electron is 9.109×10^{-31} kg.

$$\Delta E = (9.109 \times 10^{-31} \text{ kg}) \times (2.998 \times 10^8 \text{ m/s})^2 = 8.187 \times 10^{-14} \text{ J}$$

Also, $\Delta E = h\nu$; $\quad \Delta E = hc/\lambda$; $\quad \lambda = hc/\Delta E$

$$\lambda = \frac{(6.626 \times 10^{-34} \text{ J} \cdot \text{s})(2.998 \times 10^8 \text{ m/s})}{8.187 \times 10^{-14} \text{ J}} = 2.426 \times 10^{-12} \text{ m} = 2.426 \times 10^{-3} \text{ nm}$$

This is a very short wavelength indeed; it lies at the short wavelength end of the range of observed gamma ray wavelengths (see Figure 6.4).

22 Chemistry of the Nonmetals

Periodic Trends and Chemical Reactions

22.1   Metals: Sr, Ce, Rh;   nonmetals: Se, Kr;   metalloid: Sb

22.3   (a)   Cl   (b) K

(c)   K in the gas phase (lowest ionization energy), Li in aqueous solution (most positive $E°$ value)

(d)   Ne; Ne and Ar are difficult to compare because they do not form compounds and their radii are not measured in the same way as other elements. However, Ne is several rows to the right of C and surely has a smaller atomic radius. The next smallest is C.

(e)   C

22.5   (a)   Nitrogen is too small to accommodate five fluorine atoms about it. The P and As atoms are larger. Furthermore, P and As have available 3d and 4d orbitals, respectively, to form hybrid orbitals that can accommodate more than an octet of electrons about the central atom.

(b)   Si does not readily form π bonds, which would be necessary to satisfy the octet rule for both atoms in SiO.

(c)   A reducing agent is a substance that readily loses electrons. As has a lower electronegativity than N; that is, it more readily gives up electrons to an acceptor and is more easily oxidized.

22.7   (a) $NaNH_2(s) + H_2O(l) \rightarrow NH_3(aq) + NaOH(aq)$

(b) $2C_3H_7OH(l) + 9O_2(g) \rightarrow 6CO_2(g) + 8H_2O(l)$

(c) $NiO(s) + C(s) \rightarrow CO(g) + Ni(s)$ or $2NiO(s) + C(s) \rightarrow CO_2(g) + 2Ni(s)$

(d) $AlP(s) + 3H_2O(l) \rightarrow PH_3(g) + Al(OH)_3(s)$

(e) $Na_2S(s) + 2HCl(aq) \rightarrow H_2S(g) + 2NaCl(aq)$

Hydrogen, the Noble Gases, and the Halogens

22.9 $_1^1H$ - protium; $_1^2H$ - deuterium; $_1^3H$ - tritium

22.11   Like other elements in group 1A, hydrogen has only one valence electron. Like other elements in group 7A, hydrogen needs only one electron to complete its valence shell. The most common oxidation number of H is +1, like the group 1A elements; H can also exist in the -1 oxidation state, a state common to the group 7A elements.

22.13   (a) $Mg(s) + 2H^+(aq) \rightarrow Mg^{2+}(aq) + H_2(g)$

(b) $C(s) + H_2O(g) \xrightarrow{1000\,^{\circ}C} CO(g) + H_2(g)$

(c) $CH_4(g) + H_2O(g) \xrightarrow{1100\,^{\circ}C} CO(g) + 3H_2(g)$

22.15   (a) $NaH(s) + H_2O(l) \rightarrow NaOH(aq) + H_2(g)$

(b) $Fe(s) + H_2SO_4(aq) \rightarrow Fe^{2+}(aq) + H_2(g) + SO_4^{2-}(aq)$

(c) $H_2(g) + Br_2(g) \rightarrow 2HBr(g)$

(d) $2Na(l) + H_2(g) \rightarrow 2NaH(s)$

(e) $PbO(s) + H_2(g) \overset{\Delta}{\rightarrow} Pb(s) + H_2O(g)$

22.17   (a)   Ionic (metal hydride)   (b) molecular (nonmetal hydride)

(c)   metallic (nonstoichiometric transition metal hydride)

22.19   Xenon is larger, and can more readily accommodate an expanded octet. More important is the lower ionization energy of xenon; because the valence electrons are a greater average distance from the nucleus, they are more readily promoted to a state in which the Xe atom can form bonds with fluorine.

22.21   (a) IO_3^-, +5   (b) $HBrO_3$, +5   (c) **BrF_3**; Br, +3; F, -1

(d)   **NaOCl**, +1   (e) HIO_2, +3   (f) **XeO_3**, +6

22.23   (a)   potassium chlorate   (b) calcium iodate   (c) aluminum chloride

(d)   bromic acid   (e) paraperiodic acid   (f) xenon tetrafluoride

22.25   (a)   Van der Waals intermolecular attractive forces increase with increasing numbers of electrons in the atoms.

(b) F_2 reacts with water: $F_2(g) + H_2O(l) \rightarrow 2HF(aq) + 1/2\,O_2(g)$. That is, fluorine is too strong an oxidizing agent to exist in water.

(c)   HF has extensive hydrogen bonding.

(d)   Oxidizing power is related to electronegativity. Electronegativity decreases in the order given.

22.27   (a) $Br_2(l) + 2OH^-(aq) \rightarrow BrO^-(aq) + Br^-(aq) + H_2O(l)$

(b) $Cl_2(g) + 2Br^-(aq) \rightarrow Br_2(l) + 2Cl^-(aq)$

22.29   (a) square-planar   (b) trigonal pyramidal   (c)   octahedral about the central iodine

(d) linear

Oxygen and the Group 6A Elements

22.31   (a)   As an oxidizing agent in steel-making; to bleach pulp and paper; in oxyacetylene torches; in medicine to assist in breathing

(b)   Synthesis of pharmaceuticals, lubricants and other organic compounds where C=C bonds are cleaved; in water treatment

22.33 (a) $CaO(s) + H_2O(l) \rightarrow Ca^{2+}(aq) + 2OH^-(aq)$

      (b) $Al_2O_3(s) + 6H^+(aq) \rightarrow 2Al^{3+}(aq) + 3H_2O(l)$

      (c) $Na_2O_2(s) + 2H_2O(l) \rightarrow 2Na^+(aq) + 2OH^-(aq) + H_2O_2(aq)$

      (d) $N_2O_3(g) + H_2O(l) \rightarrow 2HNO_2(aq)$

      (e) $2KO_2(s) + 2H_2O(l) \rightarrow 2K^+(aq) + 2OH^-(aq) + O_2(g) + H_2O_2(aq)$

      (f) $NO(g) + O_3(g) \rightarrow NO_2(g) + O_2(g)$

22.35 (a)   Neutral   (b) acidic (oxide of a nonmetal)

      (c)   basic (oxide of a metal)   (d) amphoteric

22.37 (a)   **SeO_3**, +6   (b) $Na_2S_2O_3$, +2   (c) **SF_4**, +4   (d) H_2S, -2   (e) H_2SO_3, +4

               Oxygen (a group 6A element) is in the -2 oxidation state in compounds (a), (b) and (e).

22.39 The half reaction for oxidation in all these cases is:

      $H_2S(aq) \rightarrow S(s) + 2H^+ + 2e^-$ (The product could be written as $S_8(s)$, but this is not necessary. In fact it is not necessarily the case that S_8 would be formed, rather than some other allotropic form of the element.)

      (a) $2Fe^{3+}(aq) + H_2S(aq) \rightarrow 2Fe^{2+}(aq) + S(s) + 2H^+(aq)$

      (b) $Br_2(l) + H_2S(aq) \rightarrow 2Br^-(aq) + S(s) + 2H^+(aq)$

      (c) $2MnO_4^-(aq) + 6H^+(aq) + 5H_2S(aq) \rightarrow 2Mn^{2+}(aq) + 5S(s) + 8H_2O(l)$

      (d) $2NO_3^-(aq) + H_2S(aq) + 2H^+(aq) \rightarrow 2NO_2(aq) + S(s) + 2H_2O(l)$

22.41 (a)

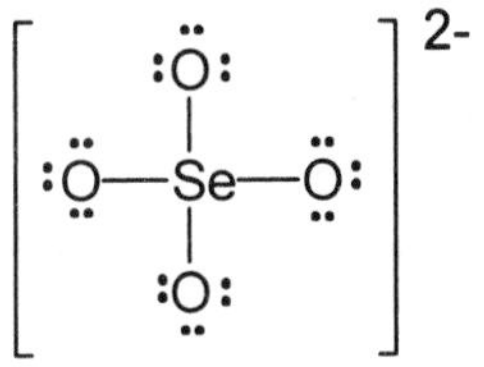

tetrahedral   bent (free rotation around S-S bond)   tetrahedral

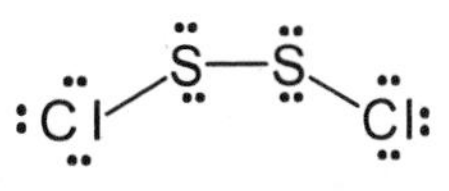

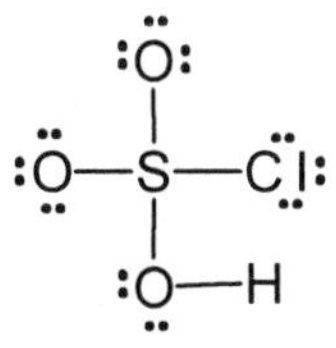

22.43 (a) $SO_2(s) + H_2O(l) \rightarrow H_2SO_3(aq) \rightleftharpoons H^+(aq) + HSO_3^-(aq)$

      (b) $ZnS(s) + 2HCl(aq) \rightarrow ZnCl_2(aq) + H_2S(g)$

      (c) $8SO_3^{2-}(aq) + S_8(s) \rightarrow 8S_2O_3^{2-}(aq)$

      (d) $SO_3(aq) + H_2SO_4(l) \rightarrow H_2S_2O_7(l)$

Nitrogen and the Group 5A Elements

22.45 (a) HNO_2, +3   (b) **N_2H_4**, -2   (c) KCN, -3   (d) $NaNO_3$, +5

      (e)   **NH_4Cl**, -3   (f) **Li_3N**, -3

22.47 (a)   :O̤=N̈—O̤—H

The molecule is bent around the central oxygen and nitrogen atoms; the four atoms need not lie in a plane.

(b) $\left[:\ddot{N}=N=\ddot{N}: \right]^{-} \longleftrightarrow \left[:N\equiv N—\ddot{\ddot{N}}: \right]^{-} \longleftrightarrow \left[:\ddot{\ddot{N}}—N\equiv N: \right]^{-}$

The molecule is linear.

(c)
$$\left[\begin{array}{c} \overset{H}{|} \quad \overset{H}{|} \\ H—N—N: \\ \underset{H}{|} \quad \underset{H}{|} \end{array} \right]^{+}$$

(d)
$$\left[\begin{array}{c} :\ddot{O}: \\ | \\ :\ddot{O}—N=\ddot{O} \end{array} \right]^{-}$$

The geometry is tetrahedral around the left nitrogen, trigonal pyramidal around the right.

(three equivalent resonance forms)
The ion is trigonal planar.

22.49 (a) $Mg_3N_2(s) + 6H_2O(l) \rightarrow 3Mg(OH)_2(s) + 2NH_3(aq)$

(b) $2NO(g) + O_2(g) \rightarrow 2NO_2(g)$

(c) $4NH_3(g) + 3O_2(g) \overset{\Delta}{\rightarrow} 2N_2(g) + 6H_2O(g)$

(d) $NaNH_2(s) + H_2O(l) \rightarrow Na^+(aq) + OH^-(aq) + NH_3(aq)$

22.51 (a) $4Zn(s) + 2NO_3^-(aq) + 10H^+(aq) \rightarrow 4Zn^{2+}(aq) + N_2O(g) + 5H_2O(l)$

(b) $4NO_3^-(aq) + S(s) + 4H^+(aq) \rightarrow 4NO_2(g) + SO_2(g) + 2H_2O(l)$

(or $6NO_3^-(aq) + S(s) + 4H^+(aq) \rightarrow 6NO_2(g) + SO_4^{2-}(aq) + 2H_2O(l)$)

(c) $2NO_3^-(aq) + 3SO_2(g) + 2H_2O(l) \rightarrow 2NO(g) + 3SO_4^{2-}(aq) + 4H^+(aq)$

22.53 (a) $2NO_3^-(aq) + 12H^+(aq) + 10e^- \rightarrow N_2(g) + 6H_2O(l)$ $E_{red}^{\circ} = +1.25\ V$

(b) $2NH_4^+(aq) \rightarrow N_2(g) + 8H^+(aq) + 6e^-$ $E_{red}^{\circ} = 0.27\ V$

22.55 (a) H_3PO_4, +5   (b) H_3AsO_3, +3   (c) Sb_2S_3, +3   (d) $Ca(H_2PO_4)_2$, +5   (e) K_3P, -3

22.57 (a)   Phosphorus is a larger atom and can more easily accommodate five surrounding atoms and an expanded octet of electrons than nitrogen can. Also, P has energetically "available" 3d orbitals which participate in the bonding, but nitrogen does not.

(b)   Only one of the three hydrogens in H_3PO_2 is bonded to oxygen. The other two are bonded directly to phosphorus and are not easily ionized because the P-H bond is not very polar.

(c) PH_3 is a weaker base than H_2O (PH_4^+ is a stronger acid than H_3O^+). Any attempt to add H^+ to PH_3 in the presence of H_2O merely causes protonation of H_2O.

(d)   White phosphorus consists of P_4 molecules, with P-P-P bond angles of 60°. Each P atom has four VSEPR pairs of electrons, so the predicted electron pair geometry is tetrahedral and the preferred bond angle is 109°. Because of the severely strained bond angles in P_4 molecules, white phosphorus is highly reactive.

22.59   (a) $2Ca_3(PO_4)_2(s) + 6SiO_2(s) + 10C(s) \xrightarrow{\Delta} P_4(g) + 6CaSiO_3(l) + 10CO(g)$

       (b) $3H_2O(l) + PCl_3(l) \rightarrow H_3PO_3(aq) + 3H^+(aq) + 3Cl^-(aq)$

       (c) $6Cl_2(g) + P_4(s) \rightarrow 4PCl_3(l)$

Carbon, the Other Group 4A Elements, and Boron

22.61   (a)   HCN   (b) SiC   (c) $CaCO_3$ (d) CaC_2

22.63   (a) $\left[:C\equiv N:\right]^-$ (b) $:C\equiv O:$ (c) $\left[:C\equiv C:\right]^{2-}$

       (d) $\ddot{S}=C=\ddot{S}$ (e) $\ddot{O}=C=\ddot{O}$ (f)

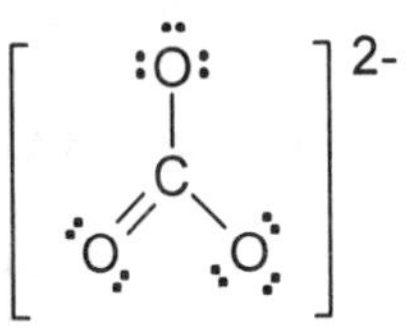

                                              one of three equivalent resonance structures

22.65   (a) $ZnCO_3(s) \xrightarrow{\Delta} ZnO(s) + CO_2(g)$

       (b) $BaC_2(s) + 2H_2O(l) \rightarrow Ba^{2+}(aq) + 2OH^-(aq) + C_2H_2(g)$

       (c) $C_2H_4(g) + 3O_2(g) \rightarrow 2CO_2(g) + 2H_2O(g)$

       (d) $2CH_3OH(l) + 3O_2(g) \rightarrow 2CO_2(g) + 4H_2O(g)$

       (e) $NaCN(s) + H^+(aq) \rightarrow Na^+(aq) + HCN(g)$

22.67   (a) $2CH_4(g) + 2NH_3(g) + 3O_2(g) \xrightarrow[\text{cat}]{800°C} 2HCN(g) + 6H_2O(g)$

       (b) $NaHCO_3(s) + H^+(aq) \rightarrow CO_2(g) + H_2O(l) + Na^+(aq)$

       (c) $2BaCO_3(s) + O_2(g) + 2SO_2(g) \rightarrow 2BaSO_4(s) + 2CO_2(g)$

22.69   (a)   **SiO_2**, +4   (b) **$GeCl_4$**, +4   (c) **$NaBH_4$**, +3   (d) **$SnCl_2$**, +2   (e) **B_2H_6**, +3

22.71   (a)   Carbon   (b) lead   (c) silicon

22.73   (a) SiO_4^{4-} (b) SiO_3^{2-} (c) SiO_3^{2-}

22.75   (a)   Diborane (Figure 22.55 and below) has bridging H atoms linking the two B atoms. The structure of ethane shown below has the C atoms bound directly, with no bridging atoms.

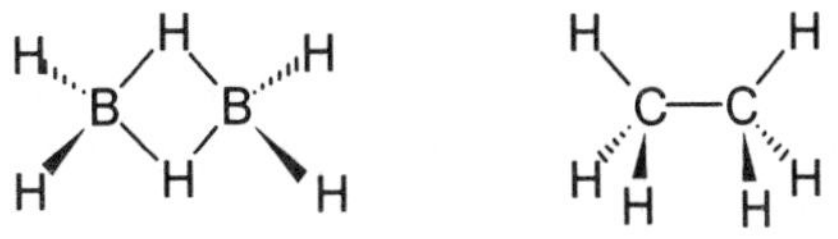

(b) B_2H_6 is an electron deficient molecule. It has 12 valence electrons, while C_2H_6 has 14 valence electrons. The 6 valence electron pairs in B_2H_6 are all involved in B-H sigma bonding, so the only way to satisfy the octet rule at B is to have the bridging H atoms shown in Figure 22.55.

(c)   A hydride ion, H^-, has two electrons while an H atom has one. The term *hydridic* indicates that the H atoms in B_2H_6 have more than the usual amount of electron density for a covalently bound H atom.

Additional Exercises

22.77   (a) $1.00 \text{ kg FeTi} \times \dfrac{1 \text{ mol FeTi}}{103.7 \text{ g FeTi}} \times \dfrac{1000 \text{ g}}{1 \text{ kg}} \times \dfrac{1 \text{ mol H}_2}{1 \text{ mol FeTi}} \times \dfrac{2.016 \text{ g H}}{1 \text{ mol H}_2} = 19.44$

$= 19.4 \text{ g H}$

(b) $V = \dfrac{19.44 \text{ g H}_2}{2.016 \text{ g/mol H}_2} \times \dfrac{0.08206 \text{ L} \cdot \text{atm}}{\text{mol} \cdot \text{K}} \times \dfrac{273 \text{ K}}{1 \text{ atm}} = 216 \text{ L}$

22.80 $BrO_3^-(aq) + XeF_2(aq) + H_2O(l) \rightarrow Xe(g) + 2HF(aq) + BrO_4^-(aq)$

22.83   (a) $H_2SO_4 - H_2O \rightarrow SO_3$ (b) $2HClO_3 - H_2O \rightarrow Cl_2O_5$

(c) $2HNO_2 - H_2O \rightarrow N_2O_3$ (d) $H_2CO_3 - H_2O \rightarrow CO_2$

(e) $2H_3PO_4 - 3H_2O \rightarrow P_2O_5$

22.86   (a) $2H_2Se(g) + O_2(g) \rightarrow 2H_2O(g) + 2Se(s)$

(b) $\Delta G^\circ = 2\Delta G^\circ_f \, H_2O(g) - 2\Delta G^\circ_f \, H_2Se(g)$

$= 2(-228.57 \text{ kJ}) - 2(15.9 \text{ kJ}) = -488.9$

$\Delta G^\circ = -RT \ln K$

$\ln K = \dfrac{-(-488.9 \times 10^3 \text{ J})}{8.314 \text{ J/K} \cdot \text{mol} \times 298 \text{ K}} = 197.33 = 197.3; \quad K = 5 \times 10^{85}$

22.89

In both structures there are unshared pairs on all oxygens to give octets and the geometry around each P is approximately tetrahedral.

22.92   (a)

$$2[5e^- + MnO_4^-(aq) + 8H^+(aq) \rightarrow Mn^{2+}(aq) + 4H_2O(l)]$$

$$5[H_2O_2(aq) \rightarrow O_2(g) + 2H^+(aq) + 2e^-]$$

$$\overline{2MnO_4^-(aq) + 5H_2O_2(aq) + 6H^+(aq) \rightarrow 2Mn^{2+}(aq) + 5O_2(g) + 8H_2O(l)}$$

(b)
$$2[Fe^{2+}(aq) \rightarrow Fe^{3+}(aq) + e^-]$$
$$H_2O_2(aq) + 2H^+(aq) + 2e^- \rightarrow 2H_2O(l)$$

$$2Fe^{2+}(aq) + H_2O_2(aq) + 2H^+(aq) \rightarrow 2Fe^{3+}(aq) + 2H_2O(l)$$

(c)
$$2 I^-(aq) \rightarrow I_2(s) + 2e^-$$
$$H_2O_2(aq) + 2H^+(aq) + 2e^- \rightarrow 2H_2O(l)$$

$$2 I^-(aq) + H_2O_2(aq) + 2H^+(aq) \rightarrow I_2(s) + 2H_2O(l)$$

(d)
$$MnO_2(s) + 4H^+(aq) + 2e^- \rightarrow Mn^{2+}(aq) + 2H_2O(l)$$
$$H_2O_2(aq) \rightarrow O_2(g) + 2H^+(aq) + 2e^-$$

$$MnO_2(s) + 2H^+(aq) + H_2O_2(aq) \rightarrow Mn^{2+}(aq) + 2H_2O(l) + O_2(g)$$

(e)
$$2 I^-(aq) \rightarrow I_2(s) + 2e^-$$
$$O_3(g) + H_2O(l) + 2e^- \rightarrow O_2(g) + 2OH^-(aq)$$

$$2 I^-(aq) + O_3(g) + H_2O(l) \rightarrow O_2(g) + I_2(s) + 2OH^-(aq)$$

Integrative Exercises

22.95 $2XeO_3(s) \rightarrow 2Xe(g) + 3O_2(g)$

$$0.654 \text{ g XeO}_3 \times \frac{1 \text{ mol XeO}_3}{179.1 \text{ g XeO}_3} \times \frac{5 \text{ mol gas}}{2 \text{ mol XeO}_3} = 9.129 \times 10^{-3} = 9.13 \times 10^{-3} \text{ mol gas}$$

$$P = \frac{(9.129 \times 10^{-3} \text{ mol})(0.08206 \text{ L} \cdot \text{atm/mol} \cdot \text{K})(321 \text{ K})}{0.452 \text{ L}} = 0.532 \text{ atm}$$

22.98   (a) $H_2(g) + 1/2 \, O_2(g) \rightarrow H_2O(l); \quad \Delta H = -285.83 \text{ kJ}$

            $CH_4(g) + 2O_2(g) \rightarrow CO_2(g) + 2H_2O(l)$

            $\Delta H = 2(-285.83) - 393.5 - (-74.8) = -890.4 \text{ kJ}$

     (b)   for H_2: $\dfrac{-285.83 \text{ kJ}}{1 \text{ mol H}_2} \times \dfrac{1 \text{ mol H}_2}{2.0159 \text{ g H}_2} = -141.79 \text{ kJ/g H}_2$

            for CH_4: $\dfrac{-890.4 \text{ kJ}}{1 \text{ mol CH}_4} \times \dfrac{1 \text{ mol CH}_4}{16.043 \text{ g CH}_4} = -55.50 \text{ kJ/g CH}_4$

     (c)   Find the number of moles of gas that occupy 1 m^3 at STP:

$$n = \frac{1 \text{ atm} \times 1 \text{ m}^3}{273 \text{ K}} \times \frac{1 \text{ K} \cdot \text{mol}}{0.08206 \text{ L} \cdot \text{atm}} \times \left[\frac{100 \text{ cm}}{1 \text{ m}} \right]^3 \times \frac{1 \text{ L}}{10^3 \text{ cm}^3} = 44.64 \text{ mol}$$

            for H_2: $\dfrac{-285.83 \text{ kJ}}{1 \text{ mol H}_2} \times \dfrac{44.64 \text{ mol H}_2}{1 \text{ m}^3 \text{ H}_2} = 1.276 \times 10^4 \text{ kJ/m}^3 \text{ H}_2$

            for CH_4: $\dfrac{-890.4 \text{ kJ}}{1 \text{ mol CH}_4} \times \dfrac{44.64 \text{ mol CH}_4}{1 \text{ m}^3 \text{ CH}_4} = 3.975 \times 10^4 \text{ kJ/m}^3 \text{ CH}_4$

22.100 First calculate the molar solubility of Cl_2 in water.

$$n = \frac{1 \text{ atm } (0.310 \text{ L})}{\frac{0.08206 \text{ L} \cdot \text{atm}}{1 \text{ mol} \cdot \text{K}} \times 273 \text{ K}} = 0.01384 = 0.0138 \text{ mol } Cl_2; \quad M = \frac{0.01384 \text{ mol}}{0.100 \text{ L}} = 0.1384$$

$$= 0.138 \, M$$

$$K = \frac{[Cl^-][HOCl][H^+]}{[Cl_2]} = 4.7 \times 10^{-4}$$

$[Cl^-] = [HOCl] = [H^+]$ Let this quantity = x. Then, $\dfrac{x^3}{(0.1384 - x)} = 4.7 \times 10^{-4}$

Assuming that x is small compared with 0.1384:

$x^3 = (0.1384)(4.7 \times 10^{-4}) = 6.504 \times 10^{-5}$; x = 0.0402 = 0.040 M

We can correct the denominator using this value, to get a better estimate of x:

$$\frac{x^3}{0.1384 - 0.0402} = 4.7 \times 10^{-4}; \quad x = 0.0359 = 0.036 \, M$$

One more round of approximation gives x = 0.0364 = 0.036 M. This is the equilibrium concentration of HClO.

22.104 (a) $SO_2(g) + 2H_2S(s) \rightarrow 3S(s) + 2H_2O(g)$ or, if we assume S_8 is the product,

        $8SO_2(g) + 16H_2S(g) \rightarrow 3S_8(s) + 16H_2O(g)$.

(b)   2000 lb coal $\times \dfrac{0.035 \text{ lb S}}{1 \text{ lb coal}} \times \dfrac{453.6 \text{ g S}}{1 \text{ lb S}} \times \dfrac{1 \text{ mol S}}{32.07 \text{ g S}} \times \dfrac{1 \text{ mol } SO_2}{1 \text{ mol S}} \times \dfrac{2 \text{ mol } H_2S}{1 \text{ mol } SO_2}$

          $= 1.98 \times 10^3 = 2.0 \times 10^3 \text{ mol } H_2S$

    $V = \dfrac{1.98 \times 10^3 \text{ mol } (0.08206 \text{ L} \cdot \text{atm/mol} \cdot \text{K})(300 \text{ K})}{(740/760) \text{ atm}} = 5.01 \times 10^4 = 5.0 \times 10^4 \text{ L}$

(c) $1.98 \times 10^3 \text{ mol } H_2S \times \dfrac{3 \text{ mol S}}{2 \text{ mol } H_2S} \times \dfrac{32.07 \text{ g S}}{1 \text{ mol S}} = 9.5 \times 10^4 \text{ g S}$

    This is about 210 lb S per ton of coal combusted. (However, two-thirds of this comes from the H_2S, which was presumably also obtained from coal.)

23 Metals and Metallurgy

Metallurgy

23.1   The important sources of iron are **hematite** (Fe_2O_3) and **magnetite** (Fe_3O_4). The major source of aluminum is **bauxite** ($Al_2O_3 \cdot xH_2O$). In ores, iron is present as the +3 ion, or in both the +2 and +3 states, as in magnetite. Aluminum is always present in the +3 oxidation state.

23.3   An ore consists of a little bit of the stuff we want, (chalcopyrite, $CuFeS_2$) and lots of other junk (gangue).

23.5   (a) $2PbS(s) + 3O_2(s) \overset{\Delta}{\rightarrow} 2PbO(s) + 2SO_2(g)$

        (b) $PbCO_3(s) \overset{\Delta}{\rightarrow} PbO(s) + CO_2(g)$

        (c) $WO_3(s) + 3H_2(g) \overset{\Delta}{\rightarrow} W(s) + 3H_2O(g)$

        (d) $ZnO(s) + CO(g) \overset{\Delta}{\rightarrow} Zn(l) + CO_2(g)$

23.7   (a) $SO_3(g)$

        (b) $CO(g)$ provides a reducing environment for the transformation of Pb^{2+} to Pb.

        (c) $PbSO_4(s) \rightarrow PbO(s) + SO_3(g)$

               $PbO(s) + CO(g) \rightarrow Pb(s) + CO_2(g)$

23.9 $FeO(s) + H_2(g) \rightarrow Fe(s) + H_2O(g)$
        $FeO(s) + CO(g) \rightarrow Fe(s) + CO_2(g)$

        $Fe_2O_3(s) + 3H_2(g) \rightarrow 2Fe(s) + 3H_2O(g)$
        $Fe_2O_3(s) + 3CO(g) \rightarrow 2Fe(s) + 3CO_2(g)$

23.11   (a)   Air serves primarily to oxidize coke (C) to CO, the main reducing agent in the blast furnace. This exothermic reaction also provides heat for the furnace.

               $2C(s) + O_2(g) \rightarrow 2CO(g) \quad \Delta H = -221 \text{ kJ}$

        (b)   Limestone, $CaCO_3$, is the source of basic oxide for slag formation.

               $CaCO_3(s) \overset{\Delta}{\rightarrow} CaO(s) + CO_2(g); \; CaO(l) + SiO_2(l) \rightarrow CaSiO_3(l)$

(c)   Coke is the fuel for the blast furnace, and the source of CO, the major reducing agent in the furnace.

$$2C(s) + O_2(g) \rightarrow 2CO(g); \quad 4CO(g) + Fe_3O_4(s) \rightarrow 4CO_2(g) + 3Fe(l)$$

(d)   Water acts as a source of hydrogen, and as a means of controlling temperature. (see Equation [23.8]). $C(s) + H_2O(g) \rightarrow CO(g) + H_2(g)$ $\Delta H = +131$ kJ

23.13 (a)   The Bayer process is necessary to separate the unwanted iron-containing solids from bauxite before electroreduction.

        (b)   The Bayer process takes advantage of the fact that Al^{3+} is amphoteric, but Fe^{3+} is not. Because it is amphoteric, Al^{3+} reacts with excess OH^- to form the soluble complex ion $Al(OH)_4^-$ while the Fe^{3+} solids cannot. This allows separation of the iron-containing solids by filtration.

23.15   Cobalt could be purified by constructing an electrolysis cell in which the crude metal was the anode and a thin sheet of pure cobalt was the cathode. The electrolysis solution is aqueous with a soluble cobalt salt such as $CoSO_4 \cdot 7H_2O$ serving as the electrolyte. (Other soluble salts with anions that do not participate in the cell reactions could be used.) Anode reaction: $Co(s) \rightarrow Co^{2+}(aq) + 2e^-$; cathode reaction: $Co^{2+}(aq) + 2e^- \rightarrow Co(s)$. Although $E°$ for reduction of $Co^{2+}(aq)$ is slightly negative (-0.277 V), we assume that reduction of water or H^+ does not occur because of a large overvoltage.

Metals and Alloys

23.17   Sodium is metallic; each atom is bonded to many nearest neighbor atoms by metallic bonding involving just one electron per atom, and delocalized over the entire three-dimensional structure. When sodium metal is distorted, each atom continues to have bonding interactions with many nearest neighbors. In NaCl the ionic forces are strong, and the arrangement of ions in the solid is very regular. When subjected to physical stress, the three-dimensional lattice tends to cleave along the very regular lattice planes, rather than undergo the large distortions characteristic of metals.

23.19   In the electron-sea model for metallic bonding, the valence electrons of the silver atoms move about the three-dimensional metallic lattice, while the silver atoms maintain regular lattice positions. Under the influence of an applied potential the electrons can move throughout the structure, giving rise to high electrical conductivity. The mobility of the electrons facilitates the transfer of kinetic energy and leads to high thermal conductivity.

23.21   The variation in densities reflects shorter metal-metal bond distances. These shorter distances suggest that the extent of metal-metal bonding increases in the series. Thus, it would appear that all the valence electrons in these elements (1, 2, 3 and 4, respectively) are involved in metallic bonding.

23.23   According to band theory, an *insulator* has a completely filled valence band and a large energy gap between the valence band and the nearest empty band; electrons are localized within the lattice. A *conductor* must have a partially filled energy band; a small excitation will promote electrons to previously empty levels within the band and allow them to move freely throughout the lattice, giving rise to the property of conduction. A *semiconductor* has a filled valence band, but the gap between the filled and empty bands is small enough to jump to the empty conduction band. The presence of an impurity may also place an electron in an otherwise empty band (producing an n-type semiconductor), or create a vacancy in an otherwise full band (producing a p-type semiconductor), providing a mechanism for conduction.

23.25   White tin, with a characteristic metallic structure, is expected to be more metallic in character. The electrical conductivity of the white allotropic form is higher because the valence electrons are shared with 12 nearest neighbors rather than being localized in four bonds to nearest neighbors as in gray tin. The Sn-Sn distance should be longer in white tin; there are only four valence electrons from each atom, and 12 nearest neighbors. The **average** tin-tin bond order can, therefore, be only about 1/3, whereas in gray tin the bond order is one. (In gray tin the Sn-Sn distance is 2.81 Å in white tin it is 3.02 Å.)

23.27   An *alloy* contains atoms of more than one element and has the properties of a metal. *Solution alloys* are homogeneous mixtures with different kinds of atoms dispersed randomly and uniformly. In *heterogeneous alloys* the components (elements or compounds) are not evenly dispersed and their properties depend not only on composition but methods of preparation. In an *intermetallic compound* the component elements have interacted to form a compound substance, for example, Cu_3As. As with more familiar compounds, these are homogeneous and have definite composition and properties.

Transition Metals

23.29   Of the properties listed, (b) the first ionization energy, (c) atomic radius and (f) electron affinity are characteristic of isolated atoms. Electrical conductivity (a), melting point (d) and heat of vaporization (e) are properties of the bulk metal.

23.31   The *lanthanide contraction* is the name given to the decrease in atomic size due to the build-up in effective nuclear charge as we move through the lanthanides (elements 58-71) and beyond them. This effect offsets the expected increase in atomic size going from the second to the third transition series. The lanthanide contraction affects size-related properties such as ionization energy, electron affinity and density.

23.33   (a) ScF_3 (b) CoF_3 (c) ZnF_2

23.35   Chromium, $[Ar]4s^13d^5$, has six valence-shell electrons, some or all of which can be involved in bonding, leading to multiple stable oxidation states. By contrast, aluminum, $[Ne]3s^23p^1$, has only three valence electrons which are all lost or shared during bonding, producing the +3 state exclusively.

23.37   (a) Cr^{3+}: $[Ar]3d^3$ (b) Au^{3+}: $[Xe]4f^{14}5d^8$ (c) Ru^{2+}: $[Kr]4d^6$
        (d) Cu^+: $[Ar]3d^{10}$ (e) Mn^{4+}: $[Ar]3d^3$ (f) Ir^{3+}: $[Xe]4f^{14}5d^6$

23.39   Ease of oxidation decreases from left to right across a period (owing to increasing effective nuclear charge); Ti^{2+} should be more easily oxidized than Ni^{2+}.

23.41 (Equation [23.26]) Fe^{2+} is a reducing agent that is readily oxidized to Fe^{3+} in the presence of O_2 from air.

23.43 (a) $Fe(s) + 2HCl(aq) \rightarrow FeCl_2(aq) + H_2(g)$

(b) $Fe(s) + 4HNO_3(aq) \rightarrow Fe(NO_3)_3(aq) + NO(g) + 2H_2O(l)$

(See net ionic equation, Equation 23.28) In concentrated nitric acid, the reaction can produce $NO_2(g)$ according to the reaction:

$Fe(s) + 6HNO_3(aq) \rightarrow Fe(NO_3)_3(aq) + 3NO_2(g) + 3H_2O(l)$

23.45 The unpaired electrons in a *paramagnetic* material cause it to be weakly attracted into a magnetic field. A *diamagnetic* material, where all electrons are paired, is very weakly repelled by a magnetic field.

Additional Exercises

23.47 $PbS(s) + O_2(g) \rightarrow Pb(l) + SO_2(g)$

Regardless of the metal of interest, $SO_2(g)$ is a product of roasting sulfide ores. In an oxygen rich environment, $SO_2(g)$ is oxidized to $SO_3(g)$, which dissolves in $H_2O(l)$ to form sulfuric acid, $H_2SO_4(aq)$. Because of its corrosive nature, $SO_2(g)$ is a dangerous environmental pollutant (Section 18.4) and cannot be freely released into the atmosphere. A sulfuric acid plant near a roasting plant would provide a means for disposing of $SO_2(g)$ that would also generate a profit.

23.49 $CO(g)$: $Pb(s)$; $H_2(g)$: $Fe(s)$; $Zn(s)$: $Au(s)$

23.52 Because selenium and tellurium are both nonmetals, we expect them to be difficult to oxidize. Thus, both Se and Te are likely to accumulate as the free elements in the so-called anode slime, along with noble metals that are not oxidized.

23.55 (a) Substitutional alloys and intermetallic compounds are both homogeneous solution alloys. Intermetallic compounds have a definite stoichiometry and properties, while substitutional alloys have a range of compositions.

(b) A paramagnetic substance has unpaired electrons and is attracted into a magnetic field. A diamagnetic substance has only paired electrons and is weakly repelled by a magnetic field.

(c) Insulators have a filled valence band with a large energy gap between the valence and the conduction band, making delocalization difficult. Semiconductors have a filled valence band but a smaller band gap, so that some electrons can move to the conduction band.

(d) In metallic conduction, metal atoms are stationary while a few valence electrons are mobile and available to carry charge throughout the substance. In electrolytic conduction, mobile ions carry charge throughout the liquid.

23.57 The equilibrium of interest is $[ZnL_4] \leftrightarrows Zn^{2+}(aq) + 4L$ $K = 1/K_f$

Since $Zn(H_2O)_4^{2+}$ is $Zn^{2+}(aq)$, its reduction potential is -0.763 V. As the stability (K_f) of the complexes increases, K decreases. Since E° is directly proportional to log K (Equation 20.18), E° values for the complexes will become more negative as K_f increases.

23.60 In a ferromagnetic solid, the magnetic centers are coupled such that the spins of all unpaired electrons are parallel. As the temperature of the solid increases, the average kinetic energy of the atoms increases until the energy of motion overcomes the force aligning the electron spins. The substance becomes paramagnetic; it still has unpaired electrons, but their spins are no longer aligned.

23.63 (a) $2NiS(s) + 3O_2(g) \rightarrow 2NiO(s) + 2SO_2(g)$

(b) $2C(s) + O_2(g) \rightarrow 2CO(g)$; $C(s) + H_2O(g) \rightarrow CO(g) + H_2(g)$

$NiO(s) + CO(g) \rightarrow Ni(s) + CO_2(g)$; $NiO(s) + H_2(g) \rightarrow Ni(s) + H_2O(g)$

(c) $Ni(s) + 2HCl(aq) \rightarrow NiCl_2(aq) + H_2(g)$

(d) $NiCl_2(aq) + 2NaOH(aq) \rightarrow Ni(OH)_2(s) + 2NaCl(aq)$

(e) $Ni(OH)_2(s) \overset{\Delta}{\rightarrow} NiO(s) + H_2O(g)$

Integrative Exercises

23.67 The first equation indicates that one mole Ni^{2+} is formed from passage of two moles of electrons, and the second equation indicates the same thing. Thus, the simple ratio (1 mol Ni^{2+}/2F).

$$67 \text{ A} \times 11.0 \text{ hr} \times \frac{3600 \text{ s}}{1 \text{ hr}} \times \frac{1 \text{ C}}{1 \text{ A} \cdot \text{s}} \times \frac{1 \text{ F}}{96,500 \text{ C}} \times \frac{1 \text{ mol Ni}^{2+}}{2 \text{ F}} \times \frac{58.7 \text{ g Ni}^{2+}}{1 \text{ mol Ni}^{2+}}$$

23.69 (a)   According to Section 20.10, the reduction of O_2 during oxidation of Fe(s) to Fe_2O_3 requires H^+. Above pH 9, iron does not corrode. At the high temperature of the converter, it is unlikely to find H_2O or H^+ in contact with the molten Fe. Also, the basic slag (CaO(l)) that is present to remove phosphorus will keep the environment basic rather than acidic. Thus, the H^+ necessary for oxidation of Fe in air is not present in the converter.

(b) $C + O_2(g) \rightarrow CO_2(g)$

$S + O_2(g) \rightarrow SO_2(g)$

$P + O_2(g) \rightarrow P_2O_5(l)$; $P_2O_5(l) + 3CaO(l) \rightarrow Ca_3(PO_4)(l)$

$Si + O_2(g) \rightarrow SiO_2$

$M + O_2(g) \rightarrow M_xO_y(l)$; $M_xO_y + SiO_2 \rightarrow$ silicates

CO_2 and SO_2 escape as gases. P_2O_5 reacts with CaO(l) to form $Ca_3(PO_4)_2(l)$, which is removed with the basic slag layer. SiO_2 and metal oxides can combine to form other silicates; SiO_2, M_xO_y and complex silicates are all removed with the basic slag layer.

23.72   97,000 A × 24 hr × $\dfrac{3600\ s}{1\ hr}$ × $\dfrac{1\ C}{1\ A \bullet s}$ × $\dfrac{1\ F}{96,500\ C}$ × $\dfrac{1\ mol\ Mg}{2\ F}$ × $\dfrac{24.31\ g\ Mg}{1\ mol\ Mg}$ × 0.96

$$= 1.0 \times 10^{6}\ g\ Mg = 1.0 \times 10^{3}\ kg\ Mg$$

23.75   (a)   (See Exercise 17.47)

$$Ag_2S(s) \rightleftharpoons 2Ag^+(aq) + S^{2-}(aq) \qquad\qquad K_{sp}$$

$$2[Ag^+(aq) + 2CN^-(aq) \rightleftharpoons Ag(CN)_2^-] \qquad\qquad K_f^2$$

$$Ag_2S(s) + 4CN^-(aq) \rightleftharpoons 2Ag(CN)_2^-(aq) + S^{2-}(aq)$$

$$K = K_{sp} \times K_f^2 = [Ag^+]^2[S^{2-}] \times \dfrac{[Ag(CN)_2^-]^2}{[Ag^+]^2[CN^-]^4} = (6 \times 10^{-51})(1 \times 10^{21})^2 = 6 \times 10^{-9}$$

(b)   The equilibrium constant for the cyanidation of Ag_2S, 6×10^{-9}, is much less than one and favors the presence of reactants rather than products. The process is not practical.

(c)
$$AgCl(s) \rightleftharpoons Ag^+(aq) + Cl^-(aq) \qquad\qquad K_{sp}$$

$$Ag^+(aq) + 2CN^-(aq) \rightleftharpoons Ag(CN)_2^-(aq) \qquad\qquad K_f$$

$$AgCl(s) + 2CN^-(aq) \rightleftharpoons Ag(CN)_2^-(aq) + Cl^-(aq)$$

$$K = K_{sp} \times K_f = [Ag^+][Cl^-] \times \dfrac{[Ag(CN)_2^-]}{[Ag^+][CN^-]^2} = (1.8 \times 10^{-10})(1 \times 10^{21}) = 2 \times 10^{11}$$

Since K >> 1 for this process, it is potentially useful for recovering silver from horn silver. However the magnitude of K says nothing about the rate of reaction. The reaction could be slow and require heat, a catalyst or both to be practical.

24 Chemistry of Coordination Compounds

Structure and Nomenclature

24.1 (a) Coordination number = 4, oxidation number = +2

(b) 5, +4   (c) 6, +3   (d) 5, +2   (e) 6, +3   (f) 4, +2

24.3 (a)

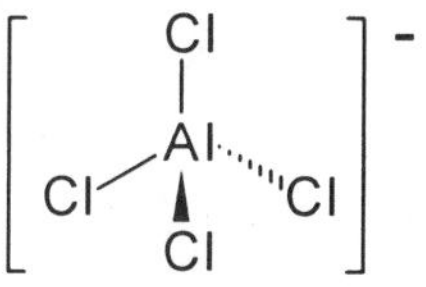

tetrahedral

(b) $\left[:N\equiv C-Ag-C\equiv N: \right]^-$ $2\bar{e}$

linear

(c)

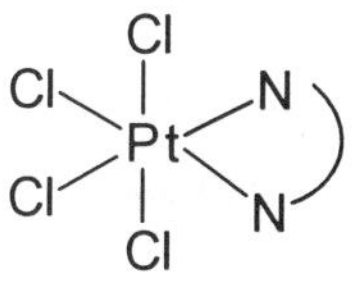

octahedral

(d)

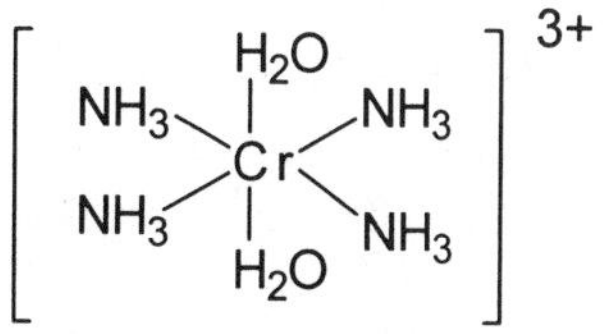

octahedral

24.5 (a) $[Cr(NH_3)_6](NO_3)_3$ (b) $[Co(NH_3)_4CO_3]_2SO_4$ (c) $[Pt(en)_2Cl_2]Br_2$

(d) $K[V(H_2O)_2Br_4]$ (e) $[Zn(en)_2][HgI_4]$

24.7 (a) *ortho*-phenanthroline, *o*-phen, is bidentate

(b) oxalate, $C_2O_4^{2-}$, is bidentate

(c) ethylenediaminetetraacetate, EDTA, is pentadentate

(d) ethylenediamine, en, is bidentate

Isomerism

24.9 (a)

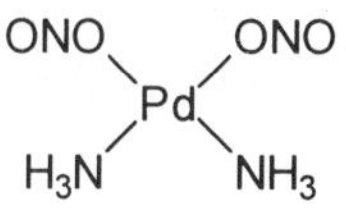

cis 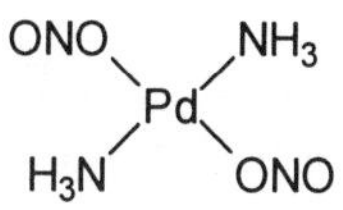   *trans*

(b) $[Pd(NH_3)_2(ONO)_2]$, $[Pd(NH_3)_2(NO_2)_2]$

(c)

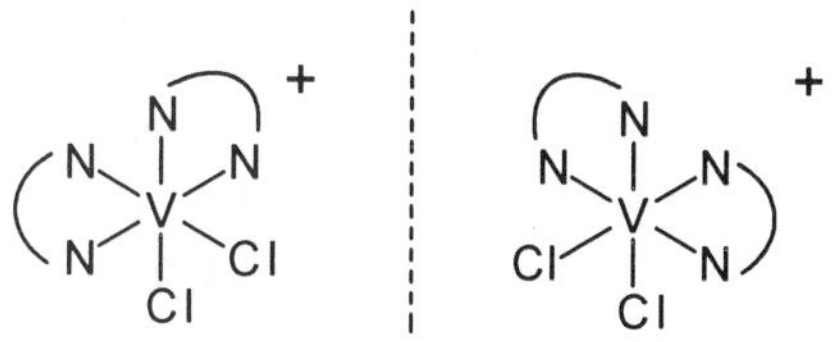

(d) $[Co(NH_3)_4Br_2]Cl$, $[Co(NH_3)_4BrCl]Br$

24.11

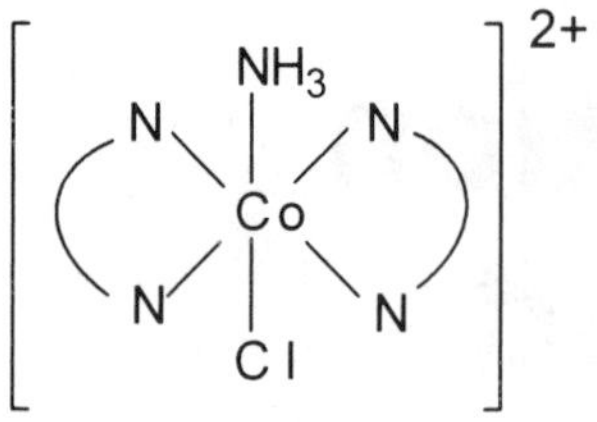

trans 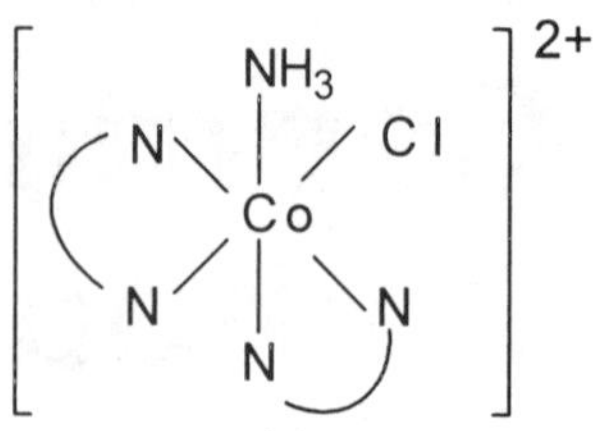   cis

The *cis* isomer is chiral.

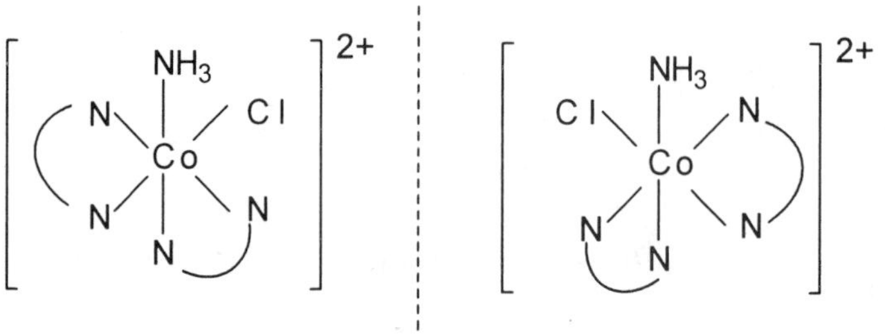

24.13 (a)

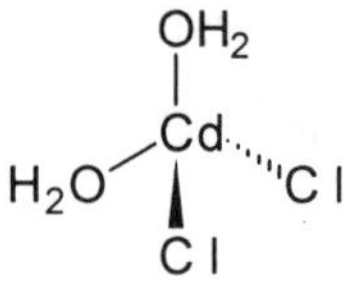

(b)

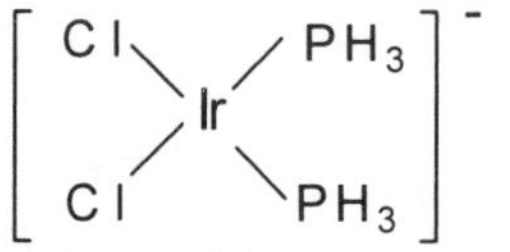

cis 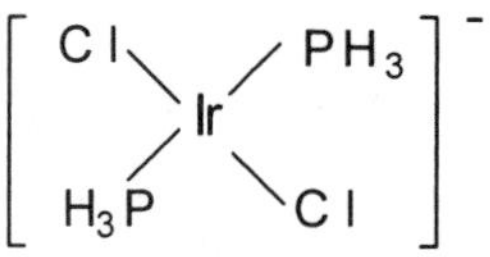   trans

(c)

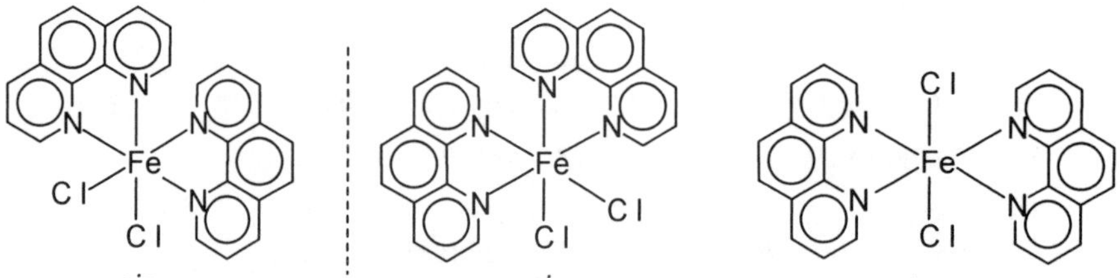

cis   cis   trans

optical isomers

(The three isomeric complex ions in part (c) each have a 1+ charge.)

Color, Magnetism; Crystal-Field Theory

24.15   Color in transition metal compounds arises from electronic transitions between d-orbital energy levels, or d-d transitions. Compounds with d^0 or d^{10} electron configurations are colorless, because d-d transitions are not possible.

(a) Zn^{2+}, d^{10}, colorless   (b) Cr^{4+}, d^2, colored   (c) Ni^{2+}, d^8, colored

(d) Al^{3+}, d^0, colorless   (e) Cd^{2+}, d^{10}, colorless   (f) Fe^{2+}, d^6, colored

24.17   (a) Ru^{3+}, d^5 (b) Cu^{2+}, d^9 (c) Co^{3+}, d^6 (d) Mo^{5+}, d^1 (e) Re^{3+}, d^4

24.19   Blue to blue-violet (Figure 24.23)

24.21   Six ligands in an octahedral arrangement are oriented along the x, y and z axes of the metal. These negatively charged ligands (or the negative end of ligand dipoles) have greater electrostatic repulsion with valence electrons in metal orbitals that also lie along these axes, the d_{z^2}, and $d_{x^2-y^2}$. The d_{xy}, d_{xz} and d_{yz} metal orbitals point between the x, y, and z axes, and electrons in these orbitals experience less repulsion with ligand electrons. Thus, in the presence of an octahedral ligand field, the d_{xy}, d_{xz} and d_{xy} metal orbitals are lower in energy than the $d_{x^2-y^2}$ and d_{z^2}.

24.23   Cyanide is a strong field ligand. The d-d electronic transitions occur at relatively high energy, because Δ is large. A yellow color corresponds to absorption of a photon in the violet region of the visible spectrum, between 430 and 400 nm. H_2O is a weaker field ligand than CN^-. The blue or green colors of aqua complexes correspond to absorptions in the region of 620 nm. Clearly, this is a region of lower energy photons than those with characteristic wavelengths in the 430 to 400 nm region. These are very general and imprecise comparisons. Other factors are involved, including whether the complex is high spin or low spin.

24.25   (a)   Mn: $[Ar]4s^2 3d^5$ (b) Ru: $[Kr]5s^1 4d^7$ (c) Rh: $[Kr]5s^1 4d^8$
          Mn^{3+}: $[Ar]3d^4$ Ru^{3+}: $[Kr]4d^5$ Rh^{3+}: $[Kr]4d^6$

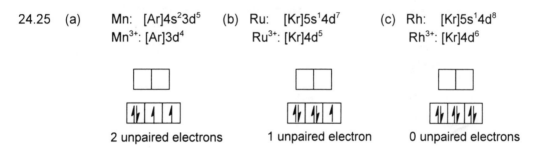

  2 unpaired electrons   1 unpaired electron   0 unpaired electrons

24.27   All complexes in this exercise are six-coordinate octahedral.

(a) d^4, high spin   (b) d^5, high spin   (c) d^6, low spin

(d) d^5, low spin   (e) d^3 (f) d^8

24.29

  high spin

Additional Exercises

24.31   (a) $[Ni(en)_2Cl_2]$; $[Ni(en)_2(H_2O)_2]Cl_2$

        (b) $K_2[Ni(CN)_4]$; $[Zn(H_2O)_4](NO_3)_2$; $[Cu(NH_3)_4]SO_4$

        (c) $[CoF_6]^{3-}$, high spin; $[Co(NH_3)_6]^{3+}$ or $[Co(CN)_6]^{3-}$, low spin

        (d)   thiocyanate, SCN^- or NCS^-;   nitrite, NO_2^- or ONO^-

        (e) $[Co(en)_2Cl_2]Cl$;   see Exercise 24.13(c) for another example.

        (f) $[Co(en)_3]Cl_3$, $K_3[Fe(ox)_3]$

24.34   (a)   In a square planar complex such as $[Pt(en)Cl_2]$, if one pair of ligands is *trans*, the remaining two coordination sites are also *trans* to each other. Ethylenediamine is a relatively short bidentate ligand that cannot occupy *trans* coordination sites, so the *trans* isomer is unknown.

        (b)   A polydentate ligand such as EDTA necessarily occupies *trans* positions in an octahedral complex. The minimum steric requirement for a bidentate ligand is a medium-length chain between the two coordinating atoms that will occupy the *trans* positions. In terms of reaction rate theory, it is unlikely that a flexible bidentate ligand will be in exactly the right orientation to coordinate *trans*. The polydentate ligand has a much better chance of occupying *trans* positions, because it locks the metal ion in place with multiple coordination sites (and shields the metal ion from competing ligands present in the solution).

24.38   (a) $AgCl(s) + 2NH_3(aq) \rightarrow [Ag(NH_3)_2]^+(aq) + Cl^-(aq)$

        (b) $[Cr(en)_2Cl_2]Cl(aq) + 2H_2O(l) \rightarrow [Cr(en_2)(H_2O)_2]^{3+}(aq) + 3Cl^-(aq)$

             green   brown-orange

             $3Ag^+(aq) + 3Cl^-(aq) \rightarrow 3AgCl(s)$

             $[Cr(en)_2(H_2O)_2]^{3+}$ and $3NO_3^-$ are spectator ions in the second reaction.

        (c) $Zn(NO_3)_2(aq) + 2NaOH(aq) \rightarrow Zn(OH)_2(s) + 2NaNO_3(aq)$

             $Zn(OH)_2(s) + 2NaOH(aq) \rightarrow [Zn(OH)_4]^{2-}(aq) + 2Na^+(aq)$

        (d) $Co^{2+}(aq) + 4Cl^-(aq) \rightarrow [CoCl_4]^{2-}(aq)$

24.42   According to the spectrochemical series, the order of increasing Δ for the ligands is $Cl^- < H_2O < NH_3$. (The tetrahedral Cl^- complex will have an even smaller Δ than an octahedral one.) The smaller the value of Δ, the longer the wavelength of visible light absorbed. The color of light absorbed is the complement of the observed color. A blue complex absorbs orange light (580-650 nm), a pink complex absorbs green light (490-560 nm) and a yellow complex absorbs violet light (400-430 nm). Since $[CoCl_4]^{2-}$ absorbs the longest wavelength, it appears blue. $[Co(H_2O)_6]^{2+}$ absorbs green and appears pink, and $[Co(NH_3)_6]^{3+}$ absorbs violet and appears yellow.

24.45 (a) False. The spin pairing energy is **smaller** than Δ in low spin complexes. It is for this reason that electrons pair up in the lower energy orbitals, in spite of the repulsive energy associated with spin pairing, rather than move to the higher energy orbital, which would cost energy in the amount Δ.

(b) True. Higher metal ion charge causes the ligands to be more strongly attracted, thus producing a larger splitting of the d orbital energies.

(c) False. Square-planar configurations are associated with a d^8 electron configuration (which Ni^{2+} has) and a ligand that produces a strong field, leading to large separations between the energy levels. Because cyanide, CN^-, is a much stronger field ligand than Cl^-, $[Ni(CN)_4]^{2-}$ is more likely to be square planar than is $[NiCl_4]^{2-}$.

24.47 Application of pressure would result in shorter metal ion-oxide distances. This would have the effect of increasing the ligand-electron repulsions, and would result in a larger splitting in the d orbital energies. Thus, application of pressure should result in a shift in the absorption to a higher energy and shorter wavelength.

24.49 (a) Only one (b) Two

(c) Four; two are geometric, the other two are stereoisomers of each of these.

Integrative Exercises

24.52 $\Delta E = hc/\lambda = \dfrac{6.626 \times 10^{-34}\ J \cdot s \times 2.998 \times 10^8\ m/s}{510 \times 10^{-9}\ m} = 3.895 \times 10^{-19} = 3.90 \times 10^{-19}\ J/photon$

$\Delta = 3.895 \times 10^{-19}\ J/photon \times \dfrac{6.022 \times 10^{23}\ photons}{1\ mol} \times \dfrac{1\ kJ}{1000\ J} = 234.6 = 235\ kJ/mol$

24.55   Determine the empirical formula of the complex, assuming the remaining mass is due to oxygen, and a 100 g sample.

$$10.0 \text{ g Mn} \times \frac{1 \text{ mol Mn}}{54.94 \text{ g Mn}} = 0.1820 \text{ mol Mn}; \ 0.182 / 0.182 = 1$$

$$28.6 \text{ g K} \times \frac{1 \text{ mol K}}{39.10 \text{ g K}} = 0.7315 \text{ mol K}; \ 0.732 / 0.182 = 4$$

$$8.8 \text{ g C} \times \frac{1 \text{ mol C}}{12.0 \text{ g C}} = 0.7327 \text{ mol C}; \ 0.733 / 0.182 = 4$$

$$29.2 \text{ g Br} \times \frac{1 \text{ mol Br}}{79.904 \text{ g Br}} = 0.3654 \text{ mol Br}; \ 0.365 / 0.182 = 2$$

$$23.4 \text{ g O} \times \frac{1 \text{ mol O}}{16.00 \text{ g O}} = 1.463 \text{ mol O}; \ 1.46 / 0.182 = 8$$

There are 2 C and 4 O per oxalate ion, for a total of two oxalate ligands in the complex. To match the conductivity of $K_4[Fe(CN)_6]$, the oxalate and bromide ions must be in the coordination sphere of the complex anion. Thus, the compound is $K_4[Mn(ox)_2Br_2]$.

24.57   Calculate the concentration of Mg^{2+} alone, and then the concentration of Ca^{2+} by difference.
M × L = mol

$$\frac{0.0104 \text{ mol EDTA}}{1 \text{ L}} \times 0.0187\text{L} \times \frac{1 \text{ mol Mg}^{2+}}{1 \text{ mol EDTA}} \times \frac{24.31 \text{ g Mg}^{2+}}{1 \text{ mol Mg}^{2+}} \times \frac{1000 \text{ mg}}{\text{g}}$$

$$\times \frac{1}{0.100 \text{ L H}_2\text{O}} = 47.28 = 47.3 \text{ mg Mg}^{2+}/\text{L}$$

0.0104 *M* EDTA × 0.0315 L = mol (Ca^{2+} + Mg^{2+})

0.0104 *M* EDTA × 0.0187 L = mol Mg^{2+}

0.0104 *M* EDTA × 0.0128 L = mol Ca^{2+}

$$0.0104 \text{ } M \text{ EDTA} \times 0.0128 \text{ L} \times \frac{1 \text{ mol Ca}^{2+}}{1 \text{ mol EDTA}} \times \frac{40.08 \text{ g Ca}^{2+}}{1 \text{ mol Ca}^{2+}} \times \frac{1000 \text{ mg}}{\text{g}} \times \frac{1}{0.100 \text{ L H}_2\text{O}}$$

$$= 53.35 = 53.4 \text{ mg Ca}^{2+}/\text{L}$$

25 The Chemistry of Life: Organic and Biological Chemistry

Hydrocarbon Structures and Nomenclature

25.1 (a) $CH_3CH_2CH_2CH_2CH_3$, C_5H_{12} (b)

$$\begin{matrix} & CH_2 & \\ H_2C & & CH_2 \\ H_2C & & CH_2 \end{matrix} \quad, \quad C_5H_{10}$$

      (c) $CH_2{=}CHCH_2CH_2CH_3$, C_5H_{10} (d) $HC{\equiv}CCH_2CH_2CH_3$, C_5H_8

      saturated: (a), (b);   unsaturated: (c), (d)

25.3 C_nH_{2n-2}

25.5 $CH_3{-}CH_2{-}CH_2{-}CH{=}CH_2$
             pentene

$CH_3{-}CH_2{-}CH{=}CH{-}CH_3$
          2-pentene

$$CH_2{=}CH{-}\overset{\overset{\textstyle CH_3}{|}}{CH}{-}CH_3$$
       3-methyl-1-butene

$$CH_2{=}\overset{\overset{\textstyle CH_3}{|}}{C}{-}CH_2{-}CH_3$$
      2-methyl-1-butene

$$CH_3{-}\overset{\overset{\textstyle CH_3}{|}}{C}{=}CH{-}CH_3$$
      2-methyl-2-butene

25.7   (a) 2,2,4-trimethylpentane   (b) 3-ethyl-2-methylpentane
        (c) 2,3,4-trimethylpentane   (d) 2,3,4-trimethylpentane
        (c) and (d) are the same molecule

25.9   (a) 109°   (b) 120°   (c) 180°

25.11   (a) 2,3-dimethylhexane   (b) 4-ethyl-2,4-dimethylnonane
         (c) 3,3,5-trimethylheptane   (d) 3,4,4-trimethylheptane

25.13   (a) 2,3-dimethylheptane   (b) *cis*-6-methyl-3-octene   (c) *para*-dibromobenzene
         (d) 4,4-dimethyl-1-hexyne   (e) methylcyclobutane

25.15 Each doubly bound carbon atom in an alkene has two unique sites for substitution. These sites cannot be interconverted because rotation about the double bond is restricted; geometric isomerism results. In an alkane, carbon forms only single bonds, so the three remaining sites are interchangeable by rotation about the single bond. Although there is also restricted rotation around the triple bond of an alkyne, there is only one additional bonding site on a triply bound carbon, so no isomerism results.

25.17 (a)   no   (b)

(c)   no   (d)   no

25.19 Assuming that each component retains its effective octane number in the mixture (and this isn't always the case), we obtain: octane number = 0.35(0) + 0.65(100) = 65.

Reactions of Hydrocarbons

25.21 (a)   A combustion reaction is the oxidation-reduction reaction of some substance (fuel) with $O_2(g)$.

$$2C_2H_6(g) + 7O_2(g) \rightarrow 4CO_2(g) + 6H_2O(g)$$

(b)   An addition reaction is the addition of some reagent to the two atoms that form a multiple bond.

(c)   In a substitution reaction, one atom or group of atoms replaces (substitutes for) another atom or group of atoms.

25.23 The small 60° C-C-C angles in the cyclopropane ring cause strain that provides a driving force for reactions that result in ring-opening. There is no comparable strain in the five- or six-membered rings.

25.25 First form an alkyl halide: $C_2H_4(g) + HBr(g) \rightarrow CH_3CH_2Br(l)$; then carry out a Friedel-Crafts reaction:

25.27 The partially positive end of the hydrogen halide, $\overset{\delta^+}{H}\!\!-\!\!\overset{\delta^-}{X}$, is attached to the π electron cloud of the alkene, cyclohexene. The electrons that formed the π bond in cyclohexene form a sigma bond to the H atom of HX, leaving a halide ion, X^-. The intermediate is a carbocation; one of the C atoms formerly involved in the π bond is now bound to a second H atom. The other C atom formerly involved in the π bond carries a full positive charge and forms only three sigma bonds, two to adjacent C atoms and one to H.

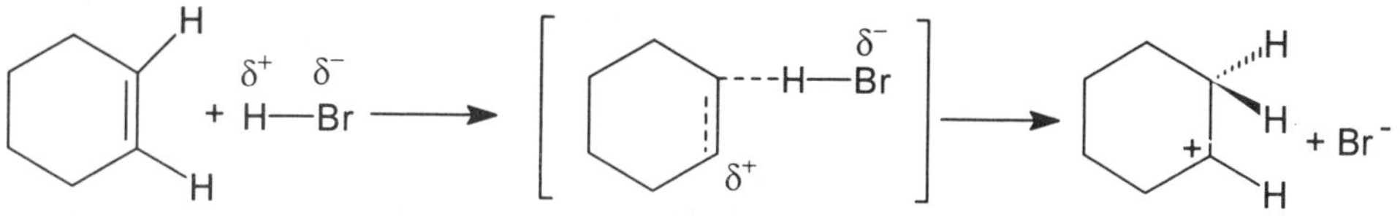

25.29 Both combustion reactions produce CO_2 and H_2O:

$C_3H_6(g) + 9/2\ O_2(g) \rightarrow 3CO_2(g) + 3H_2O(l)$

$C_5H_{10}(g) + 15/2\ O_2(g) \rightarrow 5CO_2(g) + 5H_2O(l)$

Thus, we can calculate the ΔH_{comb} / CH_2 group for each compound:

$$\frac{\Delta H_{comb}}{CH_2\ group} = \frac{2089\ kJ/mol\ C_3H_6}{3\ CH_2\ groups} = \frac{696.3\ kJ}{mol\ CH_2};\ \frac{3317\ kJ/mol\ C_5H_{10}}{5\ CH_2\ groups} = 663.4\ kJ/mol\ CH_2$$

$\Delta H_{comb}/CH_2$ group for cyclopropane is greater because C_3H_6 contains a strained ring. When combustion occurs, the strain is relieved and the stored energy is released during the reaction.

Functional Groups

25.31 (a) ketone (b) carboxylic acid (c) alcohol (d) ester (e) amide (f) amine

25.33 propionaldehyde (or propanal):

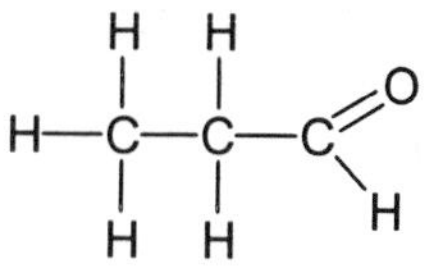

25.35 About each CH_3 carbon, 109°; about the carbonyl carbon, 120° planar.

25.37 (a)

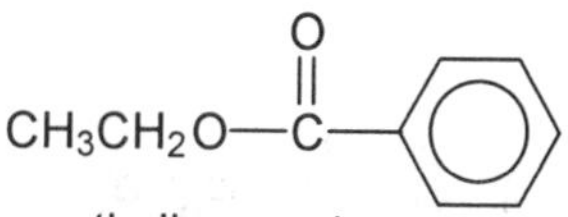

ethylbenzoate

(b)

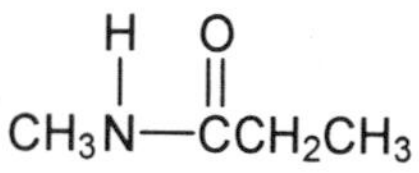

N-methylpropionamide

(c)

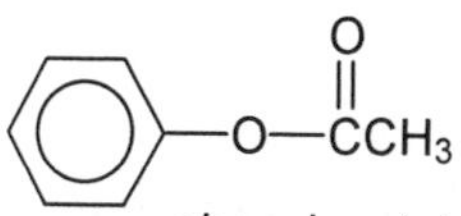

phenylacetate

25.39 (a)

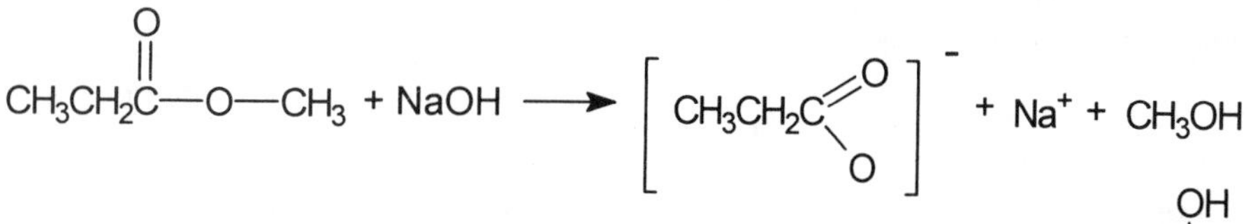

(b)

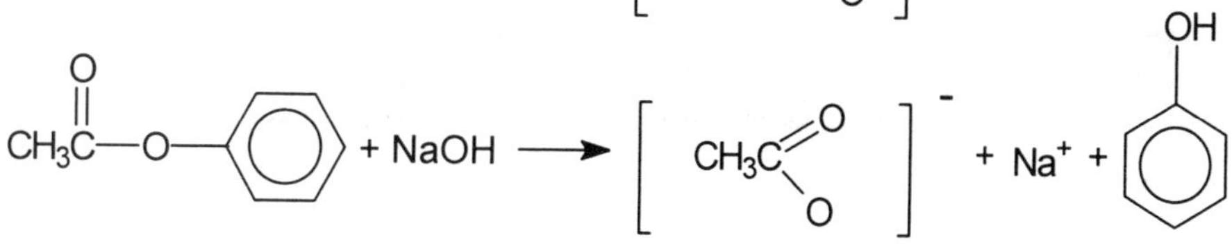

25.41   (a) $CH_3CH_2\overset{\underset{|}{OH}}{C}HCH_3$ (b) $HOCH_2CH_2OH$ (c) $H-\overset{\overset{O}{\|}}{C}-OCH_3$

(d) $CH_3CH_2\overset{\overset{O}{\|}}{C}CH_2CH_3$ (e) $CH_3CH_2OCH_2CH_3$

25.43   (a)   methanoic acid   (b) butanoic acid   (c) 3-methylpentanoic acid

Proteins

25.45   (a)   An α-amino acid contains an NH_2 group attached to the carbon that is bound to the carbon of the carboxylic acid function.

(b)   In forming a protein, amino acids undergo a condensation reaction between the amino group and carboxylic acid:

25.47   Two dipeptides are possible:

glycylvaline   valylglycine

25.49

25.51   Eight: Ser-Ser-Ser; Ser-Ser-Phe; Ser-Phe-Ser; Phe-Ser-Ser; Ser-Phe-Phe; Phe-Ser-Phe; Phe-Phe-Ser; Phe-Phe-Phe

25.53   The *primary structure* of a protein refers to the sequence of amino acids in the chain. Along any particular section of the protein chain the configuration may be helical, or it may be an open chain, or arranged in some other way. This is called the *secondary structure*. The overall shape of the protein molecule is determined by the way the segments of the protein chain fold together, or pack. The interactions which determine the overall shape are referred to as the *tertiary structure*.

Carbohydrates

25.55 Glucose exists in solution as a cyclic structure in which the aldehyde function on carbon 1 reacts with the OH group of carbon 5 to form what is called a hemiacetal, Figure 25.25. Carbon atom 1 carries an OH group in the hemiacetal form; in α-glucose this OH group is on the opposite side of the ring as the CH_2OH group on carbon atom 5. In the β (beta) form the OH group on carbon 1 is on the same side of the ring as the CH_2OH group on carbon 5.

The condensation product looks like this:

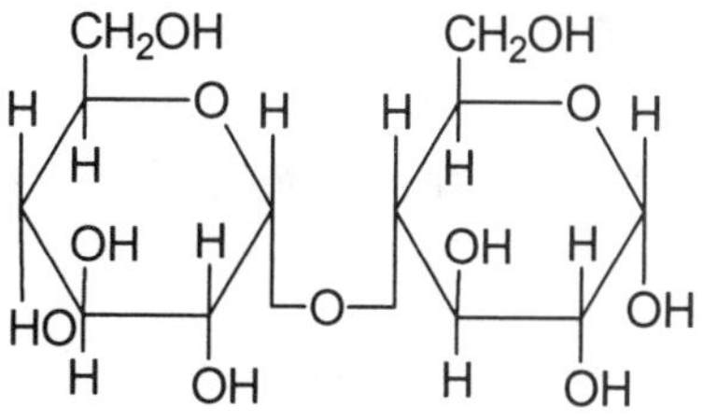

α-linkage β-linkage

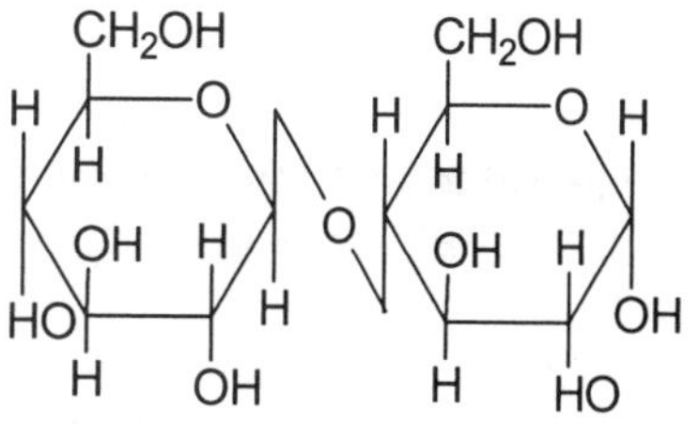

25.57 The structure is best deduced by comparing galactose with glucose, and inverting the configurations at the appropriate carbon atoms. Recall from Exercise 25.55 that both the β-form (shown here) and the α-form (OH on carbon 1 on the opposite side of ring as the CH_2OH on carbon 5) are possible.

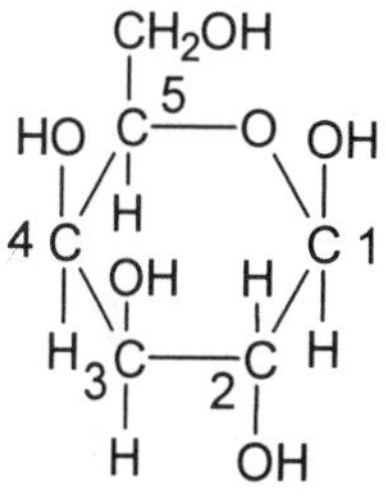

galactose

25.59 The empirical formula of glycogen is $C_6H_{10}O_5$. The six-membered ring form of glucose is the unit that forms the basis of glycogen. The monomeric glucose units are joined by α linkages.

Nucleic Acids

25.61 A *nucleotide* consists of a nitrogen-containing aromatic compound, a sugar in the furanose (5-membered) ring form, and a phosphoric acid group. The structure of deoxycytidine monophosphate is shown at right.

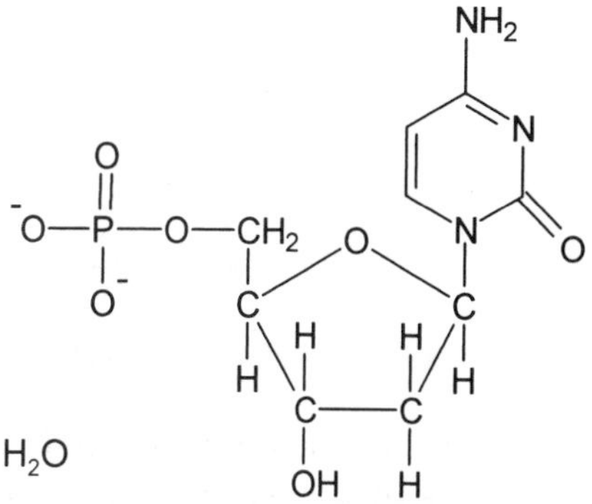

25.63 $C_4H_7O_3CH_2OH + HPO_4^{2-} \rightarrow C_4H_7O_3CH_2\text{-}O\text{-}PO_3^{2-} + H_2O$

25.65 In the helical structure for DNA, the strands of the polynucleotides are held together by hydrogen-bonding interactions between particular pairs of bases. It happens that adenine and thymine form an especially effective base pair, and that guanine and cytosine are similarly related. Thus, each adenine has a thymine as its opposite number in the other strand, and each guanine has a cytosine as its opposite number. In the overall analysis of the double strand, total adenine must then equal total thymine, and total guanine equals total cytosine.

Additional Exercises

25.67

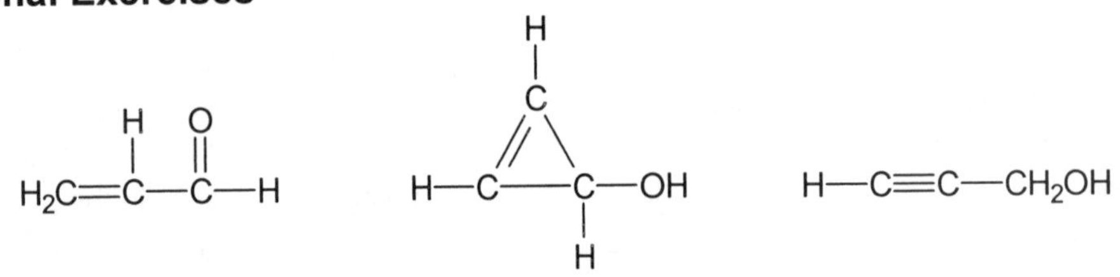

25.69

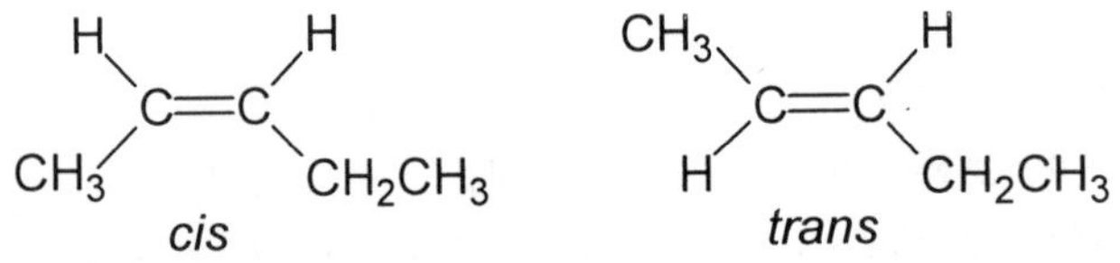

Cyclopentene does not show *cis-trans* isomerism because the existence of the ring demands that the C-C bonds be *cis* to one another.

25.71 The C-Cl bonds in the *trans* compound are pointing in exactly opposite directions. Thus, the C-Cl bond dipoles cancel (Section 9.3). This is not the case in the *cis* compound, as can be seen by drawing the structure:

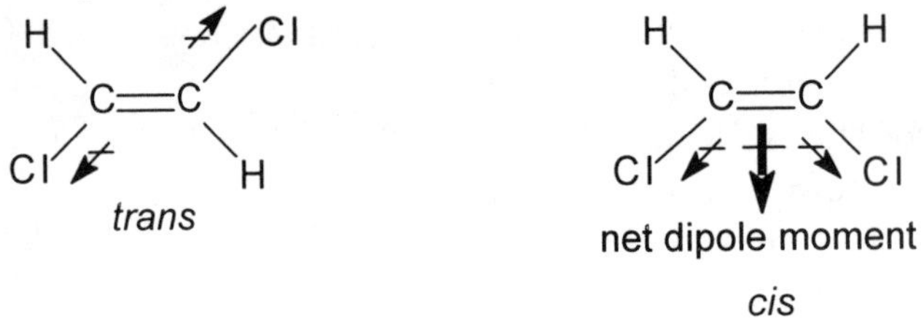

25.75 (a) 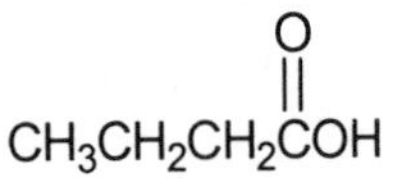 $CH_3CH_2CH_2COH$ (b) 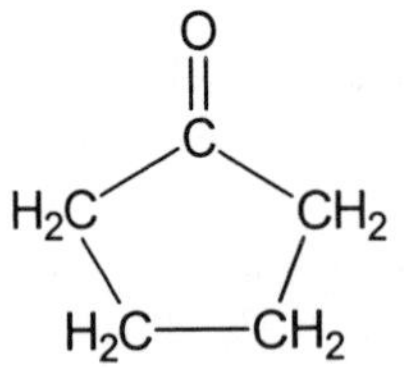 (c) 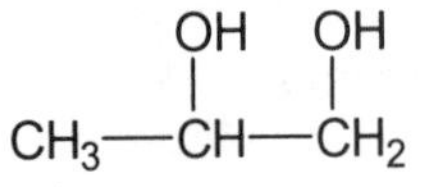 $CH_3-CH-CH_2$ with OH OH

(d)

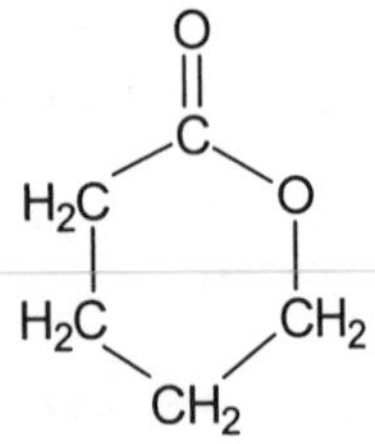

25.78 In the linear form of galactose shown in Exercise 25.57, carbon atoms 2, 3, 4 and 5 are chiral because they carry four different groups on each. In the ring form (see solution 25.57), carbon atoms 1, 2, 3, 4 and 5 are chiral.

25.81 (a) None

(b) The carbon bearing the secondary -OH has four different groups attached, and is thus chiral.

(c)   The carbon bearing the -NH_2 group and the carbon bearing the CH_3 group are both chiral.

25.83   Glu-Cys-Gly is the only possible structure.

Integrative Exercises

25.86 CH_3CH_2OH CH_3-O-CH_3
        ethanol   dimethyl ether

Ethanol contains -O-H bonds which form strong intermolecular hydrogen bonds, while dimethyl ether experiences only weak dipole-dipole and dispersion forces.

difluoromethane   tetrafluoromethane

CH_2F_2 is a polar molecule, while CF_4 is nonpolar. CH_2F_2 experiences dipole-dipole and dispersion forces, while CF_4 experiences only dispersion forces.

In both cases, stronger intermolecular forces lead to the higher boiling point.

25.88   The reaction is: $2NH_2CH_2COOH(aq) \rightarrow NH_2CH_2CONHCH_2COOH(aq) + H_2O(l)$

$\Delta G° = (-488) + (-285.83) - 2(-369) = -35.8 = -36$ kJ

25.92 $AMPOH^-(aq) \rightleftharpoons AMPO^{2-}(aq) + H^+(aq)$

$pK_a = 7.21$; $K_a = 10^{-pK_a} = 6.17 \times 10^{-8} = 6.2 \times 10^{-8}$

$K_a = \dfrac{[AMPO^{2-}][H^+]}{[AMPOH^-]} = 6.2 \times 10^{-8}$. When pH = 7.40, $[H^+] = 3.98 \times 10^{-8} = 4.0 \times 10^{-8}$.

Then $\dfrac{[AMPOH^-]}{[AMPO^{2-}]} = 3.98 \times 10^{-8} / 6.17 \times 10^{-8} = 0.65$

McGraw-Hill Technology Education

At McGraw-Hill Technology Education, we publish instructional materials for the technology education market—in particular, for computer instruction in post secondary education that ranges from introductory courses in traditional four-year universities to continuing education and proprietary schools. McGraw-Hill Technology Education presents a broad range of innovative products—texts, lab manuals, study guides, testing materials, and technology-based training and assessment tools.

We realize that technology has created and will continue to create new mediums for professors and students to use in managing resources and communicating information to one another. McGraw-Hill Technology Education provides the most flexible and complete teaching and learning tools available and offers solutions to the changing needs of the classroom. McGraw-Hill Technology Education is dedicated to providing the tools for today's instructors and students, which will enable them to successfully navigate the world of Information Technology.

- McGraw-Hill/Osborne—This division of The McGraw-Hill Companies is known for its best-selling Internet titles, Harley Hahn's *Internet & Web Yellow Pages* and the *Internet Complete Reference*. For more information, visit Osborne at www.osborne.com.

- Digital Solutions—Whether you want to teach a class online or just post your "bricks-n-mortar" class syllabus, McGraw-Hill Technology Education is committed to publishing digital solutions. Taking your course online doesn't have to be a solitary adventure, nor does it have to be a difficult one. We offer several solutions that will allow you to enjoy all the benefits of having your course material online.

- Packaging Options—For more information about our discount options, contact your McGraw-Hill Sales representative at 1-800-338-3987 or visit our website at **www.mhhe.com/it**.

McGraw-Hill Technology Education is dedicated to providing
the tools for today's instructors and students.

What does this logo mean?

It means this courseware has been approved by the Microsoft® Office Specialist Program to be among the finest available for learning *Microsoft Office Word 2003, Microsoft Office Excel 2003, Microsoft Office Access 2003*, and *Microsoft Office PowerPoint 2003*. It also means that upon completion of this courseware, you may be prepared to take an exam for Microsoft Office Specialist qualification.

What is a Microsoft Office Specialist?

A Microsoft Office Specialist is an individual who has passed exams for certifying his or her skills in one or more of the Microsoft Office desktop applications such as Microsoft Word, Microsoft Excel, Microsoft PowerPoint, Microsoft Outlook, Microsoft Access, or Microsoft Project. The Microsoft Office Specialist Program typically offers certification exams at the "Specialist" and "Expert" skill levels.* The Microsoft Office Specialist Program is the only program in the world approved by Microsoft for testing proficiency in Microsoft Office desktop applications and Microsoft Project. This testing program can be a valuable asset in any job search or career advancement.

More Information:

To learn more about becoming a Microsoft Office Specialist, visit www.microsoft.com/officespecialist

To learn about other Microsoft Office Specialist approved courseware from McGraw-Hill Technology Education, visit http://www.mhhe.com/catalogs/irwin/it/mous/index.mhtml

---

Who benefits from Microsoft Office Specialist certification?

Employers

Microsoft Office Specialist certification helps satisfy employers' needs for qualitative assessments of employees' skills. Training, coupled with Microsoft Office Specialist certification, offers organizations of every size the ability to enhance productivity and efficiency by enabling their employees to unlock many advanced and laborsaving features in Microsoft Office applications. Microsoft Office Specialist certification can ultimately improve the bottom line.

Employees

Microsoft Office Specialist certification demonstrates employees' productivity and competence in Microsoft Office applications, the most popular business applications in the world. Achieving Microsoft Office Specialist certification verifies that employees have the confidence and ability to use Microsoft Office applications in meeting and exceeding their work challenges.

Instructors

Microsoft Office Specialist certification validates instructors' knowledge and skill in using Microsoft Office applications. It serves as a valuable credential, demonstrating their potential to teach students these essential applications. The Microsoft Office Specialist Authorized Instructor program is also available to those who wish to further demonstrate their instructional capabilities.

Students

Microsoft Office Specialist certification distinguishes students from their peers. It demonstrates their efficiency in completing assignments and projects, leaving more time for other studies. Improved confidence toward meeting new challenges and obstacles is yet another benefit. Achieving Microsoft Office Specialist certification gives students the marketable skills necessary to set them apart in the competitive job market.

To learn more about becoming a Microsoft Office Specialist, visit www.microsoft.com/officespecialist

To purchase a Microsoft Office Specialist certification exam, visit www.DesktopIQ.com

---

Microsoft and the Microsoft Office Specialist Logo are either registered trademarks or trademarks of Microsoft Corporation in the United States and/or other countries.

Brief Contents

Labs

	Introduction to Microsoft Office 2003	I.1
	Overview of Microsoft Office PowerPoint 2003	PPO.1
1	Lab 1: Creating a Presentation	PP1.1
2	Lab 2: Modifying and Refining a Presentation	PP2.1
	Working Together 1: Copying, Embedding, and Linking Between Applications	PPWT1.1
3	Lab 3: Using Advanced Presentation Features	PP3.1
4	Lab 4: Creating a Presentation for a Kiosk and the Web	PP4.1
	Working Together 2: Reviewing, Embedding, and Broadcasting a Presentation	PPWT2.1
	Command Summary	PPCS.1
	Glossary of Key Terms	PPG.1
	Reference 1	PPR1.1
	Reference 2	PPR2.1
	Index	PPI.1

Detailed Contents

Introduction to Microsoft Office 2003 | I.1

What Is Microsoft Office System 2003? I.2
Office Word 2003 | I.2
Office Excel 2003 | I.4
Office Access 2003 | I.7
Office PowerPoint 2003 | I.9
Office Outlook 2003 | I.10
Common Office 2003 Features | I.11
Starting an Office 2003 Application | I.11
Using Menus | I.12
Using Shortcut Menus | I.15
Using Shortcut Keys | I.17
Using Toolbars | I.17
Displaying Toolbars on Separate Rows | I.17
Using Task Panes | I.21
Using Office Help | I.21
Using the Help Table of Contents | I.25
Exiting an Office 2003 Application | I.26
Lab Review | I.27
Key Terms | I.27
Command Summary | I.27
Lab Exercises | I.28
Step-by-Step | I.28
On Your Own | I.28

POWERPOINT

Overview of Microsoft Office PowerPoint 2003 | PPO.1

What Is a Presentation Program? | PPO.1
Office PowerPoint 2003 Features | PPO.2
Case Study for Office PowerPoint 2003 Labs | PPO.3
Before You Begin | PPO.3
Microsoft Office Language Bar | PPO.5
Instructional Conventions | PPO.5

Lab 1 Creating a Presentation | PP1.1

Objectives | PP1.1
Case Study | PP1.2
Introducing Office PowerPoint 2003 | PP1.4
Starting Office PowerPoint 2003 | PP1.5
Developing New Presentations | PP1.6
Creating a Presentation | PP1.7
Using the AutoContent Wizard | PP1.8
Viewing the Presentation | PP1.12
Using Normal View | PP1.13
Using Slide Sorter View | PP1.14
Editing a Presentation | PP1.16
Using the Outline Tab | PP1.17
Editing in the Slide Pane | PP1.23
Demoting and Promoting Bulleted Items | PP1.27
Splitting Text Between Slides | PP1.29
Saving, Closing, and Opening a Presentation | PP1.31
Saving the Presentation | PP1.31
Closing a Presentation | PP1.35
Opening an Existing Presentation | PP1.35
Checking Spelling | PP1.37
Working with Slides | PP1.40
Deleting Slides | PP1.41
Moving Slides | PP1.41
Inserting Slides | PP1.42
Selecting the Slide Layout | PP1.43
Sizing a Placeholder | PP1.45
Moving a Placeholder | PP1.46
Rehearsing a Presentation | PP1.47
Using Slide Show View | PP1.48
Formatting Slide Text | PP1.49
Changing Fonts | PP1.50
Changing Font Size | PP1.52
Adding and Removing Bullets | PP1.53

The O'Leary Series

Microsoft® Office PowerPoint® 2003

Introductory Edition

Timothy J. O'Leary
Arizona State University

Linda I. O'Leary

McGraw Hill Technology Education

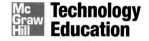

Boston Burr Ridge, IL Dubuque, IA Madison, WI New York San Francisco St. Louis
Bangkok Bogotá Caracas Kuala Lumpur Lisbon London Madrid Mexico City
Milan Montreal New Delhi Santiago Seoul Singapore Sydney Taipei Toronto

Working with Graphics	PP1.54
Inserting a Graphic from the Clip Organizer	PP1.55
Inserting a Graphic from a File	PP1.59
Sizing and Moving a Graphic	PP1.61
Previewing and Printing the Presentation	PP1.62
Previewing the Presentation	PP1.62
Specifying Printed Output	PP1.64
Changing Page Orientation	PP1.64
Printing the Presentation	PP1.65
Exiting PowerPoint	PP1.66
Concept Summary	PP1.68
Lab Review	PP1.70
Key Terms	PP1.70
Microsoft Office Specialist Skills	PP1.70
Command Summary	PP1.71
Lab Exercises	PP1.73
Screen Identification	PP1.73
Matching	PP1.74
Multiple Choice	PP1.74
True/False	PP1.76
Fill-In	PP1.76
Step-by-Step	PP1.77
On Your Own	PP1.87

Lab 2 Modifying and Refining a Presentation PP2.1

Objectives	PP2.1
Case Study	PP2.2
Replacing Text	PP2.4
Using Find and Replace	PP2.5
Creating a Simple Table	PP2.9
Using the Table Layout	PP2.9
Inserting the Table	PP2.10
Entering Data in a Table	PP2.11
Applying Text Formats	PP2.12
Sizing the Table Columns	PP2.14
Aligning Text in Cells	PP2.14
Changing the Border Size and Color	PP2.16
Adding Background Fill Color	PP2.18
Modifying and Creating Graphic Objects	PP2.20
Changing the Slide Layout	PP2.20
Recoloring a Picture	PP2.22

Duplicating a Slide	PP2.23
Inserting an AutoShape	PP2.24
Enhancing the AutoShape	PP2.25
Adding Text to an AutoShape	PP2.26
Rotating the Object	PP2.27
Working with Text Boxes	PP2.28
Creating a Text Box	PP2.28
Adding Text to a Text Box	PP2.29
Enhancing the Text Box	PP2.30
Changing the Presentation Design	PP2.30
Applying a Design Template	PP2.31
Changing the Color Scheme	PP2.34
Working with Master Slides	PP2.37
Modifying the Slide Master	PP2.38
Modifying the Title Master	PP2.42
Reapplying a Slide Layout	PP2.45
Changing and Hiding Footer Text	PP2.46
Using Special Effects	PP2.48
Animating an Object and Adding Sound Effects	PP2.49
Adding Transition Effects	PP2.51
Adding Build Effects	PP2.53
Controlling the Slide Show	PP2.56
Navigating in a Slide Show	PP2.56
Adding Freehand Annotations	PP2.57
Hiding Slides	PP2.60
Adding Speaker Notes	PP2.62
Checking Style	PP2.64
Documenting a File	PP2.69
Customizing Print Settings	PP2.71
Printing Selected Slides	PP2.71
Adding Headers and Footers to Notes and Handouts	PP2.72
Scaling Slides	PP2.73
Concept Summary	PP2.76
Lab Review	PP2.78
Key Terms	PP2.78
Microsoft Office Specialist Skills	PP2.78
Command Summary	PP2.79
Lab Exercises	PP2.81
Matching	PP2.81
Multiple Choice	PP2.81
True/False	PP2.83
Fill-In	PP2.83
Step-by-Step	PP2.84
On Your Own	PP2.93

Working Together 1: Copying, Embedding, and Linking Between Applications PPWT1.1

Case Study	PPWT1.1
Copying Between Applications	PPWT1.2
Copying from Word to a PowerPoint Slide	PPWT1.2
Embedding a Word Table in a PowerPoint Slide	PPWT1.4
Editing an Embedded Object	PPWT1.7
Linking Between Applications	PPWT1.8
Linking an Excel Chart to a PowerPoint Presentation	PPWT1.9
Updating a Linked Object	PPWT1.12
Editing Links	PPWT1.13
Printing Selected Slides	PPWT1.14
Lab Review	PPWT1.16
Key Terms	PPWT1.16
Microsoft Office Specialist Skills	PPWT1.16
Command Summary	PPWT1.16
Lab Exercises	PPWT1.17
Step-by-Step	PPWT1.17

Lab 3 Using Advanced Presentation Features PP3.1

Objectives	PP3.1
Case Study	PP3.2
Creating a New Presentation from Existing Slides	PP3.4
Copying Slides from Another Presentation	PP3.5
Saving the New Presentation	PP3.6
Enhancing the New Presentation	PP3.7
Creating a Numbered List	PP3.7
Using Format Painter	PP3.8
Modifying the Design Template	PP3.10
Creating a Custom Background	PP3.10
Applying a Slide Master to Selected Slides	PP3.12
Adding a Picture Background	PP3.15
Customizing Graphics	PP3.16
Zooming the Slide	PP3.17
Converting Graphics to Drawing Objects	PP3.18
Ungrouping an Object	PP3.20
Deleting a Graphic Element	PP3.20

Regrouping Objects	PP3.21
Changing the Stacking Order	PP3.22
Aligning Objects	PP3.23
Grouping Objects	PP3.26
Wrapping Text in an Object	PP3.26
Centering Objects	PP3.28
Creating a Chart Slide	PP3.30
Copying Data to the Office Clipboard	PP3.32
Specifying the Chart Data	PP3.34
Modifying Chart Data	PP3.38
Adding Axis Titles	PP3.38
Changing Chart Formats	PP3.40
Creating an Organization Chart	PP3.43
Adding Boxes	PP3.46
Enhancing the Organization Chart	PP3.47
Changing the Organization Chart Layout	PP3.49
Exporting a Presentation Outline to Word	PP3.52
E-mailing a Presentation	PP3.53
Delivering Presentations	PP3.55
Rehearsing Timing	PP3.56
Packaging Presentations for a CD	PP3.57
Preparing Overheads and 35mm Slides	PP3.59
Concept Summary	PP3.60
Lab Review	PP3.62
Key Terms	PP3.62
Microsoft Office Specialist Skills	PP3.62
Command Summary	PP3.63
Lab Exercises	PP3.65
Matching	PP3.65
True/False	PP3.65
Fill-In	PP3.66
Multiple Choice	PP3.66
Step-by-Step	PP3.68
On Your Own	PP3.73

Lab 4 Creating a Presentation for a Kiosk and the Web PP4.1

Objectives	PP4.1
Case Study	PP4.2
Creating a Presentation from Multiple Sources	PP4.4
Creating a New Presentation from a Design Template	PP4.4
Inserting Text from a Word Document	PP4.6

Inserting Slides from Another Presentation	PP4.8
Creating a Complex Table	PP4.12
Enhancing the Table	PP4.14
Adding Interest to the Presentation	PP4.18
Adding Animated Graphics	PP4.18
Creating a WordArt Object	PP4.20
Editing WordArt Text	PP4.23
Enhancing a WordArt Object	PP4.23
Setting Up a Presentation for a Kiosk	PP4.26
Adding Sound	PP4.26
Adding Slide Transitions	PP4.29
Making the Presentation Self-Running	PP4.30
Setting Up the Presentation for Browsing	PP4.31
Creating Custom Shows	PP4.31
Creating an Agenda Slide	PP4.34
Adding Hyperlinks	PP4.35
Using Hyperlinks	PP4.38
Adding Action Buttons	PP4.39
Changing the Button Size	PP4.42
Using Action Buttons	PP4.45
Publishing a Presentation on the Web	PP4.45
Saving the presentation as a Single-File Web Page	PP4.46
Navigating a Web Presentation	PP4.49
Saving a Presentation as a Design Template	PP4.50
Concept Summary	PP4.52
Lab Review	PP4.54
Key Terms	PP4.54
Microsoft Office Specialist Skills	PP4.54
Command Summary	PP4.55
Lab Exercises	PP4.56
Matching	PP4.56
Multiple Choice	PP4.56
True/False	PP4.58
Fill-In	PP4.58
Step-by-Step	PP4.59
On Your Own	PP4.64

Working Together 2: Reviewing, Embedding, and Broadcasting a Presentation — PPWT2.1

Case Study	PPWT2.1
Reviewing a Presentation	PPWT2.2
Adding a Comment	PPWT2.2
Sending the Presentation for Review	PPWT2.4
Combining Reviewed Presentations	PPWT2.5
Deleting a Comment	PPWT2.6
Responding to Comments and Changes	PPWT2.8
Applying Reviewer Changes	PPWT2.10
Ending the Review	PPWT2.15
Collaborating Online	PPWT2.15
Embedding a Presentation	PPWT2.16
Editing an Embedded Object	PPWT2.17
Broadcasting a Presentation	PPWT2.21
Recording a Broadcast	PPWT2.21
Playing the Broadcast	PPWT2.23
Lab Review	PPWT2.26
Key Terms	PPWT2.26
Microsoft Office Specialist Skills	PPWT2.26
Command Summary	PPWT2.27
Lab Exercises	PPWT2.28
Step-by-Step	PPWT2.28

Command Summary	PPCS.1
Glossary of Key Terms	PPG.1
Reference 1–Data File List	PPR1.1
Reference 2–Microsoft Office Specialist Skills	PPR2.1
Index	PPI.1

Acknowledgments

The new edition of The O'Leary Series has been made possible only through the enthusiasm and dedication of a great team of people. Because the team spans the country, literally from coast to coast, we have utilized every means of working together including conference calls, FAX, e-mail, and document collaboration. We have truly tested the team approach and it works!

Leading the team from McGraw-Hill are Don Hull, Sponsoring Editor, and Jennie Yates, Developmental Editor. Their renewed commitment, direction, and support have infused the team with the excitement of a new project.

The production staff is headed by James Labeots, Project Manager, whose planning and attention to detail has made it possible for us to successfully meet a very challenging schedule. Members of the production team include: Artemio Ortiz, Designer; Pat Rogondino and Cecelia Morales, Compositors; Susan Defosset, Copy Editor; Heather Burbridge, Production Supervisor; Matthew Perry, Supplement Coordinator; and Elizabeth Mavetz, Media Producer. We would particularly like to thank Pat, Cecelia, and Susan—team members for many past editions whom we can always depend on to do a great job.

Finally, we are particularly grateful to a small but very dedicated group of people who helped us develop the manuscript. Colleen Hayes, Susan Demar, and Kathy Duggan have helped on the last several editions and continue to provide excellent developmental support. To Steve Willis, Carol Cooper, and Sarah Martin who provide technical expertise, youthful perspective, and enthusiasm, our thanks for helping get the manuscripts out the door and meeting the deadlines.

Preface

Introduction

The 20th century not only brought the dawn of the Information Age, but also rapid changes in information technology. There is no indication that this rapid rate of change will be slowing—it may even be increasing. As we begin the 21st century, computer literacy will undoubtedly become prerequisite for whatever career a student chooses. The goal of the O'Leary Series is to assist students in attaining the necessary skills to efficiently use these applications. Equally important is the goal to provide a foundation for students to readily and easily learn to use future versions of this software. This series does this by providing detailed step-by-step instructions combined with careful selection and presentation of essential concepts.

About the Authors

Tim and Linda O'Leary live in the American Southwest and spend much of their time engaging instructors and students in conversation about learning. In fact, they have been talking about learning for more than 25 years. Something in those early conversations convinced them to write a book, to bring their interest in the learning process to the printed page. Today, they are as concerned as ever about learning, about technology, and about the challenges of presenting material in new ways, both in terms of content and the method of delivery.

A powerful and creative team, Tim combines his years of classroom teaching experience with Linda's background as a consultant and corporate trainer. Tim has taught courses at Stark Technical College in Canton, Ohio, Rochester Institute of Technology in upper New York state, and is currently a professor at Arizona State University in Tempe, Arizona. Tim and Linda have talked to and taught students from ages 8 to 80, all of them with a desire to learn something about computers and the applications that make their lives easier, more interesting, and more productive.

About the Book

Times are changing, technology is changing, and this text is changing, too. Do you think the students of today are different from yesterday? There is no doubt about it—they are. On the positive side, it is amazing how much effort students will put toward things they are convinced are relevant to them. Their effort directed at learning application programs and exploring the Web seems at times limitless. On the other hand, students can often be shortsighted, thinking that learning the skills to use the application is the only objective. The mission of the series is to build upon and extend this interest by not only teaching the specific application skills but by introducing the concepts that are common to all applications, providing students with the confidence, knowledge, and ability to easily learn the next generation of applications.

Same Great Features as the Office XP Edition with some new additions!

- **Introduction to Computer Essentials**—A brief introduction to the basics of computer hardware and software (appears in Office Volume I only).

- **Introduction to Outlook**—A lab devoted to Microsoft Office Outlook 2003 basics (appears in Office Volume I only).

- **Introduction to Microsoft Office 2003**—Presents an overview to the Microsoft Office 2003 components: Office Word, Excel, Access, PowerPoint, and Outlook. Includes a hands-on section that introduces the features that are common to all Office 2003 applications, including using menus, task panes, and the Office Help system.

- **Lab Organization**—The lab text is organized to include main and subtopic heads by grouping related tasks. For example, tasks such as changing fonts and applying character effects appear under the "Formatting" topic head. This results in a slightly more reference-like approach, making it easier for students to refer back to the text to review. This has been done without losing the logical and realistic development of the case.

- **Relevant Cases**—Four separate running cases demonstrate the features in each application. Topics are of interest to students—At Arizona State University, over 600 students were surveyed to find out what topics are of interest to them.

- **Focus on Concepts**—Each lab focuses on the concepts behind the application. Students learn the concepts, so they can succeed regardless of the software package they might be using. The concepts are previewed at the beginning of each lab and summarized at the end of each lab.

- All **Numbered Steps** and bullets appear in left margin space making it easy not to miss a step.

- **Clarified Marginal Notes**—Marginal notes have been enhanced by more clearly identifying the note content with box heads and the use of different colors.

    Additional Information—Brief asides with expanded discussion of features.

    Having Trouble?—Procedural tips advising students of possible problems and how to overcome them.

    Another Method—Alternative methods of performing a procedure.

- **Focus on Careers**—A new feature, appearing at the end of each lab, which provides an example of how the material covered may be applied in the "real world."

- A **Microsoft Office Specialist Skills** table, appearing at the end of each lab, contains page references to Microsoft Office Specialist skills learned in the lab.

- **End-of-Chapter Material**

  - Screen Identification (appears in the first lab of each application)

  - Matching

  - Multiple Choice

  - Fill-In

  - True/False

  Hands-On Practice Exercises—Students apply the skills and concepts they learned to solve case-based exercises. Many cases in the practice exercises tie to a running case used in another application lab. This helps to demonstrate the use of the four applications across a common case setting. For example, the Adventure Travel Tours case used in the Word labs is continued in practice exercises in Excel, Access, and PowerPoint.

  - Step-by-Step

  - On Your Own

- **Rating System**—The 3-star rating system identifies the difficulty level of each practice exercise in the end-of-lab materials.

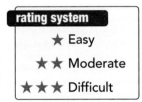

- **Continuing Exercises**—A continuing exercise icon identifies exercises that build off of exercises completed in earlier labs.

- **Working Together Labs**—At the completion of the brief and introductory texts, a final lab demonstrates the integration of the MS Office applications.

- **References**

  Command Summary—Provides a table of all commands used in the labs.

  Glossary of Key Terms—Includes definitions for all bolded terms used in the labs and included in the Key Terms list at the end of each lab.

  Data File List—Helps organize all data and solution files.

  Microsoft Office Specialist Certification Guide—Links all Microsoft Office Specialist objectives to text content and end-of-chapter exercises.

Instructor's Guide

We understand that, in today's teaching environment, offering a textbook alone is not sufficient to meet the needs of the many instructors who use our books. To teach effectively, instructors must have a full complement of supplemental resources to assist them in every facet of teaching from preparing for class, to conducting a lecture, to assessing students' comprehension. *The O'Leary Series* offers a fully-integrated supplements package and Web site, as described below.

Instructor's Resource Kit

The **Instructor's Resource Kit** contains a computerized Test Bank, an Instructor's Manual, and PowerPoint Presentation Slides. Features of the Instructor's Resource Kit are described below.

- **Instructor's Manual** The Instructor's Manual contains lab objectives, concepts, outlines, lecture notes, and command summaries. Also included are answers to all end-of-chapter material, tips for covering difficult materials, additional exercises, and a schedule showing how much time is required to cover text material.

- **Computerized Test Bank** The test bank contains over 1,300 multiple choice, true/false, and discussion questions. Each question will be accompanied by the correct answer, the level of learning difficulty, and corresponding page references. Our flexible Diploma software allows you to easily generate custom exams.

- **PowerPoint Presentation Slides** The presentation slides will include lab objectives, concepts, outlines, text figures, and speaker's notes. Also included are bullets to illustrate key terms and FAQs.

Online Learning Center/Web Site

Found at **www.mhhe.com/oleary**, this site provides additional learning and instructional tools to enhance the comprehension of the text. The OLC/Web Site is divided into these three areas:

- **Information Center** Contains core information about the text, supplements, and the authors.

- **Instructor Center** Offers instructional materials, downloads, and other relevant links for professors.

- **Student Center** Contains data files, chapter competencies, chapter concepts, self-quizzes, flashcards, additional Web links, and more.

Skills Assessment

SimNet (Simulated Network Assessment Product) provides a way for you to test students' software skills in a simulated environment.

- Pre-testing options

- Post-testing options

- Course placement testing

- Diagnostic capabilities to reinforce skills

- Proficiency testing to measure skills

- Web or LAN delivery of tests.

- Computer-based training tutorials

For more information on skills assessment software, please contact your local sales representative, or visit us at **www.mhhe.com/it**.

Digital Solutions to Help You Manage Your Course

PageOut is our Course Web Site Development Center that offers a syllabus page, URL, McGraw-Hill Online Learning Center content, online exercises and quizzes, gradebook, discussion board, and an area for student Web pages.

Available free with any McGraw-Hill Technology Education product, PageOut requires no prior knowledge of HTML, no long hours of coding, and a way for course coordinators and professors to provide a full-course Web site. PageOut offers a series of templates—simply fill them with your course information and click on one of 16 designs. The process takes under an hour and leaves you with a professionally designed Web site. We'll even get you started with sample Web sites, or enter your syllabus for you! PageOut is so straightforward and intuitive, it's little wonder why over 12,000 college professors are using it. For more information, visit the PageOut Web site at www.pageout.net.

Online courses are also available. Online Learning Centers (OLCs) are your perfect solutions for Internet-based content. Simply put, these Centers are "digital cartridges" that contain a book's pedagogy and supplements. As students read the book, they can go online and take self-grading quizzes or work through interactive exercises. These also provide students appropriate access to lecture materials and other key supplements.

Online Learning Centers can be delivered through any of these platforms:

- Blackboard.com

- WebCT (a product of Universal Learning Technology)

McGraw-Hill has partnerships with WebCT and Blackboard to make it even easier to take your course online. Now you can have McGraw-Hill content delivered through the leading Internet-based learning tool for higher education.

Computing Concepts

Computing Essentials 2004 and *Computing Today* offer a unique, visual orientation that gives students a basic understanding of computing concepts. *Computing Essentials* and *Computing Today* are some of the few books on the market that are written by a professor who still teaches the courses every semester and loves it. The books encourage "active" learning with their exercises, explorations, visual illustrations, and inclusion of screen shots and numbered steps. While combining the "active" learning style with current topics and technology, these texts provide an accurate snapshot of computing trends. When bundled with software application lab manuals, students are given a complete representation of the fundamental issues surrounding the personal computing environment.

Select features of these texts include:

- **Using Technology**—Engaging coverage of hot, high-interest topics, such as phone calls via the Internet, using the Internet remotely with a Personal Digital Assistant (PDA), and Client and Server operating systems. These Web-related projects direct the student to explore current popular uses of technology.

- **Expanding Your Knowledge**—Geared for those who want to go into greater depth on a specific topic introduced within the chapter. These projects meet the needs of instructors wanting more technical depth of coverage.

- **Building Your Portfolio**—Develops critical thinking and writing skills while students examine security, privacy, and ethical issues in technology. By completing these exercises, students will be able to walk away from the class with something to show prospective employers.

- **Making IT Work for You**—Based on student surveys, *Computing Essentials* identified several special interest topics and devoted a two-page section on each in the corresponding chapter. Making IT Work for You sections engage students by presenting high interest topics that directly relate to the concepts presented in the chapter. Topics include downloading music from the Internet, creating personal Web sites, and using the Internet to make long-distance phone calls. Many of these are supported by short video presentations that will be available via CD and the Web.

- **On the Web Explorations**—Appear throughout the margins of the text and encourage students to go to the Web to visit several informative and established sites in order to learn more about the chapter's featured topic.

- **A Look to the Future Sections**—Provide insightful information about the future impact of technology and forecasts of how upcoming enhancements in the world of computing will play an important and powerful role in society.

- **End-of-Chapter Material**—A variety of material including objective questions (key terms, matching, multiple choice, and short answer completion) and critical thinking activities. This will help to reinforce the information just learned.